D1546997

THE MEMOIRS OF W. W. KEEN, M.D.

Wand of Aesculapius

THE MEMOIRS OF

WILLIAM WILLIAMS KEEN, M.D.

Edited by W. W. Keen James

A Keen Book

Doylestown, Pennsylvania

For Uncle Bill

Copyright © 1990 by W. W. Keen James

All rights reserved.

Published by W. W. Keen James

74 East State St., Doylestown, Pennsylvania 18901-4362

Library of Congress Catalog Card Number 90-90402

ISBN: 0-9628197-0-0

Manufactured in the United States of America

CONTENTS

Foreword x

Editor's Preface xi

Author's Preface xiii

An Autobiographical Sketch 1

Some of the Social, Scientific, Economic, and Educational
    Developments During My Lifetime, with Some Remarks on
    My Surgical and Literary Life 107

Social and Economic Life 110

Personal Recollections

The Worst-Scared Man in the World 125

A Gruesome Find 128

A Tragic Post Mortem 130

Hell Hath No Fury Like a Woman Scorned 132

The Man Who Couldn't Say "Horse" 134

The Little "Scrap of Paper" in My Pocket 135

The "Umbrella Story" and the "$75,000 Fee" 137

A Distressing Night 139

When a Doctor Tried to Prove Too Much at a Murder Trial . . . 140

A Soldier of the First Napoleon 145

The First Diagnostication of a Wound of the Sympathetic Nerve
    in Man 147

1860 149

Note on My Technical Capture after Second Bull Run 156

On Anesthesia 157

Risks that Doctors, and Especially Surgeons, Constantly Run . 165

Side-to-Side Irrigation of the Interior of the Brain 169

Offers to Undergo Experiments for the Good of the Human Race . 171

The Lost Sponge 172

The Lost Fork 174

When I Fell Upon Both Feet 175

Two Family Calamities 177

When I Sat in the Seats of the Mighty 179

A Very Intelligent Horse 181

The Greatest Triumphs of the Human Voice I Know Of 185

The Hardest Question I Ever Was Asked 186

My Debt to Florence and Dora, in the "Dreadful" Summer of 1910   187

My Seventy-Fifth Birthday 192

A Soldier's Alternative 194

My Little Italian Speech and How It Grew 195

Yellow Journalism 198

Trans-Continental Telephoning 201

Orators I Have Heard 203

Presidents I Have Known 211

The Operations on President Cleveland 217

Eleven Centenary Celebrations 228

On the Bulgarian Frontier 236

An Audience by the Kaiserin 242

Personal Incidents of Travel in Persia, Bukhara, and the Caucasus   249

The Opening of the Kiel Canal 258

The Multiplied Mishaps of a Trip to Panama 259

The Woman's Medical College 266

The Ability to Endure Physical Pain 272

"Life in America One Hundred Years Ago" 278

Speech at the Annual Dinner of the British Medical Association,
   London, August 1st, 1895 278

Speech at the Annual Dinner of the British Medical Association,
   Montreal, September 2nd, 1897 281

Address in Replying to the Toast "An Impossible War" 283

Address to the Graduating Class of Nurses, Allentown Hospital
   May 27th, 1915 286

After-Dinner Speech Before the Alumni Association of the
   Jefferson Medical College, June 4th, 1915 292

The American Philosophical Society 298

My Own Impressions and Reflections on the Great War 306

The College of Physicians of Philadelphia 312

[Addendum] Some Amusing Stories 317

Appendixes

   Facsimile Page from Keen's MS   320

   Keen's Own Résumé   321

   Degrees and Honors Cited in These *Memoirs*   322

   "Auld Lang Syne" reprint   323

Notes   325

Achievements of the Friends of Medical Research in 50 Years . .   330

Selected Bibliography, Keen as Author   331

Selected Bibliography, Keen as Editor   332

Supplemental List of Doctors Mentioned in These *Memoirs* . . .   333

Index   335

ILLUSTRATIONS

Cover

W. W. Keen, 1897

Frontispiece

The Wand of Aesculapius

Plates

Map (1849) of West Philadelphia indicating Keen homestead on Chestnut St. Courtesy of the Library Company of Philadelphia.

Keen's sketches (drawn six decades later!) of the house and lot, and room arrangements of his childhood home.

Engraving (1846) of the Market St. bridge between West Philadelphia and the city. Courtesy of the Library Company of Philadelphia.

Weir Mitchell (1859). Courtesy of the College of Physicians.

Keen in 1860. Courtesy of the College of Physicians.

Keen in 1863. Courtesy of the National Library of Medicine.

Church at Centreville, Virginia (1863), Keen's field hospital at Bull Run. Alexander Gardiner photograph, from the Brady-Handy Collection of the Library of Congress.

Emma Corinna Borden, *left*, and her sister, Eudora (1863). Courtesy of the College of Physicians.

Anatomical Lecture by Dr. William Williams Keen (c. 1879), by Charles H. Stephens. Courtesy of the Pennsylvania Academy of the Fine Arts, Philadelphia. The painting was a gift to the Academy by the artist.

W. W. Keen's Clinic at the Jefferson Medical College (1893), by C. A. Weaver. Courtesy of Thomas Jefferson University Alumni Association.

The *Oneida*, field hospital for Cleveland's operations. Photograph by N. L. Stebbins, Courtesy of the Society for the Preservation of New England Antiquities.

Professor William W. Keen's Clinic, Jefferson Medical College Hospital, December 10th, 1902. Courtesy of the College of Physicians.

Keen and family (1906): Daughter Florence; daughter Corinne (with husband Walter Freeman and children Bill, Walter, Corinne, Jack, and Norman); Keen; daughter Dora; daughter Margaret (with husband Howard Butcher and children Howard, Margaret, and Dora).

Weir Mitchell, *center*, and Keen, *second right*, in 1907. Courtesy of the Franklin Inn Club.

Caricature by Wyncie King. Courtesy of the Franklin Inn Club.

Keen's Sketches

Sunday-school seating   7

Portable microscope   56

Murder victim's carotid artery and jugular vein   144

Detail of kaiserin's dress   247

Kaiserin's profile   248

Persian amphitheater   251

Woman's Medical College buildings   267

ACKNOWLEDGMENTS

My thanks to Jack Eckert, of the College of Physicians of Philadelphia; to David Holmes and Ben Wolf, of the Franklin Inn Club; to Ken Finkel, of the Library Company of Philadelphia; to Elyssa Kane, of the Pennsylvania Academy of the Fine Arts; to Laura Condon, of the Society for the Preservation of New England Antiquities; to Judy Robins, of the Thomas Jefferson University (formerly Jefferson Medical College); and Caroline Wilson--all of whom cheerfully provided data or pictures with which to enhance Keen's text.

Special thanks to cousin Frank Freeman (whose own study of Keen will include significant medical commentary) for his generosity with pictures he has gathered. Special thanks also to friend and printer Carter Gardy, for for his patience and professional assistance in the face of editorial vacillation. Friend and publisher Bill Bauhan deserves special thanks as well, for invaluable advice about the form and design of the book.

Finally, special thanks to brother Wynne, who originally enlisted my aid in providing an index for Keen's manuscript, neither of us realizing that this literary tail would end up wagging the dog. His constant encouragements has been prized.

Errors that may have crept into this edition are mine alone.

                                                        W. W. K. J.

FOREWORD

Honoring W. W. Keen, M.D.

"Hero" and "role model" are common terms in conversation, these days, but as Dr. Keen's namesake, I looked up to him as my hero. As a boy in Philadelphia who went to his home for Sunday dinner, every year from autumn to spring, I absorbed many of his ways.

He was a deacon of the Baptist Church, and I thought of him, recently, when I was at a reception where one bowl was labeled "Baptist Punch" and the other, "Regular Punch." Even at formal dinners, he served only water.

His interests included the classics. He gave me a handsome set of *Plutarch's Lives*, in which the great men of Greece were compared with the great men of Rome. My mother said that this gave me a "bowing acquaintance" with men who are our cultural ancestors.

He was near-sighted and did not play baseball, but when we played a game in which he was matched with a grandchild to carry an Easter egg in a teaspoon, he did it with such gusto that his daughters feared for his heart. He retired at 70, because he observed that people's judgment was not so good after that age.

He lost his wife, his darling "Tinny" (for Corinna), at an early age, and he carried her wedding ring on his watch chain and always spoke of her with a catch in his throat. He said to a dear friend that when the good Lord would take him, he was sure he would be greeted in heaven by his darling Tinny.

November 10, 1988   William Williams Keen Freeman

EDITOR'S PREFACE

Five times the length of Keen's initial autobiographical sketch, begun
in 1915, this literary collage offered his daughters a personal account
of his early years, the growth of his profession, and his common-sense
observations about the world at large. There is no evidence that he
ever intended to publish, in their present form, these *Memoirs* (my title).
He made a few autograph corrections to the typescript, in matters of
fact, but there has been no large-scale effort till now to nit-pick, in
matters of spelling and syntax, and the wide divergence in the clarity of
the type has led me to re-do the entirety. (A reduced facsimile page of
the original manuscript photocopy appears as an appendix, p. 320.)

   In a sense, "going public" with Keen's private document is an act of
profanation (he was always mentioned with reverence and awe), but I hope
that the wider distribution of his recollections, without the filter of
myth-guided relatives, will provoke someone to undertake a full-scale
biography of this dynamo, whose 95 years (from the administration of
Martin van Buren to the first administration of F.D.R.!) coincided with
what some have considered the zenith of the Republic.

W. W. Keen James

AUTHOR'S PREFACE

As I have never kept a regular diary, I am obliged to depend wholly upon my memory. As to various events in my long life, now verging towards four score years, my memory may be at fault, especially as to date and details of events. A lenient judgment, therefore, must be passed upon any statements found to be erroneous by those more accurately informed or who have delved among original documents.

Philad. Nov. 1. 1915   W. W. Keen

AN AUTOBIOGRAPHICAL SKETCH

By

W. W. Keen, M.D.

This sketch is only for my children, and theirs in turn. It has necessarily too many I's in it for the eyes of others. My children will pardon the apparent egotism.

I record this brief sketch of my life for my children and their descendants partly to gratify their expressed desire, partly to record some events which may otherwise be forgotten, partly to record my deep appreciation of the love of my dear children, but chiefly because of my gratitude to God for His loving kindness during a long life.

I was born January 19th, 1837, at No. 232 South 3rd St., then a residential part of the city. The house is still standing (1912), but has been long occupied only for business purposes. Adjoining it on the north, I well remember, was the Willing mansion,* which stood in a large garden extending to "Willing's Alley" and from 3rd to 4th St. In this were a number of large trees which were the favorite place for the swarms of bees from my father's garden in the rear of our own house. One of my very earliest recollections is his being called out of church to "hive" them.

---

* This may have been the Bingham mansion, the Willing mansion being at the 4th St. end of the same lot.

My father, William Williams Keen, was descended from Jöran or Göran (George) Kyn, who came over as a soldier under Gov. Printz from Sweden, in 1642. (See Gregory B. Keen's "Descendants of Jöran Kyn," in *The Pennsylvania Magazine of History and Biography*; a copy of this series of papers is bound and in my library. Also see my account [pp. 232-3] of a visit to the University of Uppsala at the celebration of the 200th anniversary of the birth of Linnaeus, in my "Eleven Centenary Celebrations.") He was the founder of Chester, Pa., and the map in *The History of Chester* (in my library) shows his large holdings of land. The Crozer Theological Seminary, of which I was made a constituent trustee, in 1867 (my first public office), and have served on the board ever since, stands on a part of this land. In a drawer in my office is a genealogy of the family, down to my father.

The name Kyn was changed to Kien by the Dutch. In those early days, people wrote little and talked much--a habit not yet lost--and they changed the spelling to preserve the pronunciation, as *Kyn* in spoken Dutch would be pronounced "K$\bar{\text{i}}$ne." In the old deed, dated 1676, in my library, the name is spelled Kien. When the English came, the spelling was changed to Keen and has so remained.

Originally, the family were Swedish Lutherans. In the Old Swedes (Gloria Dei) Church, the oldest adult grave (A.D. 1700?) is that of Matthias Keen, my great-great-great-grandfather. It is on the west side of the path running south from the south (or side) door of the church. About the time of the Revolution, which prevented the Swedish Church (i.e., in Sweden) from sending them pastors, the church became an Episcopal church and has so remained. One branch of the family settled in Oxford Township, north of the old city of Philadelphia, and a number of them are interred in Trinity

2

Episcopal Church, Oxford. A still larger number of the family are buried in the burial ground of the Pennypack (now the Lower Dublin) Baptist Church, in Bustleton.

The old substantial stone house built and occupied by my great-great-grandfather, John Keen, still stands at what was (and still may be) known as "Keen's Lane," near Tacony.* In 1797, Philadelphia was visited by its second epidemic of yellow fever. My grandmother and a sister-in-law fled the city to this old family residence, where a child was born to each of them: my father, William Williams Keen; and Rebecca Keen, daughter of Isaac & Sarah (Knowles) Keen, and later Mrs. Rebecca Miles. At my mother's funeral, in 1873, she not only appeared but returned to the house to spend the night, and we children were indignant at the good old--but quite deaf-- "Cousin Becky" Miles's intrusion upon my father's grief, at such a time. But it proved the greatest blessing to him, for she and he got to talking about old times and old friends, and it took him perforce away from his sorrow. About two weeks later, she gave me the old deed above named, and the old wills, and other family documents which are in the drawer of my office desk (later given to Corinne).

My great-grandfather Matthias Keen was twice married. His first wife was Mary Swift. His second wife was Margaret Thomas. She was of Welsh descent, a Baptist, and evidently a woman of great force of character, for she not only carried her husband from the Episcopal into the Baptist Church, but persuaded him to leave the bulk (possibly all?) of his property to *her* children only. I have no idea how much this amounted to, but the

---

* This is an error. Gregory Keen informs me it was pulled down many years ago.

3

evident injustice of it made a breach in the family which was not healed until 1843, when my father moved to West Philadelphia, to what is now 37th & Chestnut Streets. On Chestnut Street, where the Drexel Institute now stands, lived Joseph Swift Keen, the grandson of Mary Swift (the first wife of Matthias Keen), and he and my father ignored entirely the old quarrel, and the families became friends again. Gregory B. Keen is this Joseph Keen's son and the author of *The Descendants of Jöran Kyn of New Sweden.*

My father had associated with him in business his brother Joseph Keen, but my father was practically the firm. They were leather merchants and for many years, through my father's energy and enterprise, and my uncle's faithful work in the store (which was at 61 Chestnut Street, later and now re-numbered 217), did the largest leather business in Philadelphia. My father retired in the late '50s, I think. His fortune after his death was divided among my brothers George and Charles and myself, each receiving about $60,000 in value. I took 217 Chestnut St., at a valuation of $43,000 (including a mortgage of $17,100), but after it went down all the time in value and in revenue, I finally found, in 1909, a man who was willing to buy it for $24,000, including the above mortgage. This was a loss of $19,000 to me. Moreover, Father had advanced to me $11,000 (including in-terest) for my family expenses which--very properly--was deducted from my inheritance. I finally inherited only about $30,000 from my father's estate.

My mother was a descendant of Rev. Thomas Budd.* He was an Oxford M.A.

---

* I can claim also Welsh descent through Margaret Williams, on my father's side. A mixture of Swedish, English, and Welsh blood is a rather good in-heritance. Possibly there may also be other strains mingled with these three.

and the vicar, successively, of Montacute and of Martock, both in Somersetshire. Under the influence of George Fox, he became a Quaker, and when the infamous Judge Jeffreys held his "Bloody Assizes" in Ilchester (the county seat), he threw Thomas Budd into the county jail. He little knew the stern stuff of which Thomas was made. Instead of recanting his opinions, he adhered steadfastly to them for seven years till he died, still a prisoner. I am proud to reckon such a "jail bird" as an ancestor. In 1910, Florence and I visited Ilchester, Montacute, and Martock. Ilchester, although the county seat and on the main direct road from London to Exeter, Penzance, etc., has languished ever since Jeffreys' day. The inhabitants believe, so we were told, that this is the result of Jeffreys' assizes. The jail has long since disappeared, not one stone left standing upon another. All the records, too, had disappeared. The old court house alone remained, and of this I had a photograph made.

Thomas Budd's two sons emigrated to New Jersey, and many of their descendants still live there. Budd's Lake is named after them. I have in my office desk a number of papers tracing their descent, and other facts as to the family. In a newspaper there noted (I think I have copies of the issues), the family history is given at some length. Also, there is a published *History of the Budd Family*, and I have a copy of *The Early History of the Provinces of New Jersey* in my library.

My grandmother Budd's father was a farmer at Valley Forge, and I have often heard her tell how, in the dreadful winter of 1777, when the army was at Valley Forge, Washington repeatedly came to her father's farm to obtain supplies for his suffering army. She was then, I think, a girl of about twelve years of age. This fine old stone house is still standing.

We visited it 2 or 3 years ago, and Corinne took some photographs (1915).

We lived on South 3rd Street till I was a little over six years of age. My parents had eight children, of whom five died when thirteen years of age or under. I was the sixth child. There was an earlier William, and at my birth, I too was named William. There was an earlier Susan, who died before I was born, and the child next younger than I was also named Susan. She died when I was five years old. I just remember her. The eighth and last child was a boy named Baron Stow, after a warm friend of my parents, Rev. Dr. Baron Stow, of Boston. My dear father and mother had one overwhelming grief, with two of their children, the first William and first Susan, dying of scarlet fever on two successive Sundays. This was before my birth.

In 1849, my brothers George and Charles, both in ill health, were sent on a voyage to Europe. They sailed from New York, and all of us, except brother Baron, went over to see them off, for going to Europe over sixty years ago was almost like a polar expedition now. Baron, a boy of seven, was left in the care of a relative. On our return, we found that he had been taken ill with "croup" (diphtheria, we now know it really was). He rapidly grew worse and after a few days, died. Before we went to New York, we had a "daguerreotype" taken of the entire family. This was a wholly new invention, at that time, and we had to sit still for 15 or 20 minutes, I think. Only one firm in Philadelphia took such pictures, the Langenheim Brothers, who had their studio in the present Stock Exchange Building, at 3rd and Dock Streets. Having it was a great comfort to my parents, who were prostrated by the death of their "Benjamin." My nephew Frank Keen, of New Jersey, still has the daguerreotype, in excellent condition. The moment my brothers heard of Baron's death, they returned, having been away only 6 or 8 weeks.

While living on Third Street, I remember clearly going to the old First Baptist Church, then in La Grange Place, directly adjoining Old Christ Church (see my history of the First Baptist Church), whose chimes summoned us to worship. I especially well remember the Sunday school* and its circle of seats for the scholars; the teacher occupying a chair placed in a break in the circle; Rev. Dr. George B. Ide (whose daughter my brother Charles married), preaching in his sonorous voice from the high pulpit, with a red vertically-pleated curtain behind him; old General Duncan, with his long white hair and (as I learned later) his new wife, sitting just in front of us. Long after we moved to West Philadelphia, my parents still kept up their warm friendship with the old stand-bys there, Mrs. Keyser, Mrs. Inglis (née Keyser), Miss Mary Hallman, the Wattsons, Hansells, Butchers, and many other household names and faces from my childhood. Deacon Thomas Wattson was the great-grandfather of Howard Butcher, Jr., my son-in-law, and Washington Butcher was *his* grand-father.

My grandmother Budd lived on the north side of Pine Street, west of Third. I was constantly running around there. The "ice cream man" had one "freezer" of lemon and one of vanilla which he used to trundle around in a wheelbarrow and peddle out "a cent's worth" (a generous tablespoon) into a small wine glass, with which was furnished a little spoon, both glass and spoon being washed clean (?) in a pail of water that accompanied

---

* See my *History of the First Baptist Church Sunday School*, in print at its first century, in 1915.

the freezers. Then too, I recall the "A.P."s, delicious cookies made on 2nd Street below Chestnut, I think, by a certain Anne Page and embossed with her initials. They don't make such ice cream or such cookies any longer. I sometimes have a dim suspicion that an aging palate *may* have something to do with this idea (delusion?).

While I was between five and six, the "Millerite" excitement began. These followers of a man named Miller believed that the end of the world was then close at hand. Many of them ordered their "ascension robes" of white. I knew nothing of the reasons for this belief, but the rumored end of all things profoundly impressed me, and, little sinner that I was, I was really terrified at the possibility. I slept in a little trundle-bed, which was slid under my parents' four-poster during the day and drawn out at night. The windows of the bedroom faced south, and so the moon was visible. I can vividly recall my lying awake in my bed, anxiously watching the sky, and the fright I repeatedly suffered when the clouds near the moon grew thinner and the light grew brighter and brighter. I looked expectantly at the rifts in the clouds to see if the Lord was not appearing then and there on His great white throne.

Then again, I remember well the great comet of 1843, with its long narrow tail, a sight which filled me with curiosity and wonder, and, I suspect, not a little fear. Youth is always ignorant and credulous, and credulity easily culminates in superstition. This, I suppose, was the origin of my fear. My parents regarded it, I am sure, with entire equanimity.

My father's health having suffered both from his grief at the second Susan's death, in 1842, and an attack of erysipelas, he was advised by his physician to move to the "country." Accordingly, in May, 1843, he bought the lot at the southwest corner of 37th and Chestnut Streets (where the Presbyterian Church now stands), with an old stone house and a stable at the Sansom St. end of the lot. We lived there for some three or four years and then moved into the house which my father built, on a lot comprising the central 300 feet of the square on the north side of Chestnut between 36th and 37th Streets. The lot extended over 200 feet, to Ludlow Street, and contained about 1½ acres. On the rear of this lot, he built a stable and coach house, a hothouse, and a hot and a cold grapery; and he had both a flower garden and a vegetable garden, where he raised corn, potatoes, strawberries, blackberries, peas, lima beans, cabbages, lettuce, etc. He also kept a cow and some chickens, so I had "almost" a real country life. After my father's death, the place was bought--and is still occupied--by the Pennsylvania Home for Indigent Widows and Single Women.

But my father's house was only one of three buildings on this lot. At the eastern side of the lot, my father built later a house for my brother George and his family; and between that house and our own, he gave a 50-front-foot lot to the First Baptist Church in West Philadelphia (later the Epiphany Baptist Church, and still later, merged with the Berean Baptist Church into the present Chestnut Street Baptist Church), on Chestnut above 40th Street. This First Baptist Church in West Philadelphia was organized by my father, and he was its main support. Into this Church I was baptized, in 1850, when thirteen years old. With my brother Charles (he has served for over thirty years as its organist and music director, and for many years also as superintendent of the Sunday school), I entered into all its Christian and social activities.

One amusing incident, when I was a lad perhaps thirteen years old, is explained by the then rural character of West Philadelphia. The area, which was then called "Hamiltonville," was a borough, and its chief political officer was a burgess. We usually referred to it as "the village." It was entirely independent of "the city," which was limited by Vine and Cedar (now South) Streets and the two rivers. The houses, as I have described, were quite far apart. It was named after Mr. Hamilton, an English gentleman (I believe) who occupied the large yellow mansion in what is now the Woodlands but had been the estate where he lived in considerable grandeur. So far as I can recall, he had died before we moved there.

Our church, between my father's and my brother George's houses, had a basement vestry or lecture room, used during the week, the auditorium for Sunday services being above it. The floor of the vestry was two steps below the level of the ground. John Francis was the colored sexton, who had more zeal than discretion.

One Friday evening, during the prayer meeting, John, from his seat in the back of the room, discovered the ladies drawing aside their skirts and moving away from the middle aisle. The cause of the disturbance was an inoffensive toad, who had entered the door at the rear and was on his way towards the pulpit. John decided upon its removal and to effect that took a dustpan and brush. First he placed the pan behind the toad and tried to sweep him with the brush backwards into the pan, when Mr. Toad with ease hopped over the approaching brush. After two or three vain endeavors, John decided upon a rear action, instead of the frontal attack. So he placed the pan in front and tried to take him in the rear with the brush. But Mr. Toad simply hopped over the pan as easily as he had cleared the brush. The first series of failures had gotten most of us giggling, but the second

fiasco resulted, willy-nilly, in an outburst of loud laughter, and that
prayer meeting was at an end.

Later, after the death of both our parents, my brother Charles
placed a brass memorial tablet on the wall of the second Church edifice,
at the southeast corner of 37th and Chestnut Streets, commemorating the
services of our parents. This, I am told, is to be removed to the Chestnut Street Baptist Church before the building at 36th & Chestnut is torn
down.

I would like this to be seen to. [1915—It is now in place within Chestnut St Church]

My father *bought* back the lot on which the first building stood, when
the new church was built at the corner of 37th and Chestnut Streets. This
second church was begun not long before the Panic of 1857. My father was
determined that it should not fail. He begged a considerable (possibly a
large) amount from his friends, sold his own carriage and pair, sold the
grapes from his graperies, and in general curtailed his family expenses
wherever possible and "gave the money to the Lord." Such sacrifices are
as rare as they are admirable.

When we moved to West Philadelphia, in 1843, it was really "country."
The only bridge over the Schuylkill was at Market Street. The only means
of reaching the city were to walk or to have one's own carriage. It was
a great event when, to accommodate especially the businessmen, a "bus"
regularly went to the city in the morning and returned at night. Its
driver we boys used to call "Santa Anna," after the defeated Mexican
general so famous in our Mexican War, because each of them wore a wooden
"peg leg." There was a current legend that, when teased beyond endurance,
our Santa Anna would suddenly detach this wooden leg and hurl it, with
great precision, at the nearest offender.

All the streets were unpaved and were grass-grown, except where worn by the middle track of the horses and the side tracks of the wheels. There were no sidewalks. As far as I can remember, the only houses on Chestnut Street from the Schuylkill River to the present 40th Street-- beyond which were woods and farms--were Joseph Keen's house at 32nd Street; the Newton Grammar School, below 36th Street; Mr. Colladay's house (his daughter Fanny, a descendant of David Rittenhouse, was married by my brother George), at the northwest corner of 36th and Chestnut; Rudolph Evans's house, between 36th and 37th, opposite our later home; our first home, at 37th and Chestnut; two residences between 37th and 38th; Miss Ellen Price's residence, on the North side of Chestnut and occupying the entire lot from 38th to 39th; and the "Academy," just East of 40th Street. Just nine buildings in all, in the ten blocks.

A notable event was the establishment of a winter course of lectures at the Academy. Though I was old enough to go, my memory retains nothing of the lectures, though it records the fact that I headed the family procession, carrying a lantern in order to find the pitfalls, either by its aid or by falling into them. On re-reading this, I recall distinctly a lecture read in the Academy by a Mr. James Allen, of our Church. He was a well-educated Englishman, and I remember the deep impression made upon my young mind by one phrase he used, "looking through nature up to nature's God." I had never heard it before, nor did I know that it was a quotation, but the felicitous and poetic idea and wording impressed me very deeply.

About 1846-7, my father built the new residence already alluded to, and that was my home until I settled into practice in the city, in 1866. It was a large house of wood, two stories high, with an attic and a basement kitchen and dining room. It had four large Ionic columns, extending from the piazza to the roof, and stood on the north side of Chestnut between 36th and 37th (then called Margaretta and Park) Streets, across the street from the house of Rudolph Evans. Mr. Evans was a brother of Dr. Thomas W. Evans, later the well-known dentist in Paris. His oldest son John (later also a dentist in Paris--and a marquis, by purchase from the pope) and I were boon companions. One occasion I well remember. The Evans house had also a piazza in front, and under it a quite free space, which our imagination converted into a "den" for a band of bold robbers. On one occasion, I was a robber and John a policeman. The police chased us, and to avoid capture, we fled to our den, whereupon the police seized clothes poles and proceeded to dislodge us by ramming our den with these weapons. One of the poles struck me on the left cheek, barely below my eye. Had it struck even a quarter of an inch or more higher up, it would have gouged out my eye, and very possibly even have entered my brain. As it was, it made only a nasty cut, of which I still bear the scar.

Many times since then, John and I and our families have met in Paris. Only recently (1909-11), he and Mrs. Evans have both passed away. His uncle was very urgent, in 1864-5, when I was studying in Paris, that I should settle in Paris to practice. He promised me his support, an important factor since, under Napoleon III, he was an influential figure at Court, as well as in French and American society. But I decided not to stay there. What a different career I should have had, had I accepted! Providence has been very kind in helping me to decide these recurring questions, and, as it seems to me now, always rightly.

The amusements and the reading of boys and girls, in those early days, were far less varied and extensive than those of my children and grand-children. The boys played hoops, town-ball, "I spy," tag, shinny (or hockey), "prisoners' base;" and they swam, rowed, and skated. We coasted on our sleds and occasionally, when there was snow enough, had sleigh-rides. Others also fished or went out to shoot birds, in the nearby woods. I was never very strong, as a boy, and was hampered by being near-sighted, as well as short of stature; more inclined to books than to sports, I never learned to swim, fished but little, and scarcely ever used a gun.

The girls played at tag, grace hoops, battle-dore, and shuttle-cock, but it was not considered lady-like for them to swim or skate, and rarely to row. Our mixed sports at picnics (and rather rare evening parties, which began by 8 and were over by 10) were forfeits, "pussy wants a corner," post office, hunt the slipper, Jerusalem, and Copenhagen, the last of which often degenerated into too boisterous a series of almost athletic contests for a kiss.

Our reading was practically confined to the *Arabian Nights*, *Robinson Crusoe, Gulliver's Travels, The Swiss Family Robinson,* Bunyon's *Pilgrim's Progress*, and Sandford and Merton. The "Rollo" books were published when I was a grown-up boy and were, so far as I can recall, the first of the distinctly "children's books." There was no St. Nicholas--or anything approaching it in scope.

The railroads were few and short. The Pennsylvania Railroad was not a continuous line, even to Pittsburgh. Its "depot," as we then always called it, was on Dock Street; later, successively, it was on Market St. at 8th, then 11th, then 13th Street, where Wanamaker's is now. Each long car, or as we now call it, "day coach" (there were no Pullmans) was drawn

14

by a string of six or eight mules from the depot out to 32nd and Market, where it was hooked up in trains and where the engine was added. Over the Alleghenies, there were inclined planes, as no locomotives then made had power enough to scale those mountains. The cars were pulled up and let down by ropes actuated by a stationary engine at the summit. The overland rail journey was supplemented by passenger canal boats, for the waterways en route.

The telegraph was so costly, and so rarely used, that when a telegram came, all hearts were a-flutter, for it must have been about something *very* urgent or important--usually a death or other misfortune.

The sewing machine did not exist. I remember well an evening when we were reading, around the center table in the parlor (by a sperm-oil astral lamp), that my father looked up from his newspaper and said to my mother, who was sewing, "Sue, I see in the paper a statement that a man has invented what he calls a 'sewing machine.' What an absurdity! Surely no machine can ever do the work of a woman's deft fingers!"

The first steamer from Europe, the *Great Western*, arrived the year before I was born, I think. Its voyage was remarkable in many ways, one of which was that it brought to America the first copy of a new volume in *Lardner's Scientific Library* which showed conclusively that no steamship could ever cross the Atlantic. The voyage usually occupied 14 days or more; the scanty news was transferred to a pilot boat off Cape Race and thence telegraphed from Cape Race to New York. We received European news only twice a week, and every steamer's name and probable date of arrival was well known. I remember the great rejoicing there was over the first cable, in 1858, and how disappointed everybody was when, almost immediately, it failed to work. In 1857, I took my first long journey. I went as far as St. Paul, then a small town. There was no Minneapolis, but only a straggling collection of houses around Fort Snelling, and at the Falls of St. Anthony. (In fact, when I was born, even Chicago did not exist. On its site were Fort Dearborn and the few houses around it.)

Indian wars were nearly always going on. They usually began with the revolting massacre of settlers, only too often their cause no longer being the endurable wrongs done to the Indians by these same or other settlers.

I well remember the Mexican War, and the rejoicing and illuminations following the victories at Resaca de la Palma, Monterrey, and Chapultepec, and the capture of Mexico City. In celebration, my father placed a wooden bar across every row of window panes in the front of the house, with a hole opposite the center of each pane and a lighted candle at each hole. In my opinion, there never had been such victories, nor such illuminations!

Our postal facilities were primitive indeed. We had no postage stamps, and for all of Philadelphia there was only one post office, at 3rd and Dock Streets. My father took letters with him to town, in the morning, though we did have one house delivery every day. Each letter was weighed, at the post office, and the amount paid was written by the clerk, in the upper right-hand corner. This amount varied for the city, and for various distances, each, say, of 50, 100, 300, 500, or 1000 miles (I am not sure that *any* letters were sent beyond 500 miles), or some such scale. When I was at Brown, a letter to England cost 25 cents for each quarter-ounce (and 25 cents then was fully equivalent to 50 cents now). No wonder that we always used *very* thin paper--and wrote practically all the way across every page!

16

When we moved to West Philadelphia, the first school I attended was the Newton Grammar School, on the south side of Chestnut Street below 36th Street, then not only a grammar school but with grades down to a, b, and c. From there, in February, 1849, when I was just over the age limit of twelve years old, I entered the Central High School, then located on Juniper Street below Market. Its principal was, as I later found out, a fine and scholarly man, though we found him to be cold-mannered and un-genial. His name was Dr. John S. Hart, but we boys, with the perversity of pupils the world over, dubbed him "the Juniper Street Humbug" (J. S. H.). Here I first discovered that I was nearsighted. In the Newton School, we had been seated according to rank, but in the high school we were seated alphabetically, and "K" in my class came far back. I no longer could see anything written or drawn on the blackboard. Accordingly, I was advised by my teacher to go to McAllister's, then the only optician, I suspect, in Philadelphia, on the South side of Chestnut below 10th Street. I well remember old Mr. McAllister, with his tray of spectacles, putting each pair on me and bidding me look at the bricks of the houses opposite. Whether I could see distinctly, and without discomfort, the lines of mortar between the bricks was the standard by which my glasses were chosen. Even so late as 1866, when Dr. Ezra Dyer first settled in Philadelphia, he was the only man who could prescribe scientifically a pair of glasses, and so strong was the prejudice against "specialists," in those days, that Dyer's (and later still, Dr. William Thomson's) friends thought it wise to postpone for some years proposing them for fellowship in the College of Physicians, lest they should be black-balled. By contrast, in 1910, Dr. George E. de Schweinitz, purely and simply an ophthamologist, was elected the *president* of that same college.

One of my fellow students, though not my classmate, at the high school was Ignatius L. Donnelly, whose fantastic title for his Commencement address (a poem), I remember, was "Love and Whiskers." He later became well known for warmly taking the position that Bacon was the real author of Shakespeare's plays.

When Lajos Kossuth, the Hungarian patriot, visited Philadelphia, in 1849 or 1850 (having escaped after the failure of the Insurrection of 1848, when all of Europe was in political ferment), and was to be received at the high school, a number of students presented themselves as candidates for the honor of delivering an address of welcome. With true freshman impudence (I'm not sure but that I ought to say "true Keen temerity"), I wrote out my masterpiece. I did not know what form my exordium should take, so I remember I began my MS well down at the middle of page one and then consulted my pastor, Rev. Dr. E. M. Levy, as to a suitable, and as I deemed necessary, rhetorical introduction. Alas for the vanity of human wishes! What a wet blanket was thrown over me when he thought that only "Illustrious Sir" should be enough to occupy--but surely not to fill--that yawning, yearning space. And when my speech and I were rejected in toto, I believed that I had been unjustly relegated to an undeserved oblivion.

However strange it may seem, I survived this dreadful blow and spoke my first little piece in public (save some earlier appearances on the Sunday-school stage), in the Musical Fund Hall in February, 1853, receiving the wholly undeserved "degree"--Heaven save the mark!--of Bachelor of Arts, at age 16!

The Philadelphia Evening Bulletin
Wednesday, October 2, 1912

Men and Things

AN odd little relic of the enormous enthusiasm which Louis Kossuth excited when he visited Philadelphia has been placed in my hands. Men who remember the journey of the Magyar orator, statesman and warrior in the United States have said that, almost idolatrous as were the greetings to him everywhere, there was no other city, with the exception of New York, in which this feeling was so intense as it was in Philadelphia. On one or two occasions in past years we have cited here some of the unusual facts which attested the delirious state of the public mind in its welcome to the eloquent champion of Hungarian freedom. Parades, serenades, dinners and receptions were organized in his honor; public men of all parties expressed the popular impulse, and in all kinds of new current fashions his name was used as a means of obtaining public favor. Even to this day the Kossuth hat is used as a descriptive term. Probably the only other European that was received in this country at any time in the course of the nineteenth century with like fervor and acclaim was Lafayette in his old age. In Kossuth the multitude recognized the personified aspiration of humanity, in the Old World, for the blessings of freedom and opportunity; and it became, for a while, an American habit to regard with contempt or reviling every man whom he singled out as an object of scorn or wrath in his denunciations of European oppressors. The effects of his eloquence were often extraordinary in the sweep and force of his invective and the glow of his appeals. Even some of the most cautious and conservative politicians, who felt that there was something Quixotic in his transatlantic errand, admitted that they had to be careful lest they might fall under the influence of the sympathetic stir which he made in the hearts of most of their countrymen as soon as they began to listen to the music of his inspiring words.

☆ ☆ ☆ ☆ ☆

The spirit of this popular admiration is reflected in the relic which I have just mentioned. It is a book of small or pocket size that was published in Philadelphia in the early part of the winter of 1852 under the editorship of Dr. P. H. Skinner and bearing the title of "The Welcome of Louis Kossuth, Governor of Hungary, By the Youth, December 26, 1851." It was intended to be a memento of the part which the pupils in the public schools of the city had played in the great reception. In the plans for that event it appears that pains had been taken that the juvenile population should be represented and that the educational authorities had given their consent to a competition among the pupils for the honor of composing an address which the author would personally deliver in the presence of the illustrious guest. A committee of clergymen which included David Matin, John Chambers and A. D. Gillette had been appointed to examine the thirty-eight youths who prepared compositions for that purpose. These were read by them before the committee; the ages of the competitors were between twelve and sixteen; at least one, perhaps a few of them, are still living among us in their three score and ten, and the addresses which all of them submitted to the consideration of the clergymen are preserved in this little book

☆ ☆ ☆ ☆ ☆

The report of those gentlemen was highly complimentary to the style and spirit of the papers which they examined. In fact one, in reading them now, is inclined to receive an impression that English composition must have been well taught in the schools at that time. Of course they bear the marks of youthful greenness, and one smiles at the extravagance of much of the sentiment. But it may be doubted whether the pupils in the public schools at the present time would present, on the whole, a better average in both the sense and the graces of expression, notwithstanding the prevailing belief that this branch of education is conducted with more facility than it was then. Perhaps the influence of **John S. Hart**, who himself was the author of textbooks of grammar and rhetoric and whose own style as a writer on moral and educational themes was an admirable example of ease and lucid flow, had not a little to do with the attention given to English instruction, for he was, at this time, the head of the High School, and apparently it was from the High School that most of the competitors were drawn. Two of its pupils were winners of the foremost honors--one Master Malcolm A. MacNeill, aged thirteen, and the other Master John L. Painter, also aged thirteen and credited to West Kensington; and these lads were therefore chosen to act as spokesmen in conveying to Kossuth the sentiment of regard in which he was viewed in Philadelphia.

☆ ☆ ☆ ☆ ☆

The time for the presentation ceremony was the day after the Christmas of 1851, and the place the hall of the Chinese Museum, which was situated at Ninth and Sansom streets--a large part of the site of the Continental Hotel--and which contained the most capacious auditorium in the city at that time. After each of the two lads whom the committee had selected had received a gold watch as a prize for his address, Kossuth made his appearance on the platform and they were introduced to him by the Rev. Dr. Lyman Coleman. Master Painter then began his address, saluting Kossuth with "Welcome! Great Chief," comparing him to Washington, declaring that Hungary would eventually rise from its oppression, assuring its champion that there was not an American youth who would not "rather be the defeated Magyar than revel in the halls of a despotic autocrat." There was a bit of gallantry, too, in the boy's allusion to Kossuth's spouse. "Sir," he said, "we have read of the toils and hardships of your dear beloved wife who, in disguises, escaped the vigilant eye of the monster Haynaun. With such examples of female heroism, Hungary must be free; for by the virtues of our Mothers we are taught from infancy to lisp our detestation of tyranny; for disguise it as you will, a noble mind must be free and independent, and as the minds of the American youth are becoming brighter by education (for our public schools are as free as the air we breathe) every boy is taught that which is truly republican-- Liberty of Speech, of the Press, Liberty to worship God as he pleases. In behalf of the youth of Philadelphia, whom I represent, I conclude as I began: Strike for your firesides, your altars and your homes; and may the God of Battles guide the arm and hand of the Magyar band." At this point Kossuth, we are told, advanced to young Painter, placed his arms around his neck, and, in a most affectionate manner, imprinted a kiss upon his brow amidst rounds of applause. Then came the turn of Master MacNeill, who had been chosen to speak for the girls of the public schools. He described the patriotic enthusiasm of every American schoolboy, congratulated Kossuth on his appearance in the very birthplace of liberty, and bade him welcome to the protecting shade of the Star Spangled Banner. "And be assured, Sir," he said, "the schoolboy is not alone. No; the schoolgirl, too, does join him. For the same spirit which prompted America's daughters to raise floral triumphal arches to receive Washington and to throw themselves upon the protection of him who had been the defender of their mothers, still burns within their breasts, and they now unite with us in cordially and heartily welcoming him who fain would have proved himself to be a Washington to Hungary. To our midst, then, most worthy Sir, you have the most sincere welcome of the schoolboy and the schoolgirl; and in every act you undertake for the advancement of liberty, their unceasing wish to you, Sir, is Godspeed." The lad then brought forward a small volume containing the Declaration of Independence and the Constitution of the United States, and this was presented to Kossuth with the assurance that it was from its pages, in simplified and comprehensive form, that the Constitution was studied and committed to memory by the American schoolboy.

☆ ☆ ☆ ☆ ☆

Kossuth, after having kissed young MacNeill as he had young Painter, proceeded to make his reply. It was probably extemporaneous in the main, if not altogether so, although it was not only keyed to the high pitch of fine feeling that marked all his public speaking, but the diction was more expressive than that of many a native orator. Indeed, Kossuth's mastery of the English language, which he had begun to study only a few years before, was marvelous; and he was known to hold the uninterrupted attention of American audiences for three or four hours at a time. On this occasion his reply related largely to public schools and their value to the cause of national freedom. He thought that there were two marks which a man carries on his character throughout his life and which cannot be erased from it--the mark which the mother has imprinted upon his heart and the one which the teacher has imprinted upon his mind. He hoped that the hearts of men would become as pure as those of children in their love of liberty. "Indeed," he went on to say, "our Saviour, who pointed out the children to humanity in such a way, is the great teacher of the principle of brotherly love--of that brotherly love of which your city bears even the name. I hope that every man will remember that by sentiments of children the principles of mankind are sanctified and that there is a halo of piety attached to that action of mankind which is conformed to these principles." Kossuth then placed his arms around both the Painter and Mac Neill boys. "My own children," he said, "I have kissed you; take it for a father's kiss. And when you grow up to be men, though you may forget me personally, forget not that the man who represents the oppressed liberty of Europe, pleading for it before the great tribunal of the people of the United States, has imprinted a kiss upon your brows; and may that be a link for you and your companions which shall bind you through every vicissitude of life ever and ever to be warm-hearted, generous protectors and maintainers of those principles for which you feel now, in your childhood, a warm sympathy. God bless you."

☆ ☆ ☆ ☆ ☆

In the published memento to which we have been referring are given also the Addresses written by the other competitors in the examination before the committee of clergymen. The Misses Mary G. Richards, Annie Reed, Lizzie Whitehead, Jessie Elder and Marion Ash were among the girls of the Normal School, which was then situated on Sargent Street, between Ninth and Tenth, who submitted prose compositions of salutation to the hero, while Miss Malvina A. Wiley and Miss Esther C. Henck framed theirs in verse. The lads who wrote Addresses were John Henry Weill, of the Presbyterian Institute; Charles Alexander, of the Southeast Gramma School; J. Bonsall Goddard, of the Locust Street Grammar School, and William Wells, Charles H. Chubb, A. F. C. Colesberry, L. Rhoades Hall, Henry McIntire, J. L. Loudenslager, H. Cowperthwaite, Theodore McMurtrie, James H. Little, O. G. Wagner, John McClintock, J. A. Dorgan, Thomas M. Pierce, John Green, James J. Murphy, William Roberts, Samuel G. Scott, R. B. Plotts, G. M. Woodward, William Fury, Samuel K. Reynolds, R. Craige, F. B. Converse, E. D. Lockwood, and William H. Thaw. Never was liberty more rapturously exalted and the rights of mankind and the virtues of American independence more heroically acclaimed than they were by these youthful patriots. Master Chubb, aged sixteen, assured Kossuth that "despotism must fall; the seeds of destruction are sown; the watch fires of tyranny burn with an unsteady light; the sword which she once flourished over Europe is now eaten with the blood of her enemies; the ghosts of despots flit across our vision, and the sounds of their funeral dirge are wafted across the ocean by every breeze that blows over its ruffled surface--Europe will soon rejoice in the strength of her freedom." Master Alexander, aged fourteen, was sure that Hungary would do as "our mothers tell us our grandfathers did in the old days of '76," and he did not care, in bidding Louis Kossuth welcome to the land of the free, whether it "pleased or offended imperial Nicholas of the North, or his imperial protégé of Hapsburg, or the royal lady of Spain, or the bantling of despotism who crushed the young republic of Rome, or he of the Seven Hills, time out of mind the ringleader of despots." Master Colesberry, aged fifteen, expressed his ardent wish that the spark of freedom in the youth of Hungary would burst forth into mighty vengeance when they became men. "The course of a factious demagogue," he informed Kossuth, "is looked upon with scorn and contempt for its meanness; but the course of a patriot glitters with a hue of gorgeous magnificence and is regarded as beneficial in the highest degree; for in truth it can be said that men have lost their reason when they look for happiness beneath the unrelenting yoke of tyranny." Never were kings, emperors and czars handled more unmercifully than they were by these young Philadelphians, while no quarter was given to the Austrian eagle or the Russian bear. What a joyous reflection it is of the innocent thought and aspiration of wholesome boyhood; and yet how many, too, of those happy lads must have looked back, in the years of their manhood and public activity among us, with both fondness and sadness--fondness when they thought of their pure ideals, and sadness when they saw how far below them even the best men had to live in the presence of the mysteries and perplexities of the problem of life.

☆ ☆ ☆ ☆ ☆

Today there are Philadelphia households in which the memory or the tradition of that Kossuth greeting is still cherished from one generation to another.

My father's early education had been very meager but had been supplemented by extensive reading. He was a man of great intelligence, force of character, and breadth of view, and he was determined that his children should have the best possible education available, if they were willing to avail themselves of his generosity. He offered me a college course, and I eagerly accepted his proposal.

Before deciding whether to go to the University of Lewisburg, which had recently been founded by the Baptists, or to Brown University, I visited the former, in June of 1855. I went as his protégé with Deacon Thomas Wattson of the First Baptist Church, a member of the Board of Trustees at Lewisburg (and a great-grandfather of Howard Butcher Jr., my son-in-law).

To show how primitive travel conditions then were, the following account of my journey may be of interest. The Pennsylvania Railroad was not yet completed--or at least certainly did not run to Lewisburg. At Harrisburg, or some point beyond, we had to leave the railroad and proceed for forty miles in a canal boat, the only time in my life (save in Holland and on the Göta Canal, in Sweden) when I have traveled by canal boat. In the forty miles as we were approaching the mountains, there were 39 locks. It was lovely June weather, and the company consisted almost wholly of Baptists, including a large number of clergymen visiting the university for Commencement. Among us were quite a few young folks of about my own age (18 +). We had a very jolly time, telling stories, singing, walking from one lock to the next. We disembarked late in the afternoon. The moon was full, the journey delightful.

At supper, the captain, at the head of the long table, rapped for silence and asked Rev. Dr. Dowling to say grace. We all bowed our heads and waited . . . and waited. Everyone knew that Dr. Dowling was on board, but still the grace was unsaid. At last, we glanced furtively up and down the table and discovered Dr. Dowling in a most perplexing and embarrassing plight. The dentists of those days made artificial teeth wholly for show but not for use, and Dr. Dowling had taken out both uppers and lowers and put them in his pocket. He had not been forewarned and therefore needed time to find and replace them. They seemed to be the most elusive teeth any man ever possessed. But finally they were seized, and he replaced them, behind the corner of a napkin. Then, with a face as red as a beet, he arose and said grace, offered amid a very audible titter which was prevented from becoming an outburst of laughter by our respect for the cloth.

We left the boat about 4 A.M., as I remember (at all events, at early sunrise), on the bank of the canal, whence a road ran to Lewisburg. We young folks walked the few miles (probably 2 to 4) to Lewisburg, while carriages were provided for our elders.

On my return, I informed my father of my preference for Brown. With his approval, I selected Brown University chiefly on account of President Francis Wayland's great reputation, and because he had introduced, in 1850, the new system, in which the students at Brown were offered electives, for the first time, and modern science was placed on a par with the humanities. He thus antedated by many years President Eliot's work at Harvard. But on taking stock of my achievements, I found that I was far behind the entrance requirements. Accordingly, my father placed me in the school of Prof. E. D. Saunders, on 39th Street above Market (where the Presbyterian Hospital is now). Here I spent two years almost wholly on Latin and Greek. Looking back at the matter, I find it clear that if I had gone to one of the great "fitting" schools of New England (such as Phillips Academy, Andover, or Phillips Academy, Exeter), I would easily have accomplished in one year more and better work, by far, than I did in two years with Prof. Saunders. He lacked system and accuracy and worked in a sort of helter-skelter way. Still, I did fairly well.

But when I entered Brown, in September, 1855, I was measured alongside of the boys who knew every rule and every exception in *Andrews' and Stoddard's Latin Grammar*, and the same in *Harkness' Greek Grammar*. I was not at all in the same class with them. Hence, I had to put my nose to the grindstone and begin almost at the very beginning.

Earnest study for the purpose of obtaining an education was more the fashion in those days than these. Athletics were poorly developed, and as a result, the health of the students was by no means as robust as at present. I took part in the then simple football games--in which everybody played--and in 1858, we started a college rowing club. Our shell was housed on the Seekonk River, and Adoniram B. Judson and I each had a wherry, i.e., a light "lap-streak" boat rowed by one man. The day I was twenty-one (January 19th, 1858) saw my first venture in the financial field, and I made a dismal failure of it. I borrowed $100 for three months at 6 per cent, for which I gave a note to old Rev. Dr. Alva Woods (a Fellow of Brown University, father of Marshall Woods, grandfather of John Carter Brown Woods, and uncle of Mrs. George Dana Boardman), a rich but mean old skinflint. The money was obtained for the rowing club, to help pay for our boathouse. When the three months came around, the club failed to repay me, and I could not scrape together $100, and so had to ask for an extension. I paid it later, interest and all, and so rehabilitated myself and avoided going into involuntary bankruptcy!

In Providence, I became a teacher in the Sunday school almost at once and had mounted a top hat, as became a college man. On a Saturday in December, 1885, or January, 1856, came a cold drizzle which froze on the trees, and on Sunday morning, the sight was splendid. On my way to early Sunday school, I went down Waterman Street, which is quite steep and has a curve, at one point, which features a narrow and rather deep gutter, right at the turn. The pavement, alas, was almost a glare of ice. Wearing my top hat, I was carrying an umbrella and had a Bible under my arm. Just as I reached the curve and the gutter, some young ladies whom I knew were going uphill on the opposite sidewalk. I lifted my hat and, at the same moment, attempted to lift my feet over the gutter. But down I went, with my hat, my umbrella, my Bible, and I going four different ways. Naturally, the girls couldn't help bursting into uproarious laughter, which they tried in vain to repress or conceal. I picked up myself and my impedimenta, in confusion and great heat, and made my way to the church, not, it may be imagined, in exactly a Sunday school mood.

Prof. and Mrs. Lincoln and Prof. and Mrs. Angell were very kind to me at Brown. They rather took me under their wings and made me feel at home in their homes. Lincoln was superintendent of the Sunday school, and this naturally drew us together. As Angell was only seven years my senior (though I always thought of him as *far* older than I), and had very recently been married to Prof. Caswell's daughter, and as I knew the young people of the Caswell and Angell families very well, I became quite intimate there.

In my sophomore year, the first Angell baby was born. In my "Memories of Brown," I have told the story of this baby boy and his "cradle" and need not repeat it here.

Judge Greene (author of *Old Grimes*) and Mrs. Greene had three children, all girls. Mary and Sarah became my two most intimate young lady friends--friendships which have lasted through all our lives. The oldest sister, Mrs. Potter, a young widow (later the wife of C. C. Van Zandt, ex-governor of Rhode Island), I knew much less well. The elder of the other two married Samuel C. Eastman, of the Class of '57; the younger, who is still living, married Rev. Dr. Samuel W. Duncan, of the Class of '60.

The three men on the faculty to whom intellectually I owe the greatest debt were Lincoln, Chace, and Gammell. Lincoln's searching criticism of our work in Latin, his happy translations, his exact scholarship, and his broad views of what studying Latin meant (far more than a mere textual rendering) were most inspiring. Chace was a mastermind in science. He taught Physiology, Geology, and Zoology, as then understood, and made them so fascinating that I could hardly wait from one recitation to the next. Gammell taught History, and in the right way, by making it not merely a chronological record of dates and events but an unfolding of human development. That too is a study in which I have never lost interest. Each of these men encouraged questions, and independent thinking, and reasoning, so that our minds were not only stored with facts but were developed in the broadest way. Our essays with them--and with Dunn, Professor of Rhetoric--were a splendid training, and I have always attributed to the Brown method my ability to successfully explain scientific facts to non-scientific people. Many people have said to me (I hope my children and grandchildren will not think me vain in writing this. It is chiefly for their satisfaction, when I shall have long since passed away, and is for their eyes only), after having read my various published articles, in such popular magazines as *Harper's*, etc., that they have enjoyed the lucid explanations and therefore could readily understand what I was writing about. Then too, in my lectures, I have followed the same method and gotten similar results. Whenever I want to explain any subject, I first try to reduce to the simplest possible statements the elementary facts of the case. Then, proceeding one step at a time, from the now known to the as yet unknown, to show the natural development of the matter. (In the fireproof box in my middle office will be found a list of my various papers, together with lists of the offices I have held and the honors conferred on me-- lists for family eyes alone.)

My friendships among college mates included not a few in classes other than '59. For example, I knew (but very slightly) Richard Olney, of '56; Eastman and Goodwin, among others, of '57; I knew John Hay, of '58, quite well, a friendship which lasted until his death; Duncan Gordon, Kirke Porter, etc., of '60; Tom Caswell, of '61; and a few in later classes. In my own class, Poinier (my roommate for two years), George Porter and Adoniram and Elnathan Judson, and others, were close friends. Naturally, my companions were chiefly among the fraternity of the Alpha Delta Phi.

My college life was very happy. I plodded along with my studies, being especially interested in mathematics, to which I attributed my love of order and exactness--and in which I took the first prize in an extra examination for each of the first three years in college. I had never studied with a view to winning college honors, but only to do each day's

work as well as I could. When I received my appointment for the junior
exhibition, towards the end of that year, I was not a little astonished--
and I must also confess greatly pleased--to find that I had the "Oratio
Latina," which meant that I was at the head of my class and that, unless
I did less good work during the following year, I would be valedictorian,
an honor which came to me in due time.

In that same year, 1858, I saw the most magnificent sight in the
heavens that I have ever seen, Donati's comet. Every night for weeks, as
I walked from my room (No. 23 University Hall) and across the middle campus
to Deacon Bates's, for supper, I saw that glorious sight. The tail extended over nearly one-third of the heavens and spread out in a wide fan-
shaped curving triangle, far more splendid and impressive than the comet
of '43.

From my earliest childhood, and possibly even before my birth, my
father had dedicated me to the Lord. I never knew the time when he--and
I too--did not fully expect that I should enter the ministry. When I went
to college, it was to prepare me for the sacred calling. But as time went
on, I found myself insensibly changing my mind. More and more, I became
convinced that I was neither "called of God" nor fitted for the ministry.
By my senior year, when I had to make the decision whether or not to enter
a theological seminary after graduating, I felt so strongly about this
that I consulted Professors Lincoln and Angell, and upon their advice, at
the Christmas vacation, I talked with my father. It was a very hard task
for me, and a still harder one for him. I knew it was a great blow to all
his years of hope and longing. But I put the matter plainly before him,
told him why I had changed my mind, and stated that I wanted to study med-

icine. Never did I respect my dear father more. He did not hesitate for a moment, but said that if I felt that God had not called me to preach, I ought *not* to do so. Never a word of persuasion, entreaty, or command did he utter. His self-control and self-denial amazed me, for I knew how deep-rooted was his wish, cherished for over a score of years. If I wished to study medicine, he said, I should have the best education he could give me. So the matter was settled between us. But between him and God I know that there must have been a sore outpouring of his soul. It must have cost him many a tear and the deepest sorrow. But once it was settled, he never discussed it again. It was settled once for all. I am happy to be able to add that not once, but perhaps a dozen times, in later years, he said to me, "My son, I think you have found your niche."

He concurred in my desire to spend a resident graduate year at Brown, studying the branches leading up to medicine, as well as courses in general culture--especially English literature. This last was most fortunate, for, from the time I began to study medicine till now, I have had little leisure time--until recently--for general literature.

During my senior and resident graduate years, I earned some money by my own labor, for the first time in my life. I coached one classmate; I reported lectures, for the *Providence Journal* (I may possibly have preserved my reports in the scrapbook I presented, some years ago, to the library at Brown); and I played the melodeon in the New Brown Street Baptist Church. No money I have ever earned since has been so sweet to me as this. At Christmas, in 1858 and 1859, I gave to my parents and my brothers presents bought by money I had honestly earned. It was a new and real joy to me. Then I had no opportunity to earn any more until I entered the army

28

for a month in 1861, and later, in May of 1862.

One amusing event, in 1858, was my lecture in Barrington. Lizzie
Sears (daughter of the president), the two Greene sisters, Abby Judson,
and Sam Duncan accompanied me, as my guests, and we drove there from
Providence. We started in ample time and with a driver who professed to
know the way. All went on merrily, for a time, but at last, darkness
came on, in the short winter day, and the driver confessed that he was
lost. Farm houses were very few, but at last I saw a light, quite a distance back from the road (I had taken a seat on the box). I jumped off
and hastened across a rough-plowed field, for we could not find any entrance road toward the light. The first thing I knew, in the darkness, I
had run up against a sapling, which bent before my impact, but, acting
like a spring, recoiled and threw me sprawling. I had on an evening suit,
and not only was it covered with dirt, but also legs of the trousers were
very badly torn, and the swallow-tailed coat was ineffective as a covering! Learning the correct road, at the house, and also that we were far
out of our way, the driver then plied the whip, and we finally arrived at
8:30, instead of at 8, just as the audience had begun to disperse. They
were good enough to return, and while they were being seated in the
church, the girls of our party pinned up the rents and brushed off the
dirt as well as possible. I gave my lecture. I did not roam about the
platform, you may be sure, but welcomed the friendly shelter of the pulpit. But there on the very front seat below me were the five enemies of
my comfort and my equanimity who led the applause at every opportunity and
otherwise plagued the life out of me. My subject was "The Canterbury Pil-
grims," and I ended up with the first--and last--alleged "poem" I have

ever attempted! I have the MS, in my desk. I hope you *won't* read it.

Another funny--but at the time mortifying--incident happened when I asked one of Mrs. Buell's girls to go with me to a lecture by Henry Giles. When I arrived at the house, Mrs. Buell told me that "Pa Buell," as we boys always called him, had been taken ill, and she asked if I would allow her and two or three of the girls to follow us two, under my valiant protection. Just why a woman of fifty, with not two or three, but, to my consternation, five girls needed my protection was not clear. But as I wanted to be in her good graces, on account of the girls I wanted to call on, I assented. With seven ladies to get ready, naturally some time elapsed. (We went afoot, as it was quite near--and my pocketbook had been stepped on by an elephant.) When we reached the hall, every seat was occupied, and the late-comers had begun to occupy chairs in the middle aisle and at the very front. The only way to get these chairs (there were no ushers) was for me to bring them from the space under the platform. Four trips did I make, emerging in the face of the entire audience (and nearly all the college was there), holding aloft a chair in each hand--and then da capo and da capo and da capo. I suspect my face was as red as a beet, from both the exertion and from rage. Needless to say, I did not *wholly* enjoy Mr. Giles's wit and wisdom; nor do I remember even the subject. After escorting my "harem" back to the school, I returned to my room. But there I found a room full of the boys, and when I entered, a cheer arose, along with shouts of "When will you do it again?" "How many will you take *next* time?" and "How did you enjoy it?" Never again did I repeat the performance! Even today, some old graybeard at Commencement will poke me in the ribs and ask whether I admired Henry Giles's style.

```
                    Brown University, 1859
                    Program for Commencement
  1.  Latin Salutatory  - - - - - - - - - - -  Walter M. Potter

  2.  Excessive Tendencies to Association:
        An Oration of the First Class  - - - -  Albert K. Potter

  3.  The Shrine of Canterbury:
        An Oration of the Second Class - - - -  Charles H. Perry

  4.  The Versatility of Sir Walter Raleigh:
        An Oration of the First Class  - - - -  Adoniram B. Judson

  5.  The Illustrative Arts:
        An Oration of the Second Class - - - -  Lucius S. Bolles

  6.  The Tower of London:
        An Oration of the First Class  - - - -  Silas P. Holbrook

  7.  The Venetian Dominion of the Sea:
        On Oration of the Second Class - - - -  William D. King

  8.  The Social Satire of Thackeray:
        An Oration of the Second Class - - - -  George L. Porter

  9.  The Victories of Peace:
        An Oration of the First Class  - - - -  Charles M. Smith

 10.  A Knowledge of History Necessary to the Reformer:
        An Oration of the Second Class - - - -  Frederick D. Ely

 11.  The Friendship of Goethe and Schiller:
        An Oration of the First Class  - - - -  Elnathan Judson

 12.  The Position of Power:
        An Oration of the First Class  - - - -  Timothy W. Bancroft

 13.  The Future of the Slavic Race:
        An Oration of the First Class  - - - -  Charles H. Brown

 14.  The Melancholy of Cowper:
        An Oration of the First Class  - - - -  Samuel T. Poinier

 15.  Latin, the Language of Scholars:
        An Oration of the First Class  - - - -  David Weston

 16.  The Decline of Imagination in Old Age:
        The Philosophical Oration  - - - - - -  Thomas F. Tobey

 17.  The Scholar's Sentiment of Veneration for the Past:
        An Oration with the Valedictory Addresses - William W. Keen, Jr.

The Valedictory honors of the Class were awarded by the Faculty to Edward
Lawton Barker, of Newport, who declined them for the same reason that the
Class of 1835 had refused to become candidates for degrees.*
```

* This last paragraph is wrong. The following correction to Mr. Guild's
account of the Commencement of 1859 was inserted in the copy of his
History of Brown University in the John Hay Library:
    "Mr. Guild is in error. The Faculty Records [reproduced on p. 32] show
the following tables of Standing and Assignment of Parts for the Class
of 1859 at Commencement:

    1. Keen - - - - - - - 19.76   Valedictory
    2. Barker - - - - - - 19.65   Latin Salutatory
    3. W. M. Potter - - - 19.25   Classical Oration in Greek
    4. Tobey - - - - - - 19.10   Philosophical Oration
            etc.   etc.
                                [*Signed*] Harry L. Koopman"

    I never knew of Mr. Guild's erroneous statement until I read his
History, when I was preparing my *History of the Early Years of Brown University (1764-1770)*. I asked Prof. Koopman to look up the facts in the
Faculty Records, and finding them as herein stated, asked him to make the
above entry in the library copy of Guild's History. This is all I have
done, since, after 56 years, I had no desire to stir up the matter. I may
add that I gladly contributed to a fund for the comfort of Mr. Guild's
widow, when, in her old age, she was destitute. This was *after* I had discovered his error.

Standing and Assignment of Parts

Class of 1859

1.	Keen - - - - - -	19.76	Valedictory
2.	Barker - - - - -	19.65	Latin Salutatory
3.	W. M. Potter - - - -	19.25	Classical Oration in Greek
4.	Tobey - - - - -	19.10	Philosophical Oration
5.	Weston - - - - -	18.79	Oration of the First Class
6.	Brown - - - - -	18.30	" " " " "
7.	Whitney - - - - -	18.20	" " " " "
8.	V. C. Smith - - - -	17.89	" " " " "
9.	Poinier - - - - -	17.776	" " " " "
10.	Short - - - - -	17.771	" " " " "
11.	C. M. Smith - - - -	17.74	" " " " "
12.	Bowen - - - - -	17.69	" " " " "
13.	Bancroft - - - - -	17.55	" " " " "
14.	Holbrook - - - - -	16.78	" " " " "
15.	Pratt - - - - -	16.62	" " " " "
16.	E. Judson - - - -	16.33	" " " " "
17.	Colburn - - - - -	16.28	" " " " "
18.	A. K. Potter - - - -	16.25	" " " " "
19.	A. B. Judson - - - -	15.10	" " " " "
20.	Perry - - - - -	14.97	Oration of the Second Class
21.	Porter - - - - -	14.96	" " " " "
22.	Ely - - - - -	14.92	" " " " "
23.	Bolles - - - - -	14.67	" " " " "
24.	Jenney - - - - -	13.66	(No appointment)
25.	King - - - - - -	12.08	Oration of the Second Class

Blumer, having been prevented by sickness from completing his examinations, has no mark assigned him.

Candidates for the Degree of A.B.

1.	Nash - - - - - -	18.71
2.	Whipple - - - - -	15.69
3.	Fuller - - - - -	13.47

Candidates for the Degree of B.P.

1.	Andrews - - - - -	18.21
2.	Thurston - - - - -	17.92

[*Signed*]   J. B. Angell, Secretary

MY MEDICAL CAREER

I left college in June, 1860, and in September began the study of medicine at the Jefferson Medical College. I went there, rather than to the University of Pennsylvania, because the Jefferson faculty was a far stronger one than that of the university, with Gross, Pancoast, Dunglison, among others, and also because my mother's sister had married Dr. Thomas D. Mitchell, who was the Professor of Materia Medica and Therapeutics-- and, I am sorry to say, a pretty poor one. But his advice to me on one point was invaluable: i.e., to enter the office of (John H.) Brinton and (Jacob M.) Da Costa as a private pupil. Had I not done so, I should have graduated without ever having looked through a microscope, or ever having personally examined a patient, or ever having written a prescription. In my *Addresses and Other Papers*, I have described the dreadfully inadequate course and need not repeat the story here.

A still more fortunate result of my going into their office was that I made the acquaintance of Dr. S. Weir Mitchell, and on this wise. I started my studies in Dr. Brinton's office, at 1005 Walnut Street (where the Jefferson Medical College building now stands), on the first Monday in September, 1860. Two or three days laters, I was sitting at one of the front windows, with Gray's *Anatomy*--then a new book--in my lap. (Little did I ever think that my name would appear as editor on its title page.) I had a skull in my hands in order to begin the study of the bones. The afternoon sun was hot, and I had the Venetian blinds turned so as to ex- clude the direct sunlight. The slats were suddenly changed to a horizon- tal plane, and as I turned my head to see who was there, I saw a pair of eyes looking at me, and a voice outside said, "Doctor, don't you want to

33

help me with some experiments on snakes?" Now to have attained the degree
of M.D. in two or three days naturally flattered me, and snakes were very
attractive. I jumped up, laid down book and skull, and went to the front
door, where I saw a rather slender and tall young man, who introduced himself as Dr. S. Weir Mitchell. I spent a delightful afternoon with him, in
the old Philadelphia School of Anatomy (see its history, in my *Addresses
and Other Papers*), again little thinking that I later should be the head
of that school, which was the training place for myself and so many other
professors.

This was the beginning of a friendship that has endured for over 52
years (written in 1912), without a cloud even as big as a man's hand coming between us. I helped him during my entire college course in medicine
and was associated with him and Dr. George R. Morehouse, during a large
part of the Civil War, in the special Hospital for Diseases and Injuries
of the Nervous System, first in the Christian Street Hospital (the old
police station on Christian Street below 10th, which is still standing),
and later in Turner's Lane Hospital. Mitchell wrote, with suggestions
from Dr. Morehouse (and a few from me), our book called *Gunshot Wounds
and Other Injuries of Nerves*, published by Lippincott in 1864, a book
which laid the foundation for all our modern neurological surgery. A number of other papers were published under our joint names, Dr. Mitchell
writing some and I the others (see my *List of Publications*). Morehouse
was always promising, but he never put pen to paper. I remember writing
out (often till long after midnight) the "Notes of Cases" I had taken, and
all apparently for nothing: Morehouse kept these notes in his office until
they were destroyed by fire, leaving a residue of exasperation. But no,

it was not "for nothing," for it gave me exactly what I needed, training in the art of taking notes and writing out histories.

Again, after my return from Europe, in 1866, when I became head of the Philadelphia School of Anatomy, I assisted Dr. Mitchell in his later researches on snake venom. Later, I was his colleague at the Orthopedic Hospital and long did all (or nearly all) of his neurological surgery. I count it the most fortunate event of my professional life that I came early under his stimulating and elevating influence. I owe him a debt of gratitude I can never repay.*

At the end of my first year, before I had graduated in medicine, I entered the service of the United States as Assistant Surgeon of the 5th Massachusetts Regiment. In my *Addresses and Other Papers* I have narrated the most important events of my military career and will omit them here. In 1910, I joined the "Loyal Legion" and wear its button with pride. My oldest male descendant will always wear it, I hope, and remember how much of honor and patriotism it stands for.

This reminds me of a question from one of my children, when very young, of whether I was a surgeon in the *Revolutionary* War. But when I recall the fact that the period from 1776 to 1837 was only 61 years, and the period from 1837 to 1912 is 75 years, the question is not so odd after all. Throughout my own life, the Revolution has seemed as far off as the Middle Ages. How greatly our perspective varies!

---

* For fuller information as to my relations with Dr. Mitchell, see three papers by Mitchell, Billings, and myself, in *Transactions of the College of Physicians of Philadelphia,* 1905; my own paper is reprinted in my *Addresses and Other Papers*, 1905; Mitchell's lecture in Chicago (*J.A.M.A.,* May 9, 1914); J. J. Putnam's paper (*Boston Medical & Surgical Journal,* May 28, 1914); and the Weir Mitchell Memorial volume in my library. See also "The History of the Philadelphia School of Anatomy," in my *Addresses and Other Papers*.

I graduated in medicine in March, 1862, and after passing the special examination, I entered the United States Army as Assistant Surgeon, in May. As I had no intention of making the army my career, I declined my commission in the Regular Army and was instead appointed Acting Assistant Surgeon, U.S.A., or, as we were usually called by the regulars, "damned contract doctors." We--or at least I--did not appreciate the fact that we were making history, and so I kept no journal, which I now *deeply* regret.

During most of my service in the army, I was the agent of the Army Medical Museum in Washington and collected specimens from all the hospitals in Frederick, Md. (and later, in Philadelphia), and forwarded them to Washington. My own notes and specimens fill many a page and furnish many an illustration in the six splendid volumes of *The Medical and Surgical History of the War of the Rebellion*. Circular No. 6, on "Reflex Paralysis," was another important publication, setting forth a novel theory of shock which has only lately received the attention it deserves. It is a very rare pamphlet now. One copy is in the library of the College of Physicians of Philadelphia (presented by me), and I have one in my own library.

Late in July, 1864, having an especially favorable opportunity (and seeing that the war was almost over), I sailed for Europe, with Kirke Porter. We traveled in England, Scotland, Belgium, and Holland, thence up the Rhine to Switzerland, finally reaching Paris early in October. There I settled down to work, while Kirke returned to America. In particular, I worked under Nélaton, Velpeau, Maisonneuve, and Duchenne de Boulogne, as well as a number of the *chefs de clinique*.

After a hard winter's work in Paris, on French and medicine--especially surgery--I took my Easter holiday in Italy, spending Easter week in Rome.

The monarch of the "States of the Church," in 1865, was Pope Pius IX, and he and the cardinals were constantly met in the streets of Rome, he in white, with six horses, postilions, and footmen; they in scarlet, and with four horses. I heard the Miserere in the Sistine Chapel, on Good Friday, and was just back of the *Guardia Nobile* when the Pope passed up to the high altar in St. Peter's, on Easter Sunday, carried in the *sedia gestatoria*. I was blessed by him from the balcony (he overlooking the sea of over 30,000 faces in front of St. Peter's), and later saw the illumination of the dome and, for the last time, the gorgeous fireworks on the Pincian Hill. In 1866, all this had vanished. Instead of a united Italy, as now, there were Sardinia; Lombardy and Venice, under Austria; Parma; Modena; Tuscany; the States of the Church; and the two Sicilies--i.e., seven frontiers, with seven visas of passports; seven custom houses, searches, and often duties; and seven different currencies (to the joy of the money-changers and the sorrow of travelers).*

In May, 1865, I settled in Vienna for the spring term in medicine-- and also to get some German. I boarded with a German family, consisting of parents, several children, and a niece, Fräulein Victorine. She and I could communicate in French. We agreed to exchange service for service: she was to teach me German and I to teach her English. Within a very few days, she confided to me that she was *verlobt* and offered with pride to show me the letter her fiancé had written to her uncle, asking for her hand. But as I never saw it, I suspect that one or the other objected. Soon, the sentimental gave place to the practical, for the first two

---

* In fact, in 1866, the only two countries in the world where a passport was *not* required were Great Britain and the United States.

37

phrases she asked me to teach her in English were "Je vous aime" and "Donnez moi un baiser." Since her tongue could not compass the English letter *v*, her first efforts, in her most fetching way, produced, "I luf you" and "Gif me a kiss." I did not respond to either enticement!

From July to October, my brother Charles and I traveled through France, Switzerland, northern Italy, Germany, Sweden, and Norway. Early in October, he left for home, and I settled in Berlin for the winter, with Langenbeck, Virchow, and Gurlt, among others.

By February, 1866, due to over-study, I broke down with an attack of insomnia. After a month of idleness in other things--but of constant work to get well, at Dr. Beni-Barde's Hydro-Therapeutic Establishment at Auteuil (near Paris)--I recovered, attended to a few last things, and went to London for a farewell visit, and to see a bit of English surgery. In May, I returned to Philadelphia, crossing with Charley Lippitt (the future governor of Rhode Island) and Prof. N. P. Hill, my old teacher of Chemistry at Brown (and later, senator and millionaire), on the last voyage of the last side-wheeler of the Cunard Line, the *Scotia*.

I opened my office at 107 South 13th St., in June of 1866. That November, I became head of the Philadelphia School of Anatomy (see my history of that school in *Addresses and Other Papers*) and for nine years had a very successful career as a private teacher of anatomy and surgery.

From 1866 to 1875, I lectured on pathological anatomy in the summer school at Jefferson. I devoted myself heartily to my preparation for the work, especially by study of Virchow's *Cellular Pathology* and Billroth's lectures, both new books, at that time, and both full of meat. This enforced study was most useful to me later, as professor of surgery, by laying for me a foundation in pathology, without which I should have taught surgery much less effectively.

In 1873, the Chair of Anatomy at the Jefferson Medical College which had become vacant by the resignation of Prof. Joseph Pancoast was to be filled. There immediately arose a very warm contest for the place, the candidates being Drs. William H. Pancoast, William S. Forbes, John H. Brinton, and myself. I worked as hard as I could to obtain the post. As these recollections are only for my children and their descendants, I may say that the profession-at-large recognized the fact that, if ability and success as a teacher had been the determining factors, I deserved the place. (Among my letters are relevant letters of recommendation.) But Prof. S. D. Gross, though declaring that I was the best teacher among the candidates, finally threw his influence with the trustees for Dr. Pancoast, and he was elected. I do not *know* the reason for this action, but it was generally understood that, in return for this, the influence of the Pancoasts, father and son, would be thrown to Dr. Samuel W. Gross for his father's chair, when that became vacant. In view of Prof. S. D. Gross's age, this vacancy would soon occur.

Professionally, this was the greatest disappointment I ever experienced. I had worked very hard to fit myself for this chair, and I *knew* that I could fulfill its duties acceptably. Later, when the Chair of Therapeutics became vacant, so good a man as Prof. J. M. Da Costa urged me to accept an election to it, assuring me that it would be undisputed if I would accept. But I absolutely declined, on the ground that I was not fitted to teach that branch of medicine, and that, if I accepted, my teaching would be only perfunctory, and therefore obnoxious to me. (Of

the Chair of Surgery I never even thought--much less did I aspire to it--
as I felt it to be far above my abilities.)

After my defeat for the Chair of Anatomy at the Jefferson, it seemed
to me that all my hard work had been thrown away and that there was no
prospect of my having a successful career as a teacher. Gradually, my
duty became more and more clear: to do today's work today--humdrum and
simple as it might be--and, having tried my best, to leave the future to
take care of itself. If honor and preferment came, well and good; if not,
then the consciousness that I had done my level best, in the sphere in
which God had placed me, would be ample reward and would meet His approval.

In 1876, upon removal from Chestnut Street above 10th to its new home
at Broad and Cherry Streets, the Pennsylvania Academy of the Fine Arts re-
organized and enlarged its school and offered me the place of Professor
of Artistic Anatomy. This I accepted, and I occupied the position until
1890, when I resigned.

This work was most congenial and delightful. The students were in
earnest, and I threw myself with enthusiasm into the work. I collected an
excellent library on artistic anatomy for the Academy. My course consisted of about thirty lectures, combined always with demonstrations on a
living model. I also used a cadaver. On one side, the muscles were exposed *in situ* by the dissecting away of only the skin, superficial fascia,
and fat; on the other side, each muscle was dissected down to its attachment to the bones. I hung the cadaver upright (by two iron hooks inserted
into trephine openings in the sides of the skull), so that cadaver, skeleton, and living model were all in the same vertical position. No mental
transposition from a cadaver lying horizontal on a table to a skeleton and
living model in the vertical position was necessary.

40

On the living model, by voluntary, active, and resisted movements--
and by the galvanic battery (especially for the facial muscles)--the action
of the various muscles was constantly demonstrated. One outcome of these
lectures was that I wrote a paper "On the Systematic Use of the Living
Model in Teaching Anatomy," which I read at the International Medical Congress in London, in 1881 (see *Transactions* of the Congress). This led to
a very delightful acquaintance with Prof. D. J. Cunningham, then Professor
of Anatomy in Dublin, later in Edinburgh. In *Scribner's Magazine,* September, 1879, my method was described and illustrated, in an article on "The
Art Schools of Philadelphia."

I also started to write a work on artistic anatomy, because I found
that no book then written was entirely satisfactory. Those by artists had
too much art and too little anatomy, and those by anatomists too much anatomy and too little art. I have still, I think, the MS of a considerable
portion of the work, but my surgical practice (which my financial needs
made it imperative that I should not neglect) was absorbing more and more
of my time, and finally I had to relinquish the hope of finishing the proposed book, a great disappointment.

From 1878 to 1882, I was also Professor of the Anatomy of Animal Forms
as Applied to Decorative Art, in the Pennsylvania Museum and School of
Industrial Art.

These excursions into artistic and decorative anatomy were very delightful by-products, one may say, of my anatomical work. They broadened
my conception of the uses and value of anatomy and brought me into intimate
personal acquaintance with both officers and students in these two institutions. Not a few of my old pupils, especially in the Academy, have become
distinguished painters, sculptors, and illustrators.

In 1882, when Dr. Oliver Wendell Holmes retired from the Chair of Anatomy at Harvard, Dr. S. Weir Mitchell had some conversations with me (at the request of the medical faculty--or at least some of them) as to the possibility of my going to Harvard to occupy his place. It was understood that the definite appointment to the chair would be deferred for a year and was contingent upon my success during that year, a test I would have welcomed most heartily. The salary was to be only $3,000, and I was to give up all practice and devote my whole time to the duties of the chair. My financial needs (I had my wife and four children, for whose support I was almost entirely dependent upon my earnings), the meager salary, and the debarment from all practice, precluded my even seriously considering the proposition attractive, much less the possibility of accepting such a position. My growing interest in surgery, and my increasingly successful practice, convinced me that I would be far wiser to remain in Philadelphia and devote myself exclusively to surgery. Again, how fortunate was my decision!

In 1891, when Dr. Charles T. Parkes, Professor of Surgery at Rush Medical College, died, my good friend, Dr. J. Nevins Hyde, Professor of Dermatology in that flourishing school, came to see me, in Philadelphia, on behalf of the faculty, and offered me Parkes's chair. He was most kind and urgent, but after consideration, I declined this promotion, again fortunately. I was over forty and had gained a satisfactory and growing surgical clientele (Hyde declared that in Chicago, in less than five years I would have a professional income of $100,000 a year); my family ties were strong; my friends, medical, scientific, and social, were many and warm; and my religious associations were most agreeable. To break away from all these and go to the West (as Chicago then was considered) would

be a mistake for which no amount of money would compensate. The latter

makes a living; the former make a life. Though unquestionably I should

be far better off than I am now, pecuniarily, had I gone to Chicago (or

California [see below]); yet I shall leave my children a sufficiency, I

think, and the last 30 years of my life have been far more satisfactory

to me from every other aspect.

In 1880, I was offered the Chair of Surgery in the Medical Department

of the University of California, but declined it, and wisely.

San Francisco
March 7th, 1880

Friend Keen:

You probably have heard of the death of Dr. Toland. For
some time past, Dr. McLean has been delivering the lectures on
the Principles and Practice of Surgery and doing all Toland's
operations. Now that he is gone, we have to fill one, the
surgical chair, Principles and Practice of Clinical Surgery,
or make an even division of the two chairs between Dr. McLean
and the new man.

I am appointed one of a committee to fill the chair, and
upon my representation of your qualifications, the committee
have asked me to write to you and ask you if you would like to
leave the sleepy old town of Philadelphia and come out here
and accept the Chair of Principles and Practice of Surgery in
the Medical Department of the University of California. Our
regular term commences June 1st.

You would like California, no doubt. I do not believe I
over-state the matter when I say you can expect to get a practice of $20,000 per year. And with the prestige you would
naturally have from coming here to occupy the chair, you could
not be long in making yourself a practice.

Answer this the day you receive it and follow it in a few
days with a more mature answer, if you wish time.

Your old friend,

W. J. McNutt

When the Demonstratorship of Anatomy at the University of Pennsyl-

vania became vacant, by the death of Dr. H. Lenox Hodge, in 1881, Weir

Mitchell and William Pepper were very eager that I should succeed him, with a view, before long, of my then being in line to succeed Dr. Joseph Leidy, the Professor of Anatomy at the University of Pennsylvania, who could not be expected to remain much longer in active service. They did their best, as Mitchell told me, but for some reason (which neither they nor I understood), Leidy and Agnew, Professor of Surgery, both opposed my election. What a fortunate escape for me! As fortunate as my defeat for the Chair of Anatomy at the Jefferson, in 1873.

1811 Spruce Street
June 26th

Dear Doctor:

It is of no use, but I can not help in telling you how deeply I regret having lost the chance of securing as an associate in the University one who has won such a brilliant reputation as a teacher--and one for whose abilities and character I have the highest respect.

Yours sincerely,
William Pepper

When the Medico-Chirurgical College was started, in 1882, I was also urged to become one of the faculty, but I declined, as I did not like the ideas or ideals of the men at the head of the enterprise.

I also have had several other invitations to go elsewhere than Philadelphia, as a professor of surgery, but none of them were sufficiently attractive to tempt me even to consider them.

For some years, I had served as Lecturer on Surgical Anatomy at the Woman's Medical College of Pennsylvania, and when a vacancy occurred in the Chair of Surgery, in 1885, I was offered the Professorship of Surgery in that institution, a position I held until 1889.

At that time, women doctors did not occupy the same position in the

profession that they do today. In fact, they were almost tabooed, except
by a very few loyal friends. But after careful consideration, I accepted
the position, determined to do my best for their education. The young
women were earnest and capable students, and I always enjoyed the duties
of the chair.

In 1886, I met with the one appalling disaster of my life. On July
12th, my darling wife was suddenly taken from me, leaving me with four
daughters to whom I had to become both father and mother. My personal
grief almost crushed me. Had it not been for my children, I should not
have cared to live.

In the autumn of that year, I found that my grief was threatening to
impair both my health and my ability to care for my dear girls. I could
scarcely sleep. (In fact, while prior to that dreadful loss, I had been
a sound sleeper, ever since then, I have been unable to sleep, as a rule,
over 5 or 6 hours--often less, occasionally more.) I became despondent,
and I even feared a settled melancholia might come on.

One day, while I was in this condition, Mr. Henry C. Lea proposed
that I edit a new American edition of Gray's *Anatomy*. The book had had a
wonderfully successful history. It had been practically without a rival
for over thirty years but had been allowed to fall behind the times. He
offered me $400, and I accepted the offer. I would have done it for noth-
ing at all, for I was in such a mental condition that I felt that such
congenial and absorbing work was just what I needed to take me out of myself; to compel me to think of something else besides--and often in place
of--my grief; and so to help me to do my duty to my dear children, as well
as to myself.

I gave to the work all my spare time for a year--hours every day.
But when I came to the chapter on the nervous system, I found that I too,
like the book, was hopelessly behind the times. I had not been teaching
systematic human anatomy since 1875, when I closed the Philadelphia School
of Anatomy. Meanwhile, the physiological, pathological, and surgical
anatomy of the nervous system had been forging ahead by leaps and bounds.
I resolutely put my nose to the grindstone. I spent two months or more in
catching up. Then I revised, and largely re-wrote, those chapters. The
new edition was published in 1887. As it was the textbook of practically
every medical student in the United States, the appearance of my name on
the title page made me known to the entire profession (especially for the
future), and so it was of great value to me in my surgical work.

It is a pleasure to me to tell my children that this edition, even
now, after twenty-five years, is still sought, though it has been long out
of print. And Mr. Charles M. Lea said to me, only two or three years ago
(that is, 1908 or 1909), that it was the best edition of Gray's ever published.

I must add here an amusing incident connected with my editing of
Gray's *Anatomy*. When she was perhaps 9 or 10 years old, and just beginning
to make her acquaintance with English literature, Margaret came home from
school, one day, and at luncheon said that at school the girls had been
asking about me, and that she had been unable to tell them whether I had
edited Gray's *Anatomy* or Gray's "Elegy."

Now comes the object of this long prelude, to tell how my sincere efforts simply to do each day's duty met with its final rich reward. I tell
it not from vanity--my children will recognize the truth of this--but as a

lesson and a call to duty, especially to my grandchildren. My children (each in her own way, and differing sphere of action) have ever been faithful to this high ideal, as I am glad and proud to testify. I hope and believe that my grandchildren, and their children in turn, will be equally faithful, and if so, they may be sure that they will be equally successful. Even in the humblest sphere of life, duty faithfully done meets with its due reward. High and influential public station may be the goal reached. Or it may be simply that the only achievement is a clean, upright life, faithful to high ideals but without attaining to any conspicuous place, as the world counts it. But God will say to each, "Well done, good and faithful servant," and eternity counts for far more than time.

In May, 1887 (see *American Journal of the Medical Sciences*, October, 1888), when I had just finished my study of the nervous system, a hospital patient, Theodore Daveler of Lancaster, sought my advice. Had he come a year, or even three months, earlier, I should have lost *the one great opportunity of my life--and the turning point in my surgical career*. During the 25 years since my graduation in medicine, I had had a successful career as a teacher, in my private anatomical school, in the summer school of the Jefferson (from 1867 to 1875), as a lecturer on pathological anatomy (again, a most useful means of fitting me for my later work as a Professor of Surgery), and in the position I held in the Woman's Medical College. But my anatomical hopes had been blasted by my failure to obtain the Chair of Anatomy at the Jefferson; and my surgical position at the Woman's College, though of great value in training me as a teacher of surgery, was relatively an inconspicuous position, in the large world of surgery.

Daveler came to me at St. Mary's Hospital just at the critical time. Earlier, I should not have been able to make a correct diagnosis, and my future would have been a totally different one; later, I should have been only one of many brain surgeons.

My diagnosis was a brain tumor in the left motor area. The first modern operation for a brain tumor had been done in 1884, in London, by Godlee. I had witnessed Weir's operation, in 1885 or 86, but I had never before had a case of brain tumor under my own care and, of course, had never done such an operation. I was not willing, therefore, to trust my diagnosis without a consultation. Drs. S. Weir Mitchell, H. C. Wood, Morris J. Lewis, Harlan, and Charles A. Oliver kindly saw the patient with me. The conclusion they all concurred in was that the diagnosis was not clear enough to warrant so serious an operation as opening the head. I was too distrustful of my own diagnosis (which, however, I still believed to be the correct one) to operate, in the face of such an adverse decision. So I sent him home with directions to follow the treatment advised by the consultants, but I added that if he was not better in the autumn, he should come back to the hospital, and I would be willing then to operate, on my own responsibility.

He returned in the autumn, and after a minute and careful review of all the facts, and with the concurrence, then, of the former consultants, I operated on him, on December 15th, 1887. Never shall I forget my delight, and my dismay, when I removed the trephine button from his skull. There lay the tumor, just where I diagnosed it to be, but it was larger than the opening I had made--1½ inches and a *very* large opening in those days of half-inch trephines. Another button was removed, and after that,

still more bone had to be removed by bone forceps, before the tumor ($7\frac{1}{4}$"
x 6" in circumference) was entirely disclosed. Only 2 or 3 tumors larger
than this had theretofore been removed. My heart sank within me, at the
prospect of even attempting its removal. But no other course was possible, so I passed my little finger around its margin and peeled it out
as easily as one scoops a hard-boiled egg out of its shell with a spoon!
I expected a very serious hemorrhage to follow, but the amount of blood
lost was not great and was readily stopped. What a sigh of relief escaped
me when the last stitch was tied, the wound dressed, and the man put back
in bed--alive!

As I long since learned, I mismanaged the after-treatment. But he
not only survived the operation itself but also my bungling care, which
was due to my total want of experience. In 1915, twenty-eight years after
the operation, he was still living. The tumor (a fibroma), not being malignant, has of course never recurred.

Naturally, the successful removal of a brain tumor (especially of so
large a tumor), at a time when such American operations were fewer in number than the fingers of one hand, attracted a great deal of attention.
Almost immediately, two other brain cases--epilepsy resulting from definite injuries--were brought to me, and I operated in both cases with successful results.

In September, 1888, the First Congress of American Physicians and
Surgeons was held in Washington, under the presidency of Dr. John S.
Billings. Horsley and Ferrier were my guests in Philadelphia, immediately
after the congress, in which brain surgery was the leading topic. These
doctors, who had done so much to advance it in England, were both present

as guests of the congress and lent it added distinction. The general debate in the congress was participated in by Charles K. Mills, Roswell Park, Dr. (now Sir David) Ferrier, Dr. (now Sir Victor) Horsley, M. Allen Starr, E. C. Seguinn, Robert F. Weir, and myself. In the separate meeting of the American Surgical Association, I reported my three cases and had the three patients (as well as the three specimens--the tumors and the portions of brain tissue removed) present as exhibits A, B, C, etc., in connection with my paper. I especially remember that Dr. Ferrier told me that when he heard my account of the motions induced in the arm (in one of my cases) by the electric stimulation of a certain area of the brain surface, he almost jumped from his seat, as it was the first confirmation in the brain of man of his experiments on the brains of monkeys. This paper, and the successful cases there related, was the beginning of my work on cerebral surgery. (In all, I have written 39 papers on various phases of cerebral surgery.)

Another brain case which also attracted attention, by reason of its novelty and its importance, came to my clinic at the Woman's Hospital and was operated on in January, 1889.

A young boy was suffering from an inoperable tumor of the cerebellum. Its principal symptoms were increasing hydrocephalus and distressing headache. The chief indication was to relieve the poor child from pain, even if his life could not be saved. Accordingly, I trephined his skull, first on one side, and then, four weeks later, on the other. After releasing the pent-up fluid in the lateral ventricles, I washed them out, from side to side, with a warm boric acid solution, a wholly novel procedure and one which gave him great comfort. As a result of this operation, I made a careful study of the surgical anatomy of the ventricles and was the first to lay down systematic rules for the formal operation of tapping the lateral ventricles. This operation is now a well-recognized procedure and is based on my pioneer work. (*Medical News*, September 20, 1890.)

In the years that have passed since then, other, far abler, surgeons (many of them of a younger generation than my own) have done more and better work, as I most gladly testify. But while they have the joy and the rewards of their extensive and most important discoveries and improvements in diagnosis and technique, they never could have felt the thrill of those relatively few surgeons of my own age and generation who were among the "first that ever burst into that Silent Sea."

Twice have I had that satisfaction. In 1864, when, in conjunction with Weir Mitchell and Morehouse, (I being the least important but still lending a hand), we published our little book on *Gunshot Wounds and Other Injuries of Nerves*, which is the foundation of the whole modern surgery of the nervous system. Again, in 1888, when I read the above-mentioned paper on the lateral ventricles, it was far less important than the papers of physiologists and of other surgeons; yet again, I lent a hand in the establishment and development of cerebral surgery.

In the spring of 1889, less than a year after the meeting of the congress and the presentation of my early brain cases, Prof. Samuel W. Gross, who (with Prof. John H. Brinton) had succeeded to his father's Chair of Surgery at the Jefferson, unexpectedly died of pneumonia.

Shortly afterward, Dr. I. Minis Hays called upon me and said that members of the faculty had desired him to ascertain whether I would not be a candidate for the vacancy. I told him frankly that I would be willing to have my name considered, but upon two conditions. First, that if nominated, I should certainly be elected; and second, that for my election there should be no need of any personal canvass of the trustees. I would, of course, be willing to call upon each of them as a matter of courtesy, but in no sense make a canvass. These conditions having been met, I made a call upon each of the fifteen trustees, selecting a time when I was practically sure that they would not be at home so that I should only leave my card but not be exposed to the necessity of a personal interview. I was elected to the vacancy and at once began my preparation for the important and arduous task before me.

My five years' training at the Woman's Medical College, in both didactic and clinical teaching, were invaluable to me. But I never worked so hard in my life, reading textbooks and medical journals; card-cataloguing every important paper and all my own clinical cases, for ready reference; and rewriting my notes, for I always lectured extemporaneously.

I found no textbook that was satisfactory, large enough to give a fairly thorough knowledge, yet small enough to be practical, for busy students in the then lamentably brief medical course (only two years). Especially were all the textbooks deficient in that they taught nothing of surgical bacteriology, then a new but rapidly growing science. The term "Bacteriology" was first used in 1884. Since my colleague in the Chair of Pathology was a skeptic as to the role of these "bugs" (as he disdainfully referred to bacteria), I felt it to be of the utmost importance that this subject should be the foundation of a new textbook of surgery, which I at once planned. This was the genesis of the *American Text-book of Surgery*, written by thirteen of the professors of surgery in our chief

52

medical colleges which ensured both its financial and its professional success (in spite of the accidental number of its authors). It was published in 1892 by W. B. Saunders & Co., in one volume of 1209 pages, under the joint editorship of Dr. J. William White, Professor of Surgery at the University of Pennsylvania, and myself. Its *first* chapter was upon "Surgical Bacteriology," and throughout the book, bacteriology and anti- or a-septic surgery were expounded and reinforced. The amount of labor that Dr. White and I gave to this book was, I may say, enormous. Not a line of it but was read by both of us in MS and in proof, and fully discussed whenever either of us questioned the statements made or the advice given. Then we discussed each chapter with all the authors, by letter and often at length. Moreover, after we had completed our work, the whole book was read by Mr. McCreary, the most accomplished and exacting critic as to English style I have ever known, among many proofreaders. The galley proofs of the entire work were sent to each author with a request to read, criticize, and return to the editors. All serious criticisms or suggestions were then referred to the author of the chapter concerned. The result was a homogeneous whole, in careful English and representative of the best surgical thought of the profession in the United States and Canada. Its success was immediate and phenomenal. One of its peculiar features was that, as *all* of the authors had revised *all* of the chapters and made various suggestions, the book appeared with the thirteen names on the title page, but no chapter had any indication as to who was its particular author.

I have traced here, especially for my children and later descendants, the path along which I believe my Heavenly Father led me, to the un-dreamed-of distinction of the Professorship of Surgery in the Jefferson Medical College, a position of such eminence and influence that in my early professional life, I had never considered it as a possibility; nor even up to 1889 did I ever seriously aspire to it, until the so-little-expected vacancy actually occurred and the negotiations described actually took place.

For the Chair of Anatomy, I *had* intentionally prepared myself, carefully and successfully, and when it was denied me, I felt sorely disheartened. But as I looked over my future, and sought God's guidance, the one thought I had (and the one decision reached) was to do each day's duty as well as I possibly could, confidently leaving the rest in His hands. If preferment and influence came to me, because I had worked hard and successfully, well and good: I would take what came, with a certain inward satisfaction, because I tried to do my duty and to deserve success. If my career was to be that of a humble practitioner of surgery, I would still continue to do each day's work as well as I knew how and be satisfied with the approval of my own conscience and of my Maker, convinced that it is not the amount or the importance of the work done that is weighed by Him so much as the spirit of devotion to one's work, to God, and to his fellow men. This will best merit the "Well done, good and faithful servant."

The chain of events shows clearly, to my mind, the guiding hand of Providence:

1. My early teaching of anatomy and surgery, by which I not only learned a good deal about these two subjects, but also first won the power to think on my feet, and while speaking.

2. The denial of my wish for the Chair of Anatomy. My bitter disappointment, I now see, was the most fortunate happening in all my profes-

sional life. Had I been elected, I should have been a surgeon teaching anatomy as a side issue, and not, as the profession now rightly demands, an anatomist teaching anatomy and making it his life work. I should have become more and more of an anachronism, and my career would have been immensely less satisfactory than in the department I really and truly loved --and which at last, by God's help, found me. (It is but just to add that up to about 15 years ago--this written in 1912--anatomy was usually taught by a surgeon.)

3. The editing of Gray's *Anatomy*, which necessitated my studying the anatomy of the nervous system and brought my knowledge of its surgical and neurological anatomy up to date. Had I not been driven to this, I should never have done that piece of laborious study, and I should have missed entirely my one first great surgical opportunity.

4. The case of Daveler, my first case of modern brain surgery, came just after I had finished my acquisition of the new knowledge of the anatomy, physiology, and surgery of the brain. I rode just on the crest of the surgical wave which was sweeping onward toward the shore of success.

5. The First Congress of American Physicians and Surgeons, coming immediately after my first brain cases, where the surgery of the brain was the one new and striking development in the surgical world, and to which this congress lent great emphasis and éclat.

6. The vacancy, almost immediately following, in the Chair of Surgery and my election to the chair.

I came unto my own (I hope this is not too strong an expression) rather late in life, for I was 52 years old when elected, but my father had generously given me an excellent education, my health had been unusually and almost continuously good, I was tough, rather than strong, and I loved work.

In consequence of the fact that the Chair of Surgery had been divided, my salary, during all my service as Professor of Surgery, was only half that of the professors in the other chairs; i.e., mine was $2,000 a year while theirs was $4,000. My clinical work in the hospital required one, two, three hours every day (for I never delegated this work to my assistants, saving in a few minor cases which were doing well), and my clinic usually lasted three to four hours--and sometimes more--so that I gave far more time to my duties than several of my colleagues, while receiving only half their pay. But I scorned the idea of asking for more, or of calling the attention of the trustees to the inequality, if not the injustice. Moreover, a considerable and sometimes a large part of my salary I gave back to the college for various objectives, the J. M. Da Costa Laboratory, Donation Day, the Y.M.C.A., etc. In addition, I always bought my own instruments and appliances--including the first Trendelenburg chair in Philadelphia.

We had no projectoscope or epidiascope, in those days. In my Philadelphia School of Anatomy, I had bought a portable hand microscope.

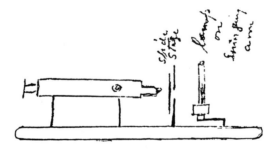

This I brought to the Jefferson, together with a large number of expensive microscope injections, which I imported from Thiersch of Leipzig. All my drawings and plates were paid for out of my salary. When I left the Jefferson, I gave all these to the college, except for a number of my instruments. These, a very large and expensive collection, I gave to the ladies of the Emergency Aid, in 1915, to be sent to the hospitals in France and Belgium. I had my microscope put in first-class order and sent it to a Baptist mission hospital in China, in 1912.

(Speaking of my clinics' duration [above] reminds me of a dream which J. Chalmers Da Costa related as a *fact*, at one of our Jefferson dinners. He dreamed that he looked in at my clinic, very late in the day, long after the lights had been turned on, and was startled at seeing me still calmly operating, while all the assistants were lying on the floor, exhausted and unconscious.)

Note, March 16th, 1916

In the *Outlook* for March 15th, 1916 (p. 624), an article entitled "Opportunity," by Lyman Abbott reads, in part, as follows:

Three elements combine, in successful achievement: opportunity, equipment, and courage. A few persons go through life unsuccessfully because they have no opportunities, more because they have no equipment, a great many because, with opportunity and equipment, they lack courage.
(E. L. Trudeau, at 17, had contracted tuberculosis as a result of nursing his brother. He later took refuge in the Adirondacks because of his delight in the free wild life of the wilderness.)
It was while he was there that Koch's discovery that tuberculosis is due to a death-dealing germ in the human body was published. Dr. Trudeau saw in this discovery a possible opportunity to fight this dread disease, and he was inspired with the purpose to undertake the fight, by his brother's untimely death, his own illness, and his sympathy with thousands of patients similarly affected. His equipment for this audacious attempt was very slight. His medical education had consisted of three years in an American medical college and six months in a hospital. He had no laboratory experience, no knowledge of the use of the microscope, and no money to fit up a proper lab-

oratory for his studies in the Adirondacks.

[There follows a description of the beginning of the Saranac Laboratory and its meager equipment.]

Out of this humble beginning have grown the great Adirondack Sanitarium and the splendid campaign carried on throughout the United States against the White Plague. A great opportunity, meager equipment, and a great heart of courage--and behold the result.

There have been many men in the world better equipped for such a campaign, but there was only one Dr. Trudeau; many women in the Civil War better equipped for nursing, but only one Clara Barton; many men at the end of that war better equipped for the education and moral emancipation of the Negro race, but only one Booker Washington. Most of us have had many more advantages than we have taken advantage of. We have passed doors of opportunity; sometimes we have not seen them, and sometimes have felt ourselves unequipped to enter them. Many times we have not had the courage to make the venture.

These three, opportunity, equipment, and courage, all apply very forcibly to my editing Gray's *Anatomy* and the case of Daveler, in relation to my career. It was for me not "an" opportunity but "the one" opportunity which led to my success. Looking backward, I now see clearly what it all meant. But at the time, I did not (and could not) foresee its weighty significance for my future. I see now that those two events comprised my opportunity. I had been equipped with a good education. As to courage, in my case, I should say it was rather the habit I had long formed of doing my work as thoroughly as I could. Almost unconsciously, I opened the door of opportunity and entered in. Had I missed it, who knows what would have been the result? That I did *not* miss it was due to my motto, "Do today's work today," to which I added, "and do it thoroughly."

"Prosaic," you say? I admit it, but I add that "the diligent performance of prosaic daily duties is the sum of successful human life."

In 1898, after the close of the Spanish-American War, President McKinley appointed me a member of the commission to investigate the alleged abuses in the management of the war, especially as to food and sanitation. In a separate MS, in the series which follows, I have given an account of this matter.

The same is true of the operations on Mr. Cleveland when he was president. That account must not be published at any time without the permission of Dr. Joseph D. Bryant of New York (who called me in consultation), in case he is living. I should also think it not only courteous but imperative to ask Mrs. Cleveland's permission, in case she is living. Dr. Bryant has prepared a full account of the operations, for the publication of which, I suppose, he will arrange. I have never seen a word of it. I have written my account for my children only.

In the summer of 1897, in Keene Valley, while abed from an injured knee, I wrote my book on *The Surgical Complications and Sequels of Typhoid Fever*, the only book then (and even now) in which this subject is treated completely. The fifteen years since it was written have largely added to the number of cases it recorded, and the percentages there given, but they have not added any new complication or sequel, except, I think, abscess of the breast.

In 1905, I published a volume of collected *Addresses and Other Papers*, and if I find time later, I shall publish one or more additional volumes to place in permanent form my most important, otherwise fugitive publications. I hope also to re-publish in one volume my papers on vivisection and antivivisection, as I think it would be of value to other writers and may have some influence in removing the chief obstacle to research.*

---

* This volume, *Animal Experimentation and Medical Progress*, I published in 1914.

From 1905 to 1910, I edited *Keen's Surgery*, in five large volumes, and in 1912, I published a sixth, supplementary, volume. (All six volumes have been republished in Spanish; a set is in my library.)

I have also published an account of the graduation ceremonies--and the attendant celebrations--of the Royal College of Surgeons of England, in 1900 (*British Medical Journal*, August 4, 1900, p. 299); and of the Royal College of Surgeons of Edinburgh, in 1905 (*Medical Library and Historical Journal*, March 1906).

In May of 1907, I represented the American Philosophical Society at the celebration of the 200th anniversary of the birth of Linnaeus by his alma mater, the University of Uppsala, and published an account of this celebration in *The Aesculapian* of December, 1908.

In January of 1908, while in Europe for the winter, I was elected president of the American Philosophic Society, the oldest and most distinguished scientific society in the United States. To sit in the chair occupied by Franklin, Rittenhouse, Jefferson, and their distinguished successors, is one of the greatest honors I have ever received.

Besides my professional papers and books, I wrote the history of the First Baptist Church of Philadelphia, in 1898, and edited the historical volume in which it was printed for our bicentennial celebration.

In January, 1907, when I was 70, I resigned my chair after having taught for 41 years in all, the last 23 having been devoted exclusively to surgery--five of them in the Woman's Medical College, and 18 in the Jefferson. In all, from 1866 to 1907, I have had over 10,000 students, and one of the pleasantest things in my life is the fact that my old students are always glad to see me, as I also am to see them.

I may say, without vanity but with what at least I please myself with thinking is a proper and just satisfaction, that I have had a more than usually successful career, both as a teacher and as a surgeon. If unsolicited honors (both American and European) be a test, I have had far more than my abilities deserve. They are a satisfaction to me, partly as a recognition of my half a century of unstinting work, but chiefly because they will be a source of pleasure, and a just pride, to my descendants.

A list of the positions I have occupied, of the honors so generously given me, and of the books and papers I have written or edited (numbering over 300) will be found in the drawer of the table in the front office. They also are given, to some extent, in *Who's Who in America*. Of two of the highest professional distinctions, one European and one American, I only learned while traveling in India, in 1901-2. In 1901, I was elected one of the eight honorary fellows of the German Surgical Society, the largest and most distinguished surgical society in the world. I am the only American surgeon who up to 1914, when Halsted was elected, had ever received that honor. And in 1902, I was elected president of the Sixth Triennial Congress of American Physicians and Surgeons (the blue ribbon of the American profession), to be held in 1903. The list of presidents is a very distinguished one, viz.:

1888	John S. Billings	1903	W. W. Keen
1891	S. Weir Mitchell	1907	R. H. Fitz
1894	A. L. Loomis	1910	E. L. Trudeau
1897	William H. Welch	1913	William C. Gorgas
1900	Henry P. Bowditch	1916	W. S. Thayer

In the late '90s, I think it was, I made a serious effort to initiate a movement for an international surgical congress. I corresponded with Billings, Czerny, Kocher, Gussenbauer, von Bergmann, Durante, and other leading surgeons in the U.S., Germany, France, Great Britain, and Italy. They all approved of the idea, and it would have materialized, but for the attitude of the British surgeons. They had no surgical society with scientific meetings, transactions, and so forth. The Royal College of Surgeons of England is a society charged with (1) the examination of students (with the Royal College of Physicians and the Society of Apothecaries) and the granting of degrees in medicine; (2) the care of the Hunterian Museum; and (3) certain funds for stated courses of lectures on surgical subjects. Their honorary fellows are from all civilized countries. Their fellows number in the hundreds and their members and licentiates several thousand. To include all of these was impossible; to include some and exclude others was equally impossible. Finally, I had to abandon the scheme.

About 1902 or 1903, the Belgian Surgical Society took the bull by the horns and organized such an international congress. They invited certain *surgeons*, in various European countries and America, to meet in Brussels, in 1905. Kocher was chosen as the first president and Depage the secretary general. The congress was a great success. Florence and Dora went with me. The delegates were entertained with lavish hospitality.

The second congress was held in 1908, again in Brussels, under the presidency of Czerny of Heidelberg. It was an even more pronounced success than the first, and Belgian hospitality outdid itself. Florence and Dora and I again were present.

The third congress was held in 1911, but I was unable to attend. Championnière was elected president; Depage was still the efficient secretary.

The fourth congress was held in New York, in 1914, with Depage now the president. I had feared that it might not be the success we wished for, and that the European surgeons would not come in great numbers. But it again proved to be a success, largely due (from the social aspect) to Dr. R. H. Harte and Dr. R. G. LeConte, of Philadelphia. The day before it adjourned, I was asked if I would accept the presidency of the fifth congress, to be held in Paris in September, 1917. I objected that I was too old (I would be nearing my 81st birthday) and would prefer that they elect someone else, either another American, or preferably a European. But their desire seemed so sincere, and they were so urgent that I finally consented. I was elected unanimously.

On August 1, 1914, the Great War (of which not the faintest suspicion existed in April) broke out. Whether the congress will ever be held I do not know. The unfortunate animosities aroused by the war and its passions would clearly indicate to me that it cannot be held in Paris--or any other capital of a belligerent nation. When the war is over, I propose writing to the Brussels International Surgical Society, which organizes the congresses, to see if it will be possible to arrange for it in Switzerland or some other neutral country.

I can truly say from my heart that I feel so unworthy of such honors that I am made more humble, rather than vain, by reason of them. When my own alma mater gave me my first LL.D., in 1891, I must confess to some pride, though never was a recipient more astonished, as well.

My highest ideal in life has been to be of service to my fellow men, and thus to serve my God. To this end, I have honestly and earnestly tried to give my patients my best services, and to make these services more and more valuable by close and constant study; to arouse in my students an enthusiasm for good true work, as well as the highest moral and professional standards of life and conduct, thus multiplying myself through them and extending an ever-widening circle of good influences; and to share in the work of diffusing knowledge by writing and editing books and papers, sharing the results of experience and discovery. For this same reason, I have been an ardent and conscientious friend of experimental research and have deemed it a professional, a moral, and a religious duty to promote research and thwart the efforts of the antivivisectionists to curtail or prevent it. I have done this because, having begun my study of surgery in 1860, and having practiced, up to 1876, the then dreadful septic surgery, and then from 1876 to 1907, having arduously worked my way up to the light, and to the glorious surgery of the present day, I speak now as an expert and of my own personal knowledge when I say that I *know* that most of the progress of modern medicine and surgery has been due, directly or indirectly, to such experimental research.

I leave to my children this brief record of my life as an evidence of God's guiding hand in every event of my life, and as an incentive to do the humble, and often irksome, tasks of daily life as faithfully and as thoroughly as possible, being sure that God is expecting just such work of us, and that if it is best for us, He will give us a high place, or if it is best for us, He will give us a lowly place. But wherever He places us, He will give us His blessing, and our final reward, according to the *spirit* in which we have rendered our service to our fellows and to Him.

William W. Keen

As my life has been prolonged far beyond my expectations, I add the following personal items.

I have been quite astonished at my own late blossoming out into an after-dinner speaker and toastmaster. I had never deemed 'it one of my accomplishments until, on August 1st, 1895, I made what I was forced to conclude was quite a successful after-dinner speech, at the British Medical Association in Queen's Hall, London (see my abridged copy from the *British Medical Journal*). Ever since then, I have been the recipient of compliments on it, from many old friends and new acquaintances. On September 2nd, 1897 (again at the British Medical Association meeting), in Montreal, I was the last of over a score of speakers, at the dinner, and in spite of the late--or rather, early--hour of 2:30, I apparently wakened an exhausted audience and seem to have satisfied them, for repeated echoes of that speech also still reach my ears, on occasion.

At the festival dinners which conclude the general meetings of the American Philosophical Society, in April, I have to preside, and I think I have succeeded in making my introductions of the speakers short and satisfactory. I have had to perform this agreeable duty for Lord Bryce (the British ambassador), M. Jusserand (the French ambassador), Count von Bernstorff (the German ambassador), and presidents Lowell, Patton, Hadley, Schurman, and Nicholls, as well as many other distinguished men. One occasion was especially noteworthy: I had on my right Mr. (as he then was) Bryce, an Englishman and the author of *The American Commonwealth*, the best book of its kind on America; and on my left, President Lowell, an American and the author of *The Government of England*, correspondingly the best book of its kind on Great Britain.

My last exploit as a toastmaster was at the dinner, in October, 1914, concluding the celebration of the 150th anniversary of the founding of Brown University (the proceedings of which have been published). The diners are said to have been satisfied. Some of them have said so to me—but then one is not apt to hear from the dissatisfied ones.

My grandchildren and their descendants may be interested in some further facts as to the various degrees that I have received. That these have been far more than I have deserved I am well aware. But as marks of a kindly and an all too generous esteem, they have been duly appreciated, by me and my daughters. I was *never* aware beforehand that they were to be conferred until they had been decided upon. (Then, of course, I had to be notified in order to be present.)

My first honorary degree, an LL.D., was given me by Brown, in 1891. It was a *very* great surprise. I value this, from my own alma mater, more than any later ones.

The LL.D.s from Northwestern (1903), Toronto (1903), and Yale (1906) require no special comment.

The LL.D. from Edinburgh, in 1905, was given in connection with the celebration of the 400th anniversary of the Royal College of Surgeons of Edinburgh, founded in 1505.

That from Saint Andrews, in 1911, was given when they celebrated the 500th anniversary of their founding, in 1411.

In the summer of 1906, I was traveling in Europe when I received letters congratulating me on my new degree from the University of Greifswald, which was celebrating the 450th anniversary of its foundation. I was much surprised, for I knew nothing about it, except through these letters, until I returned home, in the autumn. I then learned that it was an M.D. *causâ honoris*.

In 1900, the Royal College of Surgeons of England celebrated the first centenary of its new charter. The original charter dated from Henry VIII, but in 1799 it was lost (I don't know how or why), and in 1800, they were granted a new one. Before their celebration, in July of 1900, they had been authorized by law to add a new class to the existing classes (members, licentiates, and fellows), viz.: honorary fellows, not exceeding fifty in number. Sir William MacCormac, then the president, wrote to me and some other American surgeons, asking our aid in selecting four Americans for this honor, adding (in his letter to me) that my name already had been decided on for inclusion. Only thirty-five, besides the Prince of Wales (later Edward VII) and Lords Salisbury and Roseberry (the heads of the two parties), were elected. The four Americans were Warren (Boston), Weir (New York), Halsted (Baltimore), and myself. I have published an account of this celebration.

In 1905, the Royal College of Surgeons of Edinburgh celebrated the 400th anniversary of its foundation, and I was made an honorary fellow of this distinguished and ancient body. In connection with this celebration, the University of Edinburgh conferred a number of honorary degrees, including an LL.D. upon me.

In 1902, while traveling in India, I received a cablegram (forwarded from Philadelphia by mail) from Kocher, then the president of the Deutsche Gesellschaft für Chirurgie, informing me of my election as *Ehrenmitglied*

(Honorary Fellow) of this the largest and most distinguished surgical society in the world. I was not aware, until my return to the United States in October, of how high a surgical honor this was. From the volume of the *Transactions* for that year, I learned that there were only seven honorary fellows in all. Those on the list when I was elected were Lister, König, von Esmarch, von Bergmann, Macewen, Guyon, and Durante. At present (1915), I am next to the top, the list being as follows: Macewen, Keen, Guyon, Durante, Kocher, Czerny, Trendelenburg, Roentgen, and Halsted. I was the only American ever chosen until 1914, when Halsted was elected. Whether there will ever be another, following this war, the future must determine.

During my travels in India, I was also informed by letter of my election as president of the Triennial Congress of American Physicians and Surgeons (see earlier memorandum).

In 1912, the Jefferson Medical College celebrated the fiftieth anniversary of my graduation by the very graceful compliment of an Sc.D. *causâ honoris*.

In 1907, the University of Uppsala celebrated the 200th anniversary of the birth of its most distinguished graduate, Linnaeus. The only two American institutions invited to send delegates were Harvard, which had given him an honorary degree, and the American Philosophical Society, of which he had been a member. Professor Farlow, the botanist, represented Harvard, and I represented the American Philosophical Society. An account of this celebration I have also published. Their highest degree is not the LL.D., but the Ph.D. Thirteen persons, among them both Farlow and I, were so honored. This was the first time that Uppsala had *ever* awarded honorary degrees to foreigners.

While being conducted through the cathedral at Uppsala, we were told by our fine young Swedish guide (a student at the university whose English was correct and fluent) that the coat of arms on the wall of a side chapel belonged to Oxenstierna, his ancestor, who was the great chancellor of Gustavus Adolphus. "Well," said I, "I don't believe that another guest and another student can say what you and I can, that your ancestor sent my ancestor to America in 1642, 265 years ago."

I am also an honorary fellow of the Belgian Surgical Society, as well as an honorary corresponding member of the Paris Surgical Society.

In 1908, I was made an honorary fellow of the Italian Surgical Society and the Palermo Surgical Society.

In 1913, I was made an honorary fellow of the American College of Surgeons. Sir Rickman J. Godlee, president of the Royal College of Surgeons of England, Warren, Weir, and Halsted were the other--and first-- honorary fellows.

In 1901, I was chosen a fellow of the American Academy of Arts and Science, in Boston. This society was suggested by John Adams, who, while minister to France, had been so much impressed by the important work of the American Philosophical Society (see his *Life and Letters*) that he wanted a similar society in Boston. I was elected to the vacancy caused by the death of Prof. J. M. Da Costa.

I have also been elected an honorary member of a number of other medical and scientific societies, abroad and at home. (The list--I think it is complete--is with the list of my publications.) Most of these have given me diplomas (many of which will be found in the closet of my middle office). My diplomas from the Royal College of Surgeons of England and the German Surgical Society I have given to the College of Physicians.

(While on our visit to Florida, in January of 1916, on account of my long attack of grippe, Corinne suggested several subjects for me to write up. Very possibly some of these will be repetitions. If so, I must be pardoned.)

When we moved to "Hamiltonville" (now West Philadelphia), in May of 1843, my father bought the house and lot, with stable, at the southwest corner of Park (now 37th) and Chestnut, and we lived there for three or four years. He then bought the middle 300 feet of the lot (then an open and unfenced pasture, where young men and maidens gathered for summer-evening frolics) between Park and Margaretta (now 36th), on the north side of Chestnut.

In this old stone house was a fine Dutch oven, in which many good things, such as bread and pies, were baked, and many a succulent offering roasted, such as the little pig which was always served with the tradition-al lemon in its mouth. It (the oven, not the pig) was lined with fire-brick, then filled with wood and fired. It was set deep and solidly in the wall, as I remember, and was two or more feet wide and possibly three or more feet deep. When all the wood had been reduced to ashes, the oven was swept clean, the pies and meat, etc., were placed inside, and the door was tightly closed. (Our neighbors also borrowed the use of it, from time to time, to their advantage.)

The stable yard was where, when I was eight or nine years old, I chopped off the tip of my left forefinger. It was rarely the case, in those days, that anybody took a bath oftener than once a week. I was chopping a small piece of wood when my mother called me for my Saturday tub and torturous ear-gouging (as I thought it). At first I paid no attention, but at the third call, her tone had changed to one which I knew meant business. I made a sudden chop at the stick (intending then to obey), but in my haste I had aimed poorly and was duly punished for my disobedience. Fortunately, the hatchet did not take a great toll. Mother picked up the piece, washed it, and bandaged it more or less in place. In surgery, she could hardly be called an expert, and this grafting operation was a conspicuous failure.

My father later converted the stable into an excellent dwelling, but as I recall, when he gave it, rent-free, to our church for a parsonage, the village was greatly scandalized. My father insisted that inasmuch as the Founder of Christianity was born in a stable, it was logically fit for one of His ministers to live in one.

(My rough sketches [see plates] of the house and grounds at 3621 Chestnut Street leave much to be desired--a charitable judgment--but they are, in general, fairly correct, even though I am not quite certain of the topography to the north of the greenhouse, or of parts of the house itself.)

We were accustomed to spending many evenings in pleasant talk and village gossip, on the piazza. On the two cheekblocks there were two iron greyhounds, which children were always glad to mount. To the west were a few (10 or 15) fine trees, chiefly oaks and chestnuts. Among them was one fine persimmon. My unwary mouth soon taught me the lesson of watchful waiting for the well-ripened (and then delicious) fruit. These trees were the noble remnants of the primeval forest which once covered the whole territory. "The woods," as we boys called them, began in earnest (that is, where even some mild hunting could be done) at 40th and Pine and extended for a long stretch out to what is now 50th Street and Woodland Ave. (then called Darby Road), and even beyond.

On the edge of the group of trees to the west of the house stood four-square, facing south, a fine iron St. Bernard dog, which served for a base in "Prisoners' base," "I spy," and other games. Near it was a long swing.

As our grounds (including George's house and the church) covered an acre and a half, we had in front some beautiful flower beds, two large white magnolias (*M. conspicua*) and another (*M. glauca*) to the east. When in blossom, they were indeed beauties. A large copper beech grew a little to the south and east of the side porch and was highly ornamental. We had scattered at various points some excellent pear trees which father imported from France (I well remember my boyish excitement and pride over our "French importation.") There were also peach, cherry, plum, apricot, nectarine, and other fruit trees, plus trellises and espaliered grape and Lawton blackberry vines.

Besides these, we raised strawberries (with real straw between the berries and the earth to keep them clean), potatoes, lettuce, asparagus, beets, peas, beans, and other vegetables. When Michael, our gardener, farmer, coachman, ostler, and general man Friday, was digging potatoes, it was great fun for me to partially spit the useless little potato nubbins on the point of a sharp stick and launch them far, far into the air.

Michael Montague was for many years an institution--the "Fuller" of that day. He was a most faithful and industrious Irishman, as may be judged by his multifarious offices. After many years, he developed a rare and curiously slow pulse (down even below 40) and, at rare intervals, epileptic attacks. I am surprised now that we did not appreciate the danger of his driving a pair of spirited horses. One day, I remember, Hattie was

paying a call at a house near 20th and Chestnut, when two gentlemen walking

by saw that the lines had fallen from Michael's hands and that he was lying

limp on the seat. Going up to him, they discovered that he was dead, ap-

parently having choked to death in a fit. What a fortunate escape for Hattie!

Michael was succeeded by Conrad, a German and an excellent farmer.

My only recollection of him is of his reply, in broken English, to my

father when he told him he ought to get married: "No, Mr. Keen, de wimun

is queer tings. I tink I won't haf much to do mid 'em."

One of our early horses was a fine bay named

thought he could afford a pair (and our first carriage took four). At

rather long intervals, mother and I would spend a day in Kensington visit-

ing Uncle Burtis (he had married a sister of my father's), who had some

large mills. Their clattering machinery was a wonder to my youthful eyes

and ears.

Helen was the daughter of my uncle, Charles Keen, and his first wife.

His second marriage was not the success that it might have been, though

there was never any quarrel. Charley (the "Count") and "Tillie" (i.e.,

Matilda, after her mother) were the children of that marriage to Mrs. Frick,

who had two daughters by her first marriage. Our visits there were always

very formal and constrained.

Aunt Anna Reeves (Mary Banes's mother) fortunately had long been

separated from a worthless husband (as I was told, for I never saw him)

and lived very near Uncle Charlie's house on a small street (Ellen St.),

in what she facetiously called a little one-eyed house (that is, with only

one window on the first floor). Occasionally she would spend a day with us, especially when the corn was ripe. I remember how father often tricked

her by putting his own cobs on her plate and then pointing out her gluttony

in eating so many ears.

My father was very strict in some things and very unconventional in

others. He *never* allowed us boys to come to the table in our shirt sleeves,

even in the hottest weather. (It must be remembered that none of us got

more than two weeks' summer holiday.) But when the streetcars were in-

stalled on Chestnut Street, after the construction of the Chestnut St.

Bridge (in the late '60s or early '70s), father would hail an approaching

car, in a stentorian voice. (The cars stopped at any point where they were

hailed, and not only at the cross-street intersections, as now.) He would

carry two small bouquets and give them to the conductor and driver "for

their wives or sweethearts." Two or three times a week, he brought in a

basket of fruit, flowers, or vegetables to our house, when we were settled

at No. 1619 Chestnut Street. When he entered, he always "Hoo Hoo-ed!" and

the children then scurried into hiding. His pretended searching for them

on the upper shelves of the closets, while they were bursting with suppressed

laughter on the floor, and the final shouts as he at last discovered them,

who of us can forget? How much pleasure it gave us all!

He had a very blithesome spirit and was full of fun. Once, at 3621,

Michael, while digging potatoes, found a nest of field mice. My mother was

one of the few who had a quilting frame. Just then, she was having a

quilting party in our parlor, including Mrs. Wattson, Mrs. Washington Butcher,

Mrs. Standish Hansell, Mrs. Keyser and her daughter (Mrs. Inglis), and some

other friends, all from the old First Baptist Church. They were sitting

around the quilting frame, busily at work, when father came in and, opening both hands, dropped the mice in the middle of the quilt. Then such a screaming and scattering--and such fun afterwards!

My father usually wore a fine diamond breastpin in his shirt front, his only piece of jewelry, so far as I can recall.

We always had hot roast beef (and always "the finest piece of beef we have ever had on the table") for Saturday dinner, then served cold at Sunday dinner so as to give the cook as little work as possible on the Sabbath. All of the scraps from our plates father collected, at the end of the meal, cut them up very fine, then salted--and especially peppered-- them well. After dinner, we usually strolled around the garden, stable, graperies, and greenhouse, and the table-scraps were given to the chickens. They got to know this routine so well that the moment he appeared and "clucked," once or twice, they were thick around his feet, eager for the feast.

One spring (or early summer) morning, when the vines in the grapery were growing rapidly, I noticed the tender young shoots of the vines and marked on the trellis the exact point of one shoot. This was at 10:30, or just before church. Immediately after church, say around 12:30, I marked again the point of the shoot. In two hours, it had grown one and three-quarters inches, or nearly one-sixty-fourth of an inch per minute. Using a good magnifying glass, I could literally have *seen* it grow. I have often been sorry that I did not repeat this kind of observation a number of times, to determine what the maximum rate of growth might be--and not only in grape vines, but also in other plants (though vines would probably be the most favorable).

George's boys, in father's later life, were often a source of annoyance

75

to him, on account of their pranks. Father was very proud of his fine grapes and was constantly sending them to the sick, or to friends. Regularly every autumn, he took a specially fine large basket of his choicest to one or more monthly meetings of the board of directors of the Western Saving Fund. On one occasion, when the grapery was locked, two or three of the boys crept through the open ventilators in the front, lowest section. These were simply boards on hinges, and the opening was just wide enough for them to squeeze through the open space. They then reached up to every bunch in the whole house and picked off the *one lowest* grape that completed the apex of each bunch. Father was really, and justly, incensed and banished them from the house and garden for thirty days. As fruit was then very abundant, the punishment certainly fitted the offense, which was not very damaging but certainly was most irritating. (Possibly some of the pranks of my own daughters at the expense of their uncles and grandfather, in Fall River, may have been quite parallel in forgivable iniquity.)

Summer evenings, as I have said, we usually spent on the piazza, when George's family, the McLeods, Cousin Jane Burtis, and not a few other friends, would drop in. How well I remember the evenings when we adjourned to the basement dining room for cookies and ice-cold watermelon or cantaloupe. We often went around to Mrs. Burns's, on Market Street above 36th, for her ice cream and cake (or her delicious oysters, stewed or fried). Once, when Charley said to her, "Mother, they have lemon and strawberry. Which will you have?" Her prompt reply, "vanilla," was for years a joke that produced laughter.

When father was trying out a new horse to replace "Prince," who had so aged that he had to be shot and turned over to the glue factory (as we had no zoo then). Baron, who was probably not over five or six years old, calmly proceeded to cut all the hair off this totally strange horse's tail. (Fortunately, the horse kept his hoofs to himself while this was going on.) But that horse was the queerest looking beast I ever saw. While a new tail was growing, I do not remember whether or not he was provided with a caudal toupee, but my father had "to pay" for him, of course.

There were no means then known of cold storage, or even of canning. The preserving of strawberries, peaches, pears, green grapes, and other fruits--and the making of currant, grape, or other jellies--was a regular occupation of every housewife, at the appropriate season for each. Will and Sam Colladay (Fanny's brothers), or John and Louis Evans, or some other boys, and I, were sure to be on hand at such times, especially when the green grapes were being preserved. Bread spread with the "skimmings" (or "scum," as my daughters insolently call it!) was fit for a king. Our faces glistened with pleasure when such culinary stunts were announced and soon after were sticky and plastered over from ear to ear with the sweet delight.

When the tumblers--in the earliest days, we had none of the modern patent jars--were filled (and I likewise was filled), then came my job of helping my mother to cover them. We cut a round piece of rather thin writing paper, dipped it in a saucer of pure brandy, and laid it on top of the jam, jelly, or preserve. But it was my special duty to cut larger round pieces of more substantial writing paper and paste one over each tumbler, later labeling the lot. It is surprising how effectual this method proved to be. Very rarely more than two or three of all the perhaps 200 or 300 tumblers would ferment.

We had usually only two household servants, a cook and a maid who served as chambermaid and waitress. The latter function was not very burdensome, since the meals were not served in courses. She had only to place the meal on the table, remove it, and bring on the dessert. We did our own reachin', as a rule. The cook was paid $1.50 a week, the maid, $1.25, and since the basement kitchen adjoined the dining room, much labor was saved.

Later, when there were only father and mother, or those two and Helen Keen Weir (a dear, good cousin who took care of the house, as father and mother grew more feeble); or still later, when mother was an invalid and confined to her room, and there was father, and Miss Savage (the housekeeper), and occasionally myself, the "little room" (as we always called it) at the northeast corner on the first floor was used as a dining room.

Our house at 3621 was furnished comfortably, but plainly. In my drawing of the parlor, I have indicated where the principal pieces of furniture stood. There were two beautiful glass chandeliers in the front and back parlors, and it was no light job for mother, when house cleaning, to wash every one of the pendant triangular crystals, with an octagonal glass star above each crystal. My first remembrance of the solar spectrum was from my observation of those crystals.

I have also indicated on the floor plan the various chambers. One night, my father (who was subject to dreams and would often talk and even cry out in his sleep, as I have often heard him) nearly shot my mother. Our village had little or no protection at night. The streets were not lighted. There were no watchmen on duty at night, or at least I do not remember hearing about any, for we were an orderly community. Burglaries, therefore, were a rude shock to us all. My father bought a loud "watchman's rattle" and a pistol. The latter he kept under his pillow. Our only light at night was a taper, i.e., a wooden button pierced by a short wick. This floated on the surface of oil in a simple tumbler. It is even possible that this taper, which was always used in times of sickness (since it was dimmer than a candle), may not have been lighted, so that the room was almost totally dark.

At any rate, in the middle of the night, mother was moving quietly around the room, when father suddenly awakened, and in his dazed condition half awake and half asleep, and remembering recent burglaries, seized his pistol and was on the point of shooting the "burglar" when she sank down at the foot of the bed, screaming with terror. It was a very close call.

Our beds were all four-posters, of which one or two, as I remember, were of mahogany and handsomely carved. They were high enough to allow a trundle bed (a small, low bed on rollers, for a child) to be pushed under it in the daytime. Valences hung on all sides of the bed, except at the head, to conceal the presence of the trundle bed. Curtains, chiefly at the head and foot, were looped up or tied at the middle, for almost every bed.

In the early '50s, my mother, then only about 50 years old, began to fall, at intervals of months--and later, of weeks. At first, we thought it was due to awkwardness and used to tease her good humoredly. In my second year at Brown, she fell and broke her arm. After a while, we recognized the fact that her falls were due to a muscular weakness in her legs. She finally became chair-fast. Meantime, father had built an elevator from the northwest chamber to the parlor, and on to the basement dining room, though she eventually became bed-fast. Gradually, her arms--and especially her hands--became involved, so that she could not hold a teacup securely. She later had to use a glass tube, and finally she had to be fed.

With the physical failure, dear mother's mental powers were slowly failing, and for some years before her death, Miss Savage, a faithful Irish woman, had charge of the house. For perhaps twenty years before mother's death, in 1877 (aet. 73), she suffered strange attacks of partial and temporary paralysis. I think she must have had 150 or more of these attacks, over this long period of time. While sitting at table, or in her chair, she would suddenly sink down in the chair, lolling over to one side, staring vacantly, and babbling incoherent sounds. Often, she would recover herself in a few minutes. A few times, her attacks lasted for some hours, and two or three times, up to 24 hours. Every attack was followed by a little loss, both physical and mental. For the last year or two, she recognized only my father, and for the last five or six months, she recognized no one at all. Hers was a mere vegetative existence.

Dr. Sinkler made a post-mortem examination. I saw the brain after its removal. On a horizontal section, every little artery protruded slightly above the brain surface, which felt like a wire brush. This explained her attacks. The slowly-spreading hardening of her arteries had cut off the blood supply of one small area after another, and each blockage of the blood supply caused one of her attacks.

They had been married fifty-one years. It was like riving an oak in twain. Father had been a loving, considerate caretaker of mother for years, as she gradually failed. He watched over her as a mother watches over her baby. When she was gone, his occupation was gone, but he lived on for over five years after her death. He too failed physically, slowly but surely,

80

so that the elevator unexpectedly became necessary for his use also. His sight was lost, first in one eye and then in the other, so that he was almost totally blind for three or four years before his death.

I had never expected to see the day when I would thank God that my mother and my father (and, I might add, both of my brothers) had passed away, but it was literally true. My father died on August 4, 1882, just 30 days short of 85 years. My dear wife and the three older children all came down from the Adirondacks just before his death. The immediate cause was dysentery; the real cause was his age. Each of my brothers died at about 79, an age which I have just attained. If I fail physically or mentally, I pray that I may quickly pass away. I never wish to be stranded--a mere wreck--a burden to myself and my dear children.

A few other details, which may be of interest, occur to me. (I may even have described some already.)

Travel, in my youth, was far more uncommon, more costly, and less comfortable than now. It took four hours to go to New York and cost four dollars. Now it takes but two hours and costs but two dollars. There were no sleepers of any kind, so night journeys were infrequent and most uncomfortable--and usually made only on compulsion.

There were then, as now, two routes by rail from New York, the Pennsylvania and the Camden & Amboy, now a part of the Pennsylvania Railroad system. (When I was young, the Reading had no New York line.) With the one line, the traveler would go by ferryboat from New York to Amboy, then by railroad to Camden. With the other route, the ferry connection was at Jersey City, but the rail line did not extend, at first, to Philadelphia itself, but only to Tacony. Passengers and freight had to trans-ship there to a boat which brought them to, I think, the Walnut Street wharf (or was it Market Street?). When my brothers returned from Europe, in 1849, father and I were driven by Michael to the wharf in a very cold snowstorm. The boat was very late (an hour or so, if I remember rightly), and I recall very vividly how anxious we were about them. They were both in poor health. My brother Baron had died just after they left. There was no cable. The first news we had of their return was by a telegram (from Boston, I think) saying that they would arrive at 8:00 P.M., but their arrival was delayed for an hour or more. Only when we kissed them and folded them in our arms did we learn that they were much better, and that the reason for their instant return was their solicitude for father's and mother's grief over Baron's death. They had felt that our parents would be terribly depressed and lonely, with only myself, a boy of 12, at home.

The meals on the Fall River boats were somewhat typical of our public manners at that time. At supper, the ladies with their gentlemen escorts went down to table first, through the ladies cabin. Then the waiting horde of men entered. The whole meal, including the dessert (for it was really dinner), had been placed on the table. Each man helped himself, and the nimblest eater got the best meal. Some were down to the dessert by the time the laggards were only half through with the meats. The uniform price, I think, was 50 cents.

At Saratoga, I was much impressed, as a boy, with the state and style of the service at dinner. Practically everybody was first seated. The waiters were all colored. The headwaiter rang a bell (or did he blow a whistle?), the doors from the kitchen opened, and the long line of waiters entered, with almost military precision. There must have been some semblance of courses, for I remember that at the sound of the bell (or whistle), the plates were removed, and in a short time, the waiters returned with other viands, finally ending with the dessert.

The first streetcar line, horse-drawn, was the Fifth & Sixth Street Line. It required quite a long fight (as it did later, with the introduction of gasoline) before they were allowed to displace the old omnibuses. This and the other early lines were encouraged by the most liberal franchises, without any compensation to the city, and the stockholders all grew rich. The fare was six cents--or possibly $6\frac{1}{4}$ cents. During my early life, the commonest small silver were the old Spanish coins, the "fip" (or five pence, which equalled $6\frac{1}{4}$ cents), and the "levy" (probably this was a contraction for eleven pence, or $12\frac{1}{2}$ cents). The dime was not often seen, if at all. The copper cents or pennies were as large as today's quarters. We had no nickels. In the West, the "long bit" was the levy, and the "short bit" was the dime.

Paper money was not, as now, a national currency, freely circulating across the country and rarely counterfeited. There were no national banks but only state banks. One knew, in Philadelphia, all about our city banks, but when it came to banks in other parts of the state (or, worse, in far-distant other states), no one could know anything about them. Hence, counterfeits abounded. In order to guard themselves, shop-keepers, banks, and bankers, etc., subscribed to regularly-issued counterfeit detectors by which they could learn the peculiarities of each counterfeit bill. We always expected to have to compare a bill with the description of any counterfeit one-, two-, or five-dollar bill from any issuing bank from Maine to Texas. The annoyance, trouble, and delay can hardly be appreciated except by those who experienced them. Salmon P. Chase, Secretary of the Treasury during the Civil War, was, I think, the happy father of our national banks.

The limits of the city of Philadelphia were Vine Street, on the north, Cedar (now South) Street, on the south, and the two rivers. The outlying parts, though continuously built up, were called the liberties (e.g., the "Northern Liberties") or districts, such as Moyamensing, Southwark, Spring Garden, Kensington, and so forth. If a criminal reached the north side of Vine Street, or the south side of South Street, he could snap his fingers at the police. In 1854, this anomaly was ended by the consolidation of ·the city and the neighboring districts.

In my boyhood, there was but one post office, which was on Dock Street between 2nd and 3rd Streets. Each letter was weighed, and the postage was marked in ink on the right upper corner. The rate varied with the distance (such as within the city; or 100, ·250, or 500 miles, etc.). A letter to Great Britain, in the late '50s, cost 25 cents, equivalent to at least 50 cents now, for each ¼ ounce; hence the use of very thin paper and the full coverage for each sheet. (This was my constant habit, even when I was in Europe in 1864-66.) Postage could be· prepaid or collected on delivery, which caused endless delays.

There was but one polling place, the State House (now universally known as Independence Hall, just as the State House Yard is now known as Independence Square). The polls were open from 7 A.M. to 9 P.M., I think. With the long queues of impatiently waiting voters (my father often had to wait for an hour or more), in the gathering darkness, and with the rough and rowdy methods of those days, it is not surprising that belated voters

84

often left, or that there were not seldom broken heads and broken ballot boxes. Even our present bad methods are a great improvement over those of sixty years ago.

The volunteer fire department was not abolished until after (and I think it may have been several years after) I had graduated. It was a surviving relic of the day when every gentleman had his fireman's hat, cape, and boots, as well as leather fire buckets with his name and address painted on them. The early engines had two long, lengthwise handlebars, which were worked up and down by the firemen to pump water.

Later, there were a number of celebrated local fire companies, such as the Moya (that is, Moyamensing) Hose Company, the Southwark Engine Company, and so forth. Each engine required a large hose reel on a separate vehicle, which was drawn not by horses but by the men. The personnel consisted of chiefly the rougher element in the city. There was great rivalry between certain fire companies. The State House bell signaled the district in which the fire had broken out, and the various companies, in their effort to out-run their rivals to the fire, often collided at street intersections, and fights, sometimes serious, often followed.

After a long (and latterly a scandalous) career, the paid fire department was established. Then came horse-drawn engines, hose reels, hook-and-ladder companies, and now the motor vehicles, the fire towers, and separate high-pressure service in the eastern-central part of the city. The political uses of this department, and of the police, are a modern scandal, which will be eliminated in time, I have no doubt.

The first fire insurance company established (by Benjamin Franklin) in Philadelphia was the Philadelphia Contributorship for the Insurance of

Houses from Loss by Fire, in 1752. Every building insured by the company had an escutcheon on the front, just below the roof. This consisted of four hands clasped as if carrying anyone "Lady of London," as we boys used to call it. The company is now usually spoken of as "The Contributorship," but old Philadelphians more often call it the "Hand in Hand," because of the escutcheon. The company insures only real estate, and not furniture, and only in Philadelphia and its suburbs. It will only insure a certain amount on any one building (unless the fire hazard is too great), the rate varying with the risk, whether from the nature of the use of the building or from the danger of fire from the character of the environment. No more than a certain amount will be taken in any one block. Most of its policies are perpetual, i.e., not for a limited period of years. But either the company or the insured, by agreement, can terminate the policy or change the rate at any time. On 1729 Chestnut Street, for example, I originally had $10,000 worth of insurance. I deposited 2% (i.e., $200) with the company, so that at 5%, therefore, I lose $10 per year, which is the cost of my insurance. Whenever the policy is terminated, the remainder of the $200 is returned.

By its very conservative management (annual losses are very small, and sometimes there are none at all), the company has gradually accumulated a large surplus, far beyond any probable loss. Some fifteen or twenty years ago, an insurgent younger element among the policy-holders, therefore, started a rival ticket for directors, in opposition to the official ticket. Old Philadelphia was stirred to its depths, and a long line of policy-holders (men and women alike) gathered for the contest. The old fellows won, but they could take a hint as well as Queen Elizabeth, so that from then till now, a dividend of 10% on the deposit has been declared each year. I lose 5% on my deposit, but I gain 10% in dividends, with the net result that I get $10,000 insurance for nothing while they pay me $20 a year for the privilege of insuring my house.

They solicit business only in a mild way, since their income from the invested surplus more than covers all expenses and dividends, leaving more or less to be added to the ever-increasing surplus. New insurance participates in the dividends only after ten years have elapsed. About twelve years ago, I increased my insurance from ten to fifteen thousand, depositing another $100, so that for some two years past, I now lose $15 a year interest on my $300 total deposit and get $30 a year as a dividend.

The "Hand in Hand," in the early days, would not insure houses with *trees* in front of them, as these hindered the firemen. After a time, a new fire insurance company was started which *would* insure such houses. Their escutcheon was the "Green Tree," as old Philadelphians always call it (though their legal title is the Mutual Assurance Company). The company is a duplicate of the "Hand in Hand" in its methods, and a few years ago, the "Green Tree" adopted also the plan of an annual dividend on the deposit. Both companies are purely mutual, there being no traded stock.

The most remarkable achievement in amusements (and also in many practical uses), of the last five or six years, is the development of the cinematograph, usually called the cinema or cine, in Europe, and the movies, in this country. The first I ever knew of this was the work of Muybridge in photographing the movements of men, horses, etc., which he described in a book he published called *Animal Movements*, I think. As I recall it, he stationed a large series of cameras at short intervals, with

strings stretched across the path of the animal. As these were successively broken, the shutters were opened, for an instant. When placed in a
zoetrope, with slits opposite each resulting picture, the successive
photographs blended, by the persistence of vision, into a continuous moving picture.

I append a statement by "Girard" in the *Philadelphia Public Ledger*
of February 18th, 1916, as follows:

> Contrary to popular belief, the movie is not an English
> invention. It was born in Philadelphia.
> I learn from Dr. E. T. Reichert, of the University of
> Pennsylvania, that in 1861, Coleman Sellers, of this city, se-
> cured patents for the original moving picture machine. He used
> his photographs arranged radially on a horizontal axis and in
> an endless belt.
> Mr. Sellers was also the first man to produce animal move-
> ments by photograph. Mr. Muybridge, of the University, did the
> great bulk of animal movies up to the recent day when the film
> invention put the movie on the commercial map.
> Among other things, Mr. Muybridge took movie photographs
> of the heart of a dog, and it was he who suggested to Thomas A.
> Edison that he combine the moving picture with the phonograph.

The extraordinary improvements, both in technique and application,
which have followed are almost past belief. Many millions of capital are
now invested in the movies. They almost threaten to banish the actors
from the stage, which would be an irreparable loss. The wonderful and
sudden popularity of film may be judged from the statement that a Charles
Chaplin, who, I believe, does only comic stunts, has just signed a contract
for a year for $670,000. It seems incredible. Many vulgar and degrading
pictures, prize fights and worse, which are now shown should be prohibited.

But there is an immense gain. The durbar in India celebrating the
coronation of King Edward, the coronation of George V, the battles of the
present war, etc., are wonderfully realistic. In addition, the scientific

uses of the movies in explaining and demonstrating the steps of surgical operations; in showing epileptic fits and other medical conditions which are not available to be shown to students just when wanted, as illustrations to lectures or clinics; in demonstrations of mechanical processes, in the interest of education and efficiency, etc., in manufactories; in the maneuvers of military drill, entrenching, etc.; in the firing of guns (especially huge cannon), and even in following the flight of the missiles; and many other present--and probably more novel future--uses show us some of its multiform usefulness and service.

When successfully combined with the phonograph and the talking machine to render music as well as conversation and oratory, its value will be immensely increased.

(January, 1916. The following is a rather fuller account of my surgical and other literary work than that before written.)

When I began my medical studies, in 1860, the United States was almost wholly dependent upon Europe, and especially upon England, for our medical textbooks. Here and there, a few of our leading teachers wrote textbooks, but they could hardly compete with the European output. Gross's and Agnew's "Surgeries," in two and three volumes, respectively, were the most creditable and the most successful--especially Gross's.

When elected to the Chair of Surgery at the Jefferson, in 1889, as already briefly related, I found no surgical textbook founded on surgical bacteriology. I at once organized *The American Text-Book of Surgery*. The very first--and foundation--chapter was on "Surgical Bacteriology," and bacteriology pervaded every chapter. The writers were thirteen professors in the chief medical colleges of the country. This ensured an authoritative work, as well as its professional success. As to its financial success, over 40,000 copies have been *sold*. It was published in 1892 and has been followed by three later editions. Mr. W. B. Saunders at once took the cue and published a series of American Text-Books in various departments of medicine, all of them successful, and some, like our surgical work, splendidly successful. *The American Text-Book of Surgery*, as Mr. Saunders repeatedly said to me, was the beginning of the wonderful success of the W. B. Saunders Company. From then onwards, a very large number of textbooks by American authors have been published, and we are now independent of Europe. Besides textbooks in one or two volumes, a considerable number of systems of surgery, medicine, etc., have been issued. The most successful, I am told, has been *Keen's System of*

Surgery, in six volumes (1905-1913), of which nearly 14,000 sets have been printed (including review copies, etc., for professors of surgery). While I, as editor, have received a considerable compensation, the authors also have shared in the pecuniary success. Indeed, Dr. Robert W. Lovett said to me last summer (1915) that he has received more for his chapter on orthopedic surgery than for any other chapter he had ever written, adding that "in fact, more, I think, than from all the others put together."

Until, say, twenty-five years ago, the opportunities for research in this country were very scanty. Anyone who aspired to research work had to go abroad for a European training, only to find, on his return, almost no place where he could continue this fascinating work. Within the last 20 or 30 years, laboratory after laboratory has been established, and of such high quality that many Europeans are now coming *here* to learn. When I entered on my duties as Professor of Surgery at the Jefferson, European surgeons at my clinics were rarely seen. Before I resigned, in 1907, they or their chief assistants were frequent visitors.

The Rockefeller Institute, the Carnegie Institution, the Pepper Laboratory, the Jefferson Laboratory, plus research labs at Harvard, Columbia, Cornell, Chicago, Rochester (N.Y. and Minn.), and perhaps a score of others, are seething centers of ceaseless work--and good work, too. Our authors and experimenters are quoted abroad, and few journals are better or better known than the *Journal of Experimental Medicine*, *American Journal of Physiology*, *Journal of Medical Research*, *Journal of Infectious Diseases*, *Archives of Internal Medicine*, *Journal of Biological Chemistry*, and the *Journal of Pharmacology and Experimental Therapeutics*, all of them American and none, I think, over twenty-five or thirty years old.

When president of the American Medical Association (1900), I took as the subject of my presidential address "The Endowment of Medical Colleges," in which I pointed out how little had been done for medicine, as compared with theology, literature, and departments of science other than medicine. While the tide was then probably turning towards medical endowment, I have reason to believe, from what has been told me, that my address (one of the earliest on that subject) has had no little influence in that direction. Since then, truly magnificent endowments of Harvard, Yale, Columbia, the University of Minnesota, Washington University in St. Louis, Tulane, the University of Pittsburgh, and the splendid gift of the Mayo brothers, have been achieved and are amply justifying their existence.

The good fortune I had of falling at once under the stimulating influence of Weir Mitchell, at the very beginning of my medical studies, is largely accountable for my later career. I was stirred at once into authorship. My first work was in reports of cases during the Civil War, many of which will be found in the *Medical and Surgical History of the War of the Rebellion*. I later published some clinical charts and revised Flower's *Diagrams of the Nerves*. I edited twelve small volume of *American Health Primers*, for Lindsay and Blakiston. This series was republished in England by Ward and Locke, under the title *Ward and Locke's Long Life Series*. The English publishers omitted my name as editor and the names of the twelve authors, substituting "by eminent members of the medical profession." The text was so revised that all evidence of its American origin was obliterated. I sent a copy of one volume, with its English counterpart, to the *Lancet*, with a protest against such plagiarism, but the *Lancet* never uttered a word against such a scandalous outrage. I let the matter drop. Some letters on this subject will be found among my papers.

My connection with the Philadelphia School of Anatomy I have detailed in my *Addresses and Other Papers*. I had returned from my studies in Europe in the late spring of 1866. In the autumn, Dr. R. S. Sutton, who was then at the head of this ancient school, wished to remove to Pittsburgh and therefore to sell the school's good will and fixtures. He offered it to me, and after consulting with Dr. Agnew (whose pupil I had been in 1860-62) and Dr. Weir Mitchell, I took it over. The good will consisted of seven pupils; and the fixtures were a few tables and stools, two tanks for the cadavers, and a few poor miscellaneous charts, etc., for all of which, upon the advice of Agnew, I paid $600, even though it was not worth over (if even as much as) one-fourth of that sum. I took it over in November, when the students were practically all settled (though fifteen more were added to my class during that session).

My first lecture (I had never attempted anything of the kind before) was a great trial. I took as my subject "The Ligation of the Femoral Artery." Fortunately, I decided to speak extemporaneously (the method I always subsequently followed). I first demonstrated its surgical anatomy, then demonstrated the procedure for its ligation, especially warning them of the danger of a ligation of the vein, an accident which, in those days of sepsis, might easily occur in the small incisions then in vogue (for at that time, to double the length of the incision doubled the danger). I had hardly spoken for four or five minutes when my supply of saliva gave out, and it seemed to me that I should never secrete any more. As soon as I concluded, I hustled the "subject" out of the room, for I had a dreadful suspicion that I had tied the vein. As soon as I was alone, I dissected the parts and found my suspicion verified. To save my face, lest even my janitor would despise me, I removed the ligature from the vein, placed one on the artery, and never disclosed my mistake till many years afterwards, when I could afford to do so.

I taught not only systematic anatomy but also courses in operative surgery, courses which were well attended and of the greatest use to me later, as a surgeon. In addition, I also gave courses, for several years, in artistic anatomy which fitted me for my later position as Professor of Artistic Anatomy in the Pennsylvania Academy of the Fine Arts.

One of the sessions of the School of Anatomy I opened with an address on "The Early History of Practical Anatomy." I gave a good deal of time to research on this matter, and it taught me more than my lecture taught my auditors. Even today, I really find it quite interesting. When I closed the school, in 1875, I published a *History of the Philadelphia School of Anatomy*, which is a serious and valuable record of the good work done in the 65 years of this "School of the Prophets," from which came so many of our distinguished teachers. It was closed in 1875 because the United States government bought the site for the new post office.

Other later teachers of anatomy have opened anatomical and surgical schools with the same name, but even though they have a legal right to use the name, they are in no sense a continuation of the original Philadelphia School of Anatomy. I have written an account of these schools which will be found among my papers.

In 1898, I published my *Surgical Complications and Sequels of Typhoid Fever*, which still (1915) is the only book on the subject. Though its statistics are no longer valid (they have improved very greatly), its principles are still entirely valid. I think I have never seen any complication or sequel, except typhoid abscess of the breast, which is not described in this book. (See also, in my list of papers, No. 234, with a table of 158 cases of typhoid perforation.)

In 1898, I also published the bicentenary history of the First Baptist Church. In 1905, I published my volume of *Addresses and Other Papers*.

In 1914, I published my various papers on vivisection, in a volume entitled *Animal Experimentation and Medical Research* (Houghton Mifflin).

In the October 24, 1903, issue of *The Outlook*, I published a little paper on "The Cheerfulness of Death." It expressed thoughts which had been long floating about in my mind. I republished it in my *Addresses and Other Papers*, and the American Baptist Publication Society later republished it as a little pamphlet. Nothing I have ever written has brought me so many kind messages and letters. It has been a great comfort to many.

I also have contributed chapters to a number of other works, a list of which is in my fireproof box. In the same list are articles I have published in medical and other journals, numbering well over three hundred.

Among the papers in that list, I may mention some of the most important. Nos. 1, 2, 3, and 6 were published in conjunction with Drs. Mitchell and Morehouse; No. 16 deals with a remarkable, and in my own experience unique, case of osteoporosis; Nos. 18 and 23 were on a new diagnostic sign of the sprain fracture of the ankle-joint; No. 20, a very rare instance of necrosis of the entire petrous portion of the temporal bone resulting from a similar injury to one described in *Hamlet*; Nos. 29 and 30 (written with William Thomson) describe a pathological demonstration of

the anatomical distribution of the optic nerve in the retina. This demonstration was accepted as final by Flint, in his five-volume *Physiology*,
and, I believe, by most if not all later writers.

No. 45 demonstrated the enervation of the internal and external in-
tercostal muscles, by experiments on a criminal who was executed by hang-
ing; Nos. 56, 65, and 72 were early papers describing and advocating
cholecystotomy. No. 61 advocated the systematic use of the living model
in teaching anatomy, a method commended and adopted by Cunningham of
Dublin (and later of Edinburgh).

No. 63 was my first paper on Dupuytren's contraction; later papers
on this subject were Nos. 99, 100, and 295.

No. 73 was on stretching the facial nerve in tic convulsif.

No. 74 was an early case of appendicitis. (See also Nos. 125 and
132.) No. 75 was the first instance of nephrectomy for a gunshot wound
of the kidney; No. 76 described two cases of aneurism at ages 18 and 8, a
very rare condition in the young.

No. 82 was a lesson in septic surgery; Nos. 86, 88, 89, and 90 first
described and formulated the tapping of the lateral ventricles as a definite surgical operation. In one, I tapped and drained both lateral ventricles and irrigated them from side to side, a wholly new procedure.

No. 87 was an early case of hysterectomy; No. 94 was an early case
of nephrorrhaphy for floating kidney and was followed by Nos. 114 and 118.

Nos. 101 and 102 were among the very early papers on the surgery of
the brain and spinal cord and were followed by Nos. 109, 115, 119, 120,
120, 121, 128, 131, 133, 134, 140, 141, 142, 156, 159, 162, 164, 168, 171,
176a, 181, 184, 185, 186, 189, 204, 215, 238, 240, 241, 250, 268, 270a,

272, 288, 291, and 322. There are 38 papers in all, each dealing with intra-cranial surgery in one of its many phases. By consulting them, one can see what I accomplished in cerebral and spinal surgery. This group of papers is by far the most important work I have done, surgically speaking. Daveler's case opened the door of opportunity to me, as I have described, and I entered in. I was so far in the lead that even better men later could not catch up in reputation at least for many years. A stern chase was indeed a long chase.

No. 104 described a new operation for prominent ears; No. 109 described a case of the removal of the hand center.

No. 115, the 38th paper on cerebral surgery, was another, and elaborate, paper on the surgery of the lateral ventricles, which cost me a year of incessant labor. It was far too long to read, at the Berlin International Medical Congress, in 1890, so I read a very brief abstract. Both the abstract and and the full paper were handed by me in person to Prof. E. Sonnenburg, the secretary of the surgical section, and he "lost" the full paper (strange to say, not the little abstract but the bulky full text)! Only the abstract was published. He never even apologized for the unpardonable carelessness. Alas, I had no carbon copy, and I had neither the time nor the courage to re-write it. Carbon paper was then quite a new device. Never since then have I omitted to have one or more carbon copies of every paper or address.

No. 124 described a new operation for spasmodic wry neck by the division of the posterior nerves; No. 130 described a new and exact method of lengthening tendons; No. 135 showed what an apparently useless kidney was capable of doing.

No. 137 described what is, so far as I know, the only case of amputation at the hip-joint for a large sarcoma, in a woman five months pregnant. She recovered, had her baby, and resumed her missionary work in Brazil. She lived on for some years, but eventually died from a recurrence.

No. 138 was the first case in America, I think, of the removal of a tumor from the liver. (See also Nos. 147, 201, and 222a.)

No. 139 was the most difficult operation I ever performed in the neck. Two lives were at stake. No. 160 is a similar but less difficult case.

No. 143 described a most extensive operation for the cure of a fecal fistula, the result of appendicitis.

No. 145 was one of the earliest papers describing gangrene of the testicle, which resulted from the torsion of the spermatic cord.

No. 151 described a case of ovariotomy in which the tumor removed weighed 111 pounds and the young girl (aet. 14+), after recovery, weighed only 68 pounds. (My son-in-law, Dr. Walter Freeman, warned me that if I was not careful, I might sometime "throw away the wrong piece.")

No. 157 proposed distention of the bladder with air instead of water, in suprapubic cystotomy.

No. 165 described the case of an operation wound of the thoracic duct, with records of four other cases of this rare accident.

No. 166 was an elaborate paper dealing with the control of hemorrhage in the arm, clavicle, and scapula.

No. 170 was a case of the amputation of the shoulder girdle. In it I reported also a case of extensive thoracoplasty by a new method, which I later discovered had already been done by Schede (though this was unknown to me at the time). Accordingly, I gave him the credit in my published paper. (See also No. 210.)

No. 174 reported six cases of the suture of the musculo-spiral nerve. (See also Nos. 207, 245, 255, and 259.)

No. 187 was an elaborate paper on renal traumatisms; No. 193 described the resection of the sternum for tumors; No. 197 reported 25 cases of the resection of the rectum; No. 203 described one of the earliest cases of primary tuberculosis of the breast.

No. 213, the Cartwright lectures, on the surgery of the stomach were an elaborate study of the subject.

No. 216 was an extraordinary case of a urinary fecal fistula following appendicitis, with the appendix opening into the bladder.

No. 219 described an improved method of laryngectomy, while No. 220 described two very unusual cases of surgery of the trachea.

No. 237 was a case of multiple neuro-fibromata of the ulnar nerve.

No. 239 reported a nephrotomy for a huge aneurism of the renal artery (by far the largest renal aneurism ever operated on), with twelve other collected cases of aneurism of the renal artery.

No. 246 recorded a case of the ligature of the abdominal aorta in which the patient lived for 48 days after the operation, the longest period on record. It was the 12th such operation ever done. I proposed and figured an instrument for the temporary compression of the aorta.

No. 248, on the progress of surgery in the 19th century, was one of a series of similar "Century" papers printed in the *New York Sun*, in the first months of the 20th century (that is, in 1901), and later republished by Harper and Brother under the title *The Progress of the Century*.

No. 262, on "The Duties and Responsibilities of Trustees of Public

Medical Institutions," has been reprinted by Dr. J. McKeen Cattell, in a volume entitled *Medical Research and Education* (Science Press, 1913).

No. 273, on interileo abdominal amputation, described a new method of amputation of the leg and one half of the pelvic girdle. (Kocher embodied this new method in the later editions of his *Operative Surgery*.)

No. 275 was a paper on the massage of the heart following a chloroform collapse, with notes of 25 other similar cases. Among my newspaper clippings will be found a letter I published in the London *Times* describing the lies told, in relation to this case, by the *New York Evening Journal* of W. R. Hearst. (See also my MS, below, on "Yellow Journalism.")

No. 276 was a case of a huge parotid tumor (weighing 7 pounds), with recovery.

No. 279, on "The Danger of Allowing Warts and Moles to Remain lest they Become Malignant," with 25 illustrative cases, drew the attention of the profession to a little-considered yet serious danger and evoked great interest. This is one of the most useful papers I ever wrote, though Osler's humorous comment to me was, "From brain tumors to warts and moles: the first evidence of senility." (See also No. 326.)

No. 295 described a new method of operating in Dupuytren's contraction.

No. 297, "The Service of Missions to Science and Society," was my presidential address before the American Baptist Missionary Union, in 1906, and showed what missionaries had done, with references to original authorities.

No. 299, on tumors of the carotid gland, was an exhaustive study of this subject. All the recorded cases were collected and figured.

No. 301 described the case of a sacro-coccygeal tumor (teratoma) with an opening entirely through the sacrum and a sinus passing through the opening and communicating with the rectum, the sinus resembling a bronchus, the only case on record, so far as I know, of such an anomaly. The patient (Helen White, my great-great-niece) is now a finely developed girl. The tumor was removed, and the sinus finally was successfully closed.

No. 303, "The Symptomatology, Diagnosis, and Surgical Treatment of Cervical Ribs," with histories of all the recorded cases I could find, was the most important paper on this subject up to that time. All the later papers I have seen have recorded only later individual cases.

No. 305 recorded an extraordinary, and I think unique, case of an extensive burn of the top of the head, with necrosis of the entire osseous cap of the cranium.

No. 333, the last in the present list, was the Ether Day Address, on October 16th, 1915, at the Massachusetts General Hospital.

Several numbers have been interpolated, bringing the total to nearly 340 papers. If to these are added the books, chapters in books, and the addresses I have written, etc., I think I cannot be accused of having spent an idle life.

In the *Medical News*, of which I was one of the editorial staff for some years, I wrote many of the editorials (most of them in bound volumes in my library), to which I have affixed my initials.

My influence has always been thrown, I think, in favor of the highest ideals in medicine; of the best opportunities for research; of the most advanced methods of instruction; of everything that would lead to the elevation of our guild and to the benefit of suffering humanity.

The medical secretary, the typewriter, the telephone, and the automobile, all the products of the last twenty-five years, have doubled or tripled the efficiency of every doctor. How much more, therefore, may our successors be able to accomplish!

My intellectual life has been influenced most of all by the instructors and friends I have been fortunate in having. In Brown University, Professors Chace, Gammell, Lincoln, and Angell were the most influential.

To the analytical method which I learned at Brown, as I have already stated before (but it deserves emphasis by repetition), I attribute my success as a teacher. I always tried to reduce each problem to its simplest known terms and then proceed, step by step, to the more complex and the unknown. Often, I have tingled from head to foot when suddenly, in the midst of a lecture--like a spark struck at a blow--a happy apposite illustration, phrase, or argument has occurred to me, and I have been all aglow with enthusiasm. I was always in dead earnest, in my efforts to make clear to my students, and to impress upon them, the great truths of surgery. Every lecture was a new subject, on which I had read the latest literature. I never tired in my efforts to turn out the best doctors, so far as my department was concerned. I never spared time, labor, or painstaking preparation.

Of mathematics I was very fond, in college, and to that discipline I attribute my deeply-ingrained sense of order and exactness. I also endeavored to use the plainest and best English.

The chief commendation I have had from lay readers of my magazine articles has been that they could *understand* them. I could ask no better praise.

I adopted the following method of composition, in all written papers and addresses.

First, I gathered all my material and, for some time, mulled over the subject.

My secretary put markers at reference points for all the authorities I wished to consult or to quote. Then I drew up a skeleton of my address or paper, with the chief headings and a more or less full list of subheadings. Next, I dictated, or sometimes wrote, a rough sketch. This my secretary typewrote, with wide intervals between the lines. This rough copy I interlined, added to, and cut out some parts, transposing others. If time allowed, I preferred to lay aside this sketch, for some days, and then attack it afresh. The MS was often (usually, in fact) a very tangled mess, which I finally gave to my secretary to decipher. She then made a fair copy on rather stiff paper, with wide spaces between the lines for easy reading. This final copy contained the facts and arguments as I apprehended them. Then it underwent a close scrutiny, purely from the point of view of obtaining a good English style.

By this time, I was so familiar with the text that I needed to read from the MS only at brief intervals, so that I could look at my audience most of the time (the only way ever to hold the attention of any audience). I always had my MS in loose sheets, and as I finished each page, I placed it at the back, so that I always had a few loose final sheets which would not remain stiff and upright but insisted on falling over, thus making them difficult to read.

On one occasion, familiarity with the text of my address stood me in good stead, as I gave a formal introductory address at the beginning of the winter session of the Woman's Medical College. I picked up the MS lying on my desk, but by some curious chance, I did not notice that I had left on the desk three or four of the final sheets. During the address, all went well till, as I slipped the "last" sheet slightly aside, ready to place it behind the others, I was startled to see page *one* staring me in the face. My mind worked at high pressure, during the minute it took to read the few lines of the last sheet I had with me. I debated whether to own up, in confusion, and stop, or to rely on my familiarity with what I had written and chance it, speaking extemporaneously while pretending to be reading from my text. I at once chose the latter. I placed the last leaf at the back and continued the address, glancing, from time to time, at page one as if reading. When I had spoken what I believed to be the equivalent of a page, I slipped page one to the back; then after a time, page two; and finally, page three. Only one person caught on to my trick, a friend sitting almost directly behind me who, happening to look at my MS, saw pages 1, 2, and 3 slipped behind the others, in turn. Drops of cold sweat accumulated on my forehead, during the brief ordeal. But I won.

Weir Mitchell's influence I have already acknowledged. The friends I have had in the Jefferson, the University of Pennsylvania, the College of Physicians, the American Surgical Association, the American Philosophical Society, the Wistar Party, the Franklin Inn Club, and my many friends in Europe have all been of the greatest service to me, in stimulating my intellectual life and work.

I have often been surprised at my changed attitude towards hemorrhage during operation. How vividly I recall my first operation on a living patient, a simple amputation of the forearm, in an army hospital, in 1862. I was greatly alarmed after the very first incision, lest the patient might bleed to death before I could secure the arteries. I remember well that shortly afterwards, I asked an older surgeon to amputate for me at the shoulder joint. Though I had often done it on a cadaver, I shrank from doing it because I was actually afraid of the hemorrhage. But I ended up being as little afraid as anyone could possibly be of even the most furious hemorrhage. If it did occur, I met it with imperturbable coolness, sure of my mastery by means I had often used with success. This is, I think, the severest test of an experienced surgeon. When the warm blood is gushing as if from a fireplug over the hands of the surgeon, and he knows that it can continue for only a very few minutes without destroying life, if he can retain his equanimity and his perfect mental poise, giving short, sharp orders and adopting (almost, it would seem, by intuition) just the right means for arresting the hemorrhage, then he can be implicitly relied upon. I am amazed at myself when, after such a sudden and not unseldom unexpected emergency, I have found myself the victor and undisturbed in mind. I have returned unspoken but fervent thanks to God for my having attained to such self-control.

I have always been a firm believer in the Christian religion. My ideas have been liberalized, as time has gone by, but I have not believed in the almost total secularization of the Sabbath, in fact the total neglect of its religious duties--and pleasures. Were the attendance on the services of the Sabbath entirely given up, organized Christianity would wholly disappear, and the influence of the churches would be entirely eliminated. What a disaster this would be to the world is hard to assess.

The future life is, to me, a logical necessity, even apart from revelation. I cannot possibly believe that such master minds as those of the sages of Antiquity, or the more modern instances such as Dante, Shakespeare, Goethe, Kant, Huxley, Tyndall, Darwin, Kelvin, Holmes, Whittier, and thousands of others--great poets, authors, scientists, historians, anthropologists, archeologists, preachers, lawyers, doctors, orators, artists, statesmen, etc.--all should be capable of development to such wonderful heights of intellectual achievement and then be snuffed out by death and vanish. It would resemble a man who could construct the most perfect telescope, spectroscope, steam engine, telephone, or wireless (and the mind of man far exceeds all these), and then throw them all, unused, into the scrap heap. I do not believe that God is so illogical. There *must* be another and a better world. Otherwise, God (or, if one prefers it, Nature)--and I write it reverently--would be a monumental bungler.

Never did I feel more absolutely convinced of the existence of the other world than when I personally had to face it, when I was operated on in 1910. I was absolutely and perfectly calm. A few days before I started for Rochester, Minnesota, three or four of the members of the American Philosophical Society met me, at my request, and I told them of the seriousness of the operation, and of the possibility (or even, as I believed, the probability) of my death, so that they might not be taken by surprise. I left town on a Saturday, the day after the November meeting of the Society. (Before the meeting, I had given a dinner party for the speaker and enjoyed it heartily.) As I took the ether, I do not think my pulse was quickened by even a single beat, evidence of what comfort a supreme faith in religion, in God, and my Saviour can be in such a time of trial.

106

SOME OF THE SOCIAL, SCIENTIFIC, ECONOMIC, AND EDUCATIONAL
DEVELOPMENTS DURING MY LIFETIME, WITH SOME REMARKS ON MY
SURGICAL AND LITERARY LIFE (January, 1916)

In my reminiscences and in the histories of my own church and of the
early years of Brown University, I have touched slightly on these subjects,
but some more detailed account of the wonderful progress the world has
made, during my long lifetime, may be of interest. I write from memory,
and so some of the dates and data may be erroneous, but not seriously
so, I hope.

All of the world's achievements (except those of medicine and surgery, as noted at the end of my Ether Day Address), however, sink into
insignificance in the light of the present horrible war. The history of
its causes and its authors will only be fully known 50, or even 100,
years from now. Had Germany and Austria *dared* to publish *textually* the
notes which passed between Berlin and Vienna (and there *were* such notes:
see the official introduction to the first German White Book), allowing
the world to know how much of a hand Germany had, through von Tschirsky
(the German ambassador to Vienna), in framing the ultimatum to Serbia, I
believe that it would be clear that the Kaiser was responsible for the
war. Had he lifted only his little finger, Austria would have called a
European congress; or the ultimatum would have been preceded by conferences between the powers; or a reasonable time would have been given
Serbia, during which the powers could have effected some arrangement to
satisfy and protect Austria, while at the same time preserving the peace
of the world.

I hold the Kaiser responsible for all the sorrow, suffering, poverty, death, and destruction resulting from the war. He opened it by violating

a solemn treaty (a mere "scrap of paper") and by desolating Belgium. This

treatment of Belgium can be seen as a logical outcome of the Kaiser's

speech to his soldiers, when he sent them to China, at the time of the

Boxer Rebellion:

> Spare nobody, take no prisoners. Use your weapons in a
> manner to make every Chinaman for a thousand years to come
> forego the wish to as much as look askance at a German.*

Had the bungling, stupid German diplomacy sought, from pole to pole,

anything which would have more firmly consolidated anti-German sentiment

among the Americans (indeed, of the whole civilized world), it could not

have discovered a more efficient means than the destruction of the *Lusi-*

tania and, later, of the *Ancona*. Words fail to describe the utter detes-

tation I feel, not for the German people but for the military autocracy

and the army. (I feel as kindly towards my personal friends in Germany as

I ever did.)

As president of the American Philosophical Society, and of the Fifth

International Surgical Congress (which is to meet in Paris in September of

1917), I feel that I am not at liberty to declare my sentiments publicly.

I have carefully refrained, therefore, from any expression of opinion

which could reach my German or Austro-Hungarian friends. Privately, how-

ever, I feel at liberty to (and do) express my abhorence of Germany's

brutal methods. The report of Lord Bryce's commission (as well as numer-

ous statements to me by friends of what they have seen and known) has con-

vinced me of the truth of otherwise unverifiable rumors, even as though

the Kaiser's admonition to his troops had not been uttered.

---

* Schierbrand, Wolf V. *The Kaiser's Speeches*. Harper Bros., New York, 1903.

I feel such an aversion to Germany's conduct that, although I esteem my individual German friends as much as ever, I shall never again set foot on German soil--or on a German steamer. I shall never again buy anything "Made in Germany," and never again trust a promise of the German government. (Of course, I include Austria, a mere tail to the German kite.) For twenty centuries, "Punic faith" has been a hissing and a reproach. It has been left to the 20th century to substitute "Germanic faith" as still less honorable. The violation of Luxembourg and Belgium was their first step. They now claim to have found in Brussels documents which warrant this. These documents have been published in full, and they say simply that "*IF* Germany violates its treaty obligations," then so and so will be done. But granting that these documents ever *did* justify Germany's tearing up a "scrap of paper," the motives of Germany are to be judged by what she knew *at the time of her violation of solemn treaty pledges*, and not by evidence found later.

Then her violation of all international law (to say nothing of the laws of God and humanity), in murdering innocent non-combatants on the high seas, with the sinking of the *Lusitania* and the *Ancona*, make one shudder with revulsion. Her scientists have devised means for the use of chlorine and bromine gases, diabolical weapons which place her outside the realm of civilization.

Now, though three of the guarantors of the neutrality of the Suez Canal in time of war, Germany, Austria, and Turkey are massing troops to destroy the canal, tearing up another "scrap of paper."

I would wish to eliminate such an enemy of civilization from my consciousness. May she drink to the very dregs the cup of sorrows she has pressed to the lips of so many innocent sufferers.

109

SOCIAL AND ECONOMIC LIFE

Life was rather primitive when I was born. The population of the United States was, I think, about 16,000,000, and of Philadelphia, about 200,000.

One could not walk a block (or, in Philadelphia parlance, a square), even when I was a young man, without meeting the Quaker dress, including drab, "coal-scuttle" bonnets and drab dresses for the women and drab, "shad-bellied" coats (with no lapel or turn-over collar) and broad-brimmed hats for the men. One now has to go to the 5th Street Meeting or the 12th Street Meeting on "First Day" (the Quaker Sunday) to see them still.

Public lands were deemed so inexhaustible that one could buy them for $1.25 an acre, and great land-grants were given out to aid in the construction of the various railroads to the Pacific built in the '60s and '70s. In 1862, Senator Morrill introduced a bill, which passed, giving to one university in each state large grants of land to encourage the foundation of agricultural departments. It was wonderful that this should have been done during the throes of the Civil War, and at its most serious stage. This was a great help to a few universities, especially Cornell and Minnesota (the latter now probably valued at $100,000,000!), but many of the colleges and universities, unfortunately, mis-managed this splendid gift.

The first murder trial I remember, as a boy (and I read every word of it), was that of Prof. Webster for the murder of Prof. Parkman, both of the Harvard Medical School.

The Pullman and sleeping car have come in during my adult life. It was a characteristic remark of some German surgeons, attending the Fourth

International Surgical Congress, in New York (in April, 1914), when asked

how they liked the sleeping cars, that they were satisfied, adding, how-

ever, that their wives "did not like the upper berths."

My father never used any other than a quill pen, shaping it himself

and cutting the nib on his left thumbnail. In England, I have often been

annoyed, in the coffee room, by the *scratch, scratch* of such pens. In

December, 1915, I saw that members of Parliament would no longer be sup-

plied with them. Steel pens, at least those made in Manchester, by Gil-

lott, only came in during my late boyhood. The conundrum was asked, "Why

is Gillott a corrupter of morals?" The answer: "Because he makes people

steel pens and tells them they do right."

The typewriter appeared towards the end of the 19th century.

"Girard" (Mr. Herman L. Collins) in the March 4th, 1916, *Ledger* says:

> Things they didn't find in Philadelphia 40 years ago, when
> President Grant opened the Centennial:
> Half our present population, one ten-story building, a
> trolley car, a telephone, a foot of street paved with wood or
> asphalt, a wireless station, a typewriter, a typesetting ma-
> chine, a phonograph, a national bank or a trust company with
> $5,000,000 deposits, compared with about $95,000,000 today; an
> automobile, an electric light in the street, an electric pro-
> pelled train, a "movie" theatre, an electric fan, a City Hall,
> filtered water, an aeroplane, a million-dollar hotel, a man
> with a million income, a school or college with 1000 students.

Hoe's and other fast power printing presses are probably less than

forty years old. Compressed air, as a powerful motor in riveting, drill-

ing, and mining, is a novelty probably not over 25 years old.

I have seen the rise of the air brake; the X ray (1895); the movies,

from the earliest attempt by Muybridge to the present pervasive develop-

ment; and the whole advance of wireless telegraphy and the telephone.

The first Atlantic cable was initiated in 1858. After about four hundred messages (the first of which was between Queen Victoria and President Buchanan), it failed. Only by the persistence of Cyrus W. Field was a new cable laid, in 1866, and it has been a success ever since. The laying of the first cable was celebrated with great rejoicings, illuminations, etc.--and the New York city hall was destroyed by fire as a result.

The whole modern development of electricity has taken place within the last forty years. In 1876, at the Centennial Exhibition, the *sole* modern electrical exhibit was one arc light, installed by Prof. Farmer on the main building. The dynamo, the hydroelectric plant, and the trolley system followed still later, together with all the varied uses of electricity for obtaining light, power, heat, telephone, and telegraphy.

The automobile as a common vehicle scarcely antedates the 20th century.

The Rural Free Delivery service and the Parcel Post are quite recent, the latter within about three years. Artificial ice, that great boon to the tropics (and a great boon even in the temperate zones) dates only about 35 years back.

Sky-scraper buildings have become necessary, by the increasing value of land, and have been made possible by the development of cement and reinforced concrete, the elevator (the vertical railway), and by steam- and hot-water-heating, as well as by forced-air ventilation.

In science, the most wonderful discovery has been that of radioactivity, by which our views of physics and chemistry, and even the very constitution of matter itself, have been wholly revolutionized. This alone has made the last fifteen years, or so, a time of extraordinary progress.

Moreover, chemistry alone has progressed as never before. The extraordinary development of modern applied chemistry, within almost every industry, is best seen in the complex programs of the Congresses of Applied Chemistry. Scientific, or theoretical, chemistry seeks the quieter atmosphere of the American Philosophical Society, the National Academy of Sciences, the American Academy of Arts and Sciences, and other technical scientific societies.

The synthesis of urea, one of the many substances believed to be obtained only as the result of the vital forces of plants or animals, has led the way to the production of a number of marvelous such substances in the chemist's laboratory, which is replacing Nature's vital laboratory.

Synthetic rubber, indigo, gasoline, and many other substances are either commercially profitable now or doubtless will be soon. The multitude of new colors and medicines of the coal-tar groups show what can be done in this department. Often the by-products are even more valuable than the main product.

Astronomy, of which I can give only a few details, has progressed in a marvelous fashion. The wonderful discovery or Uranus, by Adams and Le Verrier, by mathematical calculations based on planetary disturbances in the orbits of Neptune and Jupiter, reads like a fairy tale, as its location was so accurately predicted that the planet itself was immediately found.

The extraordinary development of astronomical instruments, as at the Mt. Wilson Solar Observatory (among others), and the results obtained, almost outstrips the imagination. Bauer, of the Carnegie Institution, has been able to correct the large errors in the sailing charts and marine tables, by the world-wide voyage of the non-magnetic ship *Carnegie*, making the seas far safer.

Epoch-making Inventions by People of the United States in the Last 50 Years

[*National Geographic Magazine, December 1916*]

Invention	Inventor	Year
Telephone	Bell	1876
Typewriter	Sholes	1878
Cash register	Patterson	1885
Incandescent lamp	Edison	1880
Electric furnace-reduction	Cowles	1885
Talking machine	Edison	1878
Electrolytic alkali production	Castner	1890
Transparent photograph film	Eastman	1888
Motion-picture machine	Edison	1893
Buttonhole-sewing machine	Reece	1881
Carborundum	Acheson	1896
Calcium carbide	Willson	1888
Artificial graphite	Acheson	1896
Split-phase induction motor	Tesla	1887
Air brake	Westinghouse	1869
Electric welding	Thomson	1889
Type-bar casting	Mergenthaler	1885
Chain-stitch shoe-sewing machine	French & Myers	1881
Single-type composing machine	Lanston	1887
Continuous-process match machine	Beecher	1888
Chrome tanning	Schulz	1884
Disk harrow (modern type)	Hardy	1896
Welt machine	Goodyear	1871
Electric lamp	Brush	1879
Recording adding machine	Burroughs	1888
Celluloid	Hyatt	1870
Automatic knot-tying harvester machine	Appleby	1880
Water gas	Lowe	1875
Barbed-wire machine	Glidden	1875
Rotary converter	Bradley	1887
Automatic car-coupler	Janney	1873
High-speed steel-maker	Taylor & White	1901
Dry-air blast-furnace process	Gayley	1894
Railway block signals	Robinson	1872
Trolley car	VanDepoele/Sprague	1887
Harveyized armor plate	Harvey	1891

Inventions for Foreigners During the Same Period

Invention	Inventor	Year
Electric steel	Heroult (French)	1900
Dynamite	Nobel (Swedish)	1867
Artifical alizarene (dye)	Graebe & Lieberman (German)	1869
Siphon recorder	Thompson (English)	1874
Gas engine, Otto cycle	Otto (German)	1877
Wireless telegraphy	Marconi (Italian)	1900
Smokeless powder	Vielle (French)	1886
Diesel motor	Diesel (German)	1900
Centrifugal creamer	De Laval (Swedish)	1880
Manganese steel	Hadfield (English)	1884
Electric transformer	Gaulard & Gibbs (English)	1883
Cyanide process for extracting metal	Arthur & DeForrest (English)	1888
Mantle burner	Welsbach (Austrian)	1890
Coke oven by-product	Hoffman (Austrian)	1893

When I was in college, Fraunhofer's lines, in the solar spectrum, were only a curious phenomenon, entirely unknown as to their cause or meaning. Now, the spectroscope has shown, by these lines, the chemical composition of the sun, the planets, the stars, and even of the nebulae and the comets. It has shown the composition of the whole visible universe to be almost identical, in the essential elements. New elements also have been added, by the spectroscope, to those already known.

In engineering, the progress has been no less astonishing. The skyscrapers have already been mentioned. Instead of the walls' being built on a perimeter foundation supporting the floors, a forest of steel now rises from a central foundation bearing up the floors, which in turn carry the walls, whose only function now is to keep out the weather. The walls can begin on any story, instead of from the ground up.

The great bridges, the long tunnels, and the viaducts and canals of the last fifty years are exceeded only, perhaps, by the pyramids.

The Suez Canal, the Soo Canal, the Kiel Canal, and, of course, the Panama Canal are a few of the greatest artificial waterways of the world. Many of the lesser canals cannot be mentioned. The greatest of all, that at Panama, was made possible only, first, by the conquest of yellow fever; second, by the development of cement and concrete construction; and third, by the invention of huge steam shovels. When we visited the canal, the last time, the walls of the great locks were nearing completion, and Col. Sibert said to me that if concrete and cement had not been available, there could have been no canal: the only substitution could have been dressed granite, and the enormous cost (plus the very much longer time required) would have made the canal impossible.

The wonderful irrigation projects, again, made possible only by great dams of concrete and cement, have been devised and built practically entirely since about 1900, I think. The Great American Desert of my boyhood geography lessons has been made to blossom like the rose, by the magic touch of water.

Of mining and metallurgy, so successfully prosecuted in the United States, South America, and Africa, I can say only that chemical discoveries and the inventive genius of man have wholly revolutionized these entire industries.

On the ocean, I have seen the wooden sailing ships give place to iron and steel ships. In war, they are now armored against enemies and propelled by steam from coal (and latterly by oil). The frigate has been replaced by the battleship, the dreadnought, and the super-dreadnought. The small guns, with projectiles weighing a few pounds, have given place to enormous cannon and 12-, 14-, and 16-inch shells (the largest of which weigh over half a ton and cost, I believe, half a thousand dollars each), which, by smokeless powder, can be hurled over twenty miles. By modern high explosives they are shattered into a thousand deadly fragments at their target, wrecking forts and regiments alike.

The barbarous practice, introduced by the Germans in the present horrible war, of using asphyxiating gases is a new and devilish invention worthy only of German *Kultur* and efficiency.

Yet, so far as forts and ships are concerned, the great guns can destroy the former, while a mine or a torpedo (of relatively small cost) can destroy in a moment the proudest and costliest ship afloat. Young Hammond's torpedo, dirigible by wireless as far as six miles off shore (or

116

even by wireless from an aeroplane), is the latest most wonderful--and most terrible--development of maritime warfare.

The mine, the torpedo boat, the torpedo-boat destroyer, the submarine and various aerial means of attack (especially the last two) immediately preceeded, or have been chiefly developed during, the Great War now going on, alas, on the most horrifying and gigantic scale the world has ever seen.

While other arts and sciences which can increase man's power of destructiveness are utilized in this war, I thank God that *my* profession exists, even in war, only to heal and to help.

What a terribly long list of wars I have seen!

In my youth, Indian wars were almost continuous in the West, as I have already mentioned.

The first patient I ever sat up with at night (in 1861) was an army officer whose cheek had been penetrated by an arrow, in an Indian fight. The need for my services was that the arrow point had wounded the internal maxillary artery, producing a secondary hemorrhage.

I well remember the Mexican War, followed by the Civil War and the Spanish-American War.

In Europe, I recall well the uprisings of 1848, which were put down by the various armies. Then followed the Crimean War, 1854-5; the Franco-Austro-Italian War of 1859 (the year I graduated from Brown); the Schleswig-Holstein War (1864), in which Prussia and Austria robbed poor Denmark of Schleswig-Holstein; the Austro-Prussian War of 1866; the Franco-Prussian War of 1870; the Russo-Turkish War of 1877-8; and finally the cataclysm of 1914-16, which *one man*, the German Kaiser, could have prevented by lifting a finger. If the Devil doesn't get the Kaiser, to use my father's old expression, there's no using in having a Devil!

In Asia and Africa I have seen the Boer War, 1899-1901; the Tai Ping Rebellion, in China; the Sino-Japanese War of 1895; the Boxer War of 1900; the Russo-Japanese War of 1904-5; and many military expeditions or small wars, as in India, Burma, Cochin, China, Java, Egypt, and the Sudan. Africa has been partitioned among the powers of Europe. Included is the Congo, with its horrible Belgian atrocities, which were reported to me personally by missionaries who were eye-witnesses to them.

Even now, it is not certain that the attempted spoliation of China by the European powers, halted by John Hay, may not yet be carried out, once Europe has recuperated from the present war.

The maps of Europe, Asia, and Africa (and, to a large extent, of the Americas) have been made over and over and soon will have to be re-made yet once more. Thank God that the beastly cruel, unspeakable Turk will probably be finally driven out of Europe, after nearly five centuries of misrule.

Politically, the changes during my lifetime have been very marked.

The United States has (not "have") grown enormously. In 1837, the population was very small, and the West was scarcely settled. Territories beyond the Mississippi, Iowa, Missouri, Arkansas, Louisiana, and Texas, have all since attained statehood. The Mexican War added a large territory. The Canal Zone was undreamed of. We had no colonial possessions, but now we have Puerto Rico, Hawaii, Guam, and the Philippines. We are showing that, like the English, we have the colonizing instinct (if the wretched Philippine policy of the Democrats does not destroy it).

In Europe, the unification of Italy and of Germany; the happy passing

118

of the temporal power of the popes; the separation of Norway and Sweden; the changes, in France and Portugal, from monarchy to republic; the shrinkage of Turkey; and the kaleidoscopic changes in the Balkans are the most striking.

In Asia, the marvelous rise of Japan, and the possibilities of China, make the West watch with anxiety.

Africa, with modern sanitation, may, in time, become a civilized continent.

Christian missions are working wonders among the teeming millions in Asia and Africa. (See my "Service of Missions to Science and Society.")

South America is feeding Europe and in time may feed us if, as seems likely, constant revolutions are replaced by stable governments, as in the A, B, C nations.

What effects the Great War will produce no one would now venture to predict.

The explorers have been busy. In America, the great deserts of the southwest are now manageable, and the Rocky Mountains, believed to be an impossible barrier, even in 1842, have been conquered. A network of railways had bound together the East and the West, and the North and South. When I returned from Europe, in 1866, not a mile of railroad existed west of the Mississippi, so that Prof. (afterwards, Senator) N. P. Hill, my old teacher of Chemistry at Brown, had to tote all of his heavy mining machinery by wagon from St. Louis to Denver, over a month away.

In 1842, Marcus Whitman, a missionary at Fort Walla Walla, heard the boast of the first British immigrants, who had just arrived across the Rockies, that all of that country would be British. Mounting his horse, he rode, in mid-winter, across the Rockies and the prairies, and all the way to Washington, in order to warn Webster, then Secretary of State. Webster was about to relinquish the Oregon Territory (now Washington, Oregon, and Idaho) to the British, in exchange for some paltry fishing concessions in the Atlantic. Whitman then sought President Tyler, who assured him that if he could conduct emigrants across the Rockies to settle the area, the proposed treaty would not be signed. The following spring, Whitman led 800 emigrants over the mountains and into the fertile valley of the Willamette, and that great empire in the northwest was saved to the United States.

Alaska, on the map of 1852, was a Russian possession, and as uncharted as mid-Africa. Not even the great Yukon River appears. "Seward's Folly" has proved to be a vision of far-sighted statesmanship. Alaska has already repaid a hundred-fold the $7,200,000 it cost, and it is only beginning to be developed.

Africa has been explored and, to a great extent, civilized. The Mountains of the Moon (Pliny's *Montani Lunae*) have been conquered; and the Niger and the Congo (whose mouths only are on maps, as late as 1863) have been explored. The sources of the once-mysterious Nile have been found. The great Lakes Tanganyika and Victoria Nyanza, etc., have been discovered. And peace and plenty have been brought to the fellaheen of Egypt by the English government, the great dams on the Nile.

The part played by Livingstone, Stanley, and a host of other explorers and missionaries is too long a story for details here.

The polar regions have yielded nearly all their secrets. The north magnetic pole was discovered by Sir James Ross in 1831, six years before I was born; the south magnetic pole was located by Shackleton, in 1909; the geographical north pole was discovered by Perry, in 1909, and the southern counterpart, in 1911, by Amundsen. Undeterred by the sad fate of both De Long and Scott, Stefansson and other explorers are now at work to complete our knowledge of the circumpolar regions, both north and south, while in the torrid equatorial regions all around the world, explorers are equally busy and equally successful.

Slavery has been at last abolished, thank God, from the United States, the only civilized nation which so long practiced it, and in the few spots where it still exists, it is vanishing.

Anthropology, archeology, and philology are all cooperating to uncover the history, civilization, and manners and customs of the past, and to give written languages and dictionaries to the benighted races and peoples of the present.

The Rosetta stone, the Moabite stone, the Nestorian tablet, and the excavations in Palestine, Mesopotamia, Egypt, and northern Africa, plus Central, South, and North America, all are unfolding wonderful stories of past civilizations which were wholly unknown, in my boyhood.

Philanthropy and education, in the United States, have forged ahead hand in hand, at a marvelous rate. The stupendous gifts by Rockefeller, Carnegie, and scores of other multi-millionaires, have endowed colleges, universities, boards, institutions, institutes, foundations, etc., which are doing splendid service to God and man.

Women's colleges (beginning with Vassar) and co-educational colleges have multiplied exceedingly and have done a world of good.

In literature and art, painting, sculpture, and music, plus the domestic arts and crafts, we have progressed only moderately well, but we are doing better and better. Some outstanding names appear, but in bulk we have lagged far behind in the race. But we have been busy, first of all, in getting a living, in subduing forests, in building railroads and cities, and gradually in accumulating the means for a leisure class, some (and in time many) of whose members will give themselves to the things of the spirit, rather than to the things of the flesh.

In business, equally great changes have occurred. The factory system and co-partnerships, combining the capital, skill, and energy of two or more individuals, have given place to corporations (gigantic ones, of late) and these, in turn, to so-called trusts, which, when rightly managed, are a boon to both capital and labor. All these I have seen develop. Labor unions, too, have arisen, and again, if rightly managed, are to be encouraged.

I must have been a rather unwelcome baby, for I was born in the panic year of 1837. I went to college in 1855, and in 1857 came another severe panic. Others followed in 1873 and 1893, and just after we started around the world, in 1901; and again in 1907, just after we went abroad for an indefinite stay.

The Great War *may* establish New York as the world's financial center and the dollar as the world's unit of exchange, but he would be a rash prophet who would declare that these things *will* happen.

In medicine, I have witnessed all but one of the great modern discoveries. Vaccination was introduced by Jenner in 1796. But since I was born, anesthesis came in (in 1846) and antisepsis began with Lister's first paper, in 1867, and was well established by, say, 1879. A new science, bacteriology, was for thirty years slowly struggling into existence, but it was only given its name in 1884. These three have revolutionized both surgery and medicine, in all their branches. I have pointed out, in various papers, the splendid results of these discoveries and cannot recount them here. (See my *Addresses and Other Papers*; also my "Ether Day Address," etc.)

I can point out only a few of the world-wide benefits from the discoveries made in our laboratories and clinics. I record here again my profound conviction, based on personal knowledge, that research by animal experimentation has been the main factor in all this wonderful and beneficial progress. I therefore have deemed it a scientific, a humanitarian, and a Christian duty to combat, by every means in my power, the efforts of the antivivisectionists. I have been lied about, malignantly attacked, and called all manner of names, but the abuse has had no more effect upon me than the proverbial water on a duck's back. I have felt, like Luther: "*Hier stehe ich; ich kann nicht Anders.*"

Bacteriology has disclosed to us the causes of many formerly obscure diseases: plague, syphilis, cerebro-spinal meningitis, cholera, typhoid, leprosy, pneumonia, and tetanus, among others. Even the filterable viruses (e.g., infantile paralysis) have yielded up their secrets. As a result, we have developed antitoxins with which to cure (or better still, to prevent) many of the maladies.

No other American research organization has done so much for the relief of humanity as the Rockefeller Institute.

With some diseases, such as cancer, hydrophobia, yellow fever, and smallpox, plus children's diseases, such as scarlet fever, we still are in the dark as to the cause, but happily, with yellow fever and smallpox we have the means of preventing them.

In a number of diseases, for example, yellow fever, the plague, sleeping sickness, and typhus, we have discovered the means of their diffusion by various insects and therefore can largely (or in some cases, entirely) prevent their spread, and so avert the terrible epidemics which have wasted the world, in past ages.

The Rockefeller Foundation has undertaken (or soon will undertake) campaigns encircling the earth, and with every prospect of ultimate success, to eradicate leprosy, yellow fever, and hookworm disease. What can stir the imagination more than such a prospect! What possibly could do more for the whole human race! And yet a few fanatics rail at the founder of the Rockefeller philanthropies as though he were the embodiment of cruelty!

Typhoid fever, hitherto the curse of armies and the autumnal reaper of death, has now been entirely banished from the United States Army, has been only a minor factor in the Great War, in Europe, and is rapidly lessening (and ought to practically disappear) among our civilian population. If only the public would insist upon--and obtain--clean water and clean milk and employ broadcast the antityphoid vaccination. What a glorious time this is in which to live and witness (and still more, to aid in bringing about) such splendid results of research!

PERSONAL RECOLLECTIONS

by

W. W. Keen, M. D.

THE WORST-SCARED MAN IN THE WORLD

Two months after I had graduated from Jefferson Medical College, I entered the army, by examination (in May, 1862), and was made executive officer of the Eckington Military Hospital, in the then outskirts of Washington. The hospital had been a country residence, in which I had one room which served as bedroom and office, and on the grounds of which were a number of tents for the patients.

At about 10 o'clock, one Sunday morning, a soldier sought my advice. In order to make a diagnosis, I was obliged to make an instrumental examination, which caused so much pain that I had to use an anesthetic. The only place where I could do this was in my own room and on my own bed.

I had been brought up, by Prof. Samuel D. Gross at the Jefferson (where I had been one of his clinical assistants), to use chloroform. Accordingly, I called one of my assistants, who gave the patient chloroform on a folded towel, after the most approved method. Just as I was about to begin the examination, my assistant suddenly said, "Doctor, he's not breathing!" I looked down at his face and saw it was getting purple; his chest was not moving, and his pulse could not be felt. I instantly seized a knife and cut across his temporal artery. Not a drop of blood escaped. We quickly began artificial respiration and continued it for over an hour, but it was all in vain. The man was stone dead.

On inquiry, in order to notify his friends, I found that he was a relative of an assistant postmaster general, a high government official

125

who I naturally feared might be extremely hostile. At noon, I rode into Washington, feeling very blue and with all sorts of fears and much compunction of conscience, to see the assistant postmaster general and make a clean breast of the whole sad affair. I found him to be a most kindly considerate man who, when I had explained everything in detail, felt that I was not in the least to blame. He even gladly consented to my request for a post mortem in order to ascertain, if possible, the cause of death.

The post mortem was made at about 5 or 6 P.M. The man's death having been instantaneous, there was not the least rigor mortis, that muscular rigidity which, when one dies slowly, sets in soon after death. The body was as limp as when one has fainted.

I should explain here how we remove the brain for examination. One sweep of the knife is made down to the bone, over the top of the head from one ear to the other. (The hair is previously parted along this line so that when it is brushed again into its ordinary place, the incision is completely hidden.) The whole front half and back half of the scalp are then detached from the skull, the first being drawn down as a flap over the face and the other, low down on the back of the head. On the temples--a very important point, in this narrative--are two strong muscles which pull the lower jaw tight up against the upper jaw. (By placing a finger on the temple while repeatedly chewing, one can feel it contracting.) As soon as they are uncovered, on displacing the scalp, these two muscles are divided, by knife, at the level where the intention is to saw all around the skull. This detaches the entire top of the skull from the lower part and makes easy the removal of the brain.

My assistant (quite nervous himself, as he was the one who had given

126

the chloroform) was stooping to steady the head while I used the saw. I
had sawn all across the forehead and then swept the saw gradually towards
the temple. With the first full sweeps of the saw, to and fro, the patient loudly champed his jaws at us several times! My assistant instantly dropped the head and leaped backwards, holding up both hands in horror,
and exclaimed, "Good God! isn't he dead?!" I stood trembling and aghast
with the same idea in my mind. A cold sweat broke out all over me. My
heart gave one great convulsive leap, then stood still, then began to beat
at race-horse speed, while I was gasping for breath. And no wonder.

Consider all the circumstances: a callow youth, just graduated . . .
his first fatal case . . . the sudden death . . . the influential relative
. . . the possibility of a civil or military inquisition, with an uncertain
outcome. . . the scalp on the top of the head wholly torn loose, and
the top of the skull half sawed off (surely a mortal wound if the man was
not really dead). And now this sudden seeming protest, by the corpse, at
what I was doing. All this, and more, passed in an instant through my
brain in frightful sequence. Is it any wonder that I was, for a moment,
the worst-scared man in the world?

But a moment's reflection explained the matter. I had failed to completely sever the fibers of the temporal muscles, and as the saw caught
them in its teeth, in its to-and-fro movement, the muscles would be taut,
at the extreme ends of the excursion, but relaxed at the middle. The body
being absolutely limp from the absence of rigor mortis, the lower jaw
would drop, as the muscles relaxed, only to snap vigorously against the
upper jaw, when the muscles were made taut again. Besides this, no hemorrhage occurred from the extensively divided scalp.

In a few moments, we had sufficiently regained our self-command to realize that the man was surely already dead and to continue the post mortem, but it was with unsteady hands and perturbed minds. Finally, when I rolled the brain out of the skull into my left hand, my assistant, with a sort of ghostly smile and a sigh of relief, turned and said, "Well, doctor, he's dead now, anyhow!"

The brain and heart both proved to be normal, in our dead soldier, and the chloroform, analyzed in the surgeon general's laboratory, was found to be pure. The only explanation of the fatality is that it was one of those undoubted, but rare, cases of a peculiar and individual susceptibility to the effect of chloroform which kills in a moment and without premonition.

But it was a long time before that horrible scene ceased to haunt me, and even now, after fifty years, I can sometimes plainly hear that sudden champing of the dead man's teeth--and never without a shudder.

A GRUESOME FIND

A client once sought Benjamin Harrison (later president of the United States) and engaged him to search for the body of a relative that was supposed to have been removed from the grave and taken to one of the anatomical study rooms in Cincinnati.

In the course of his search, Harrison came to the Medical College of Ohio, where Dr. Phineus S. Conner, an old friend during my college days, was a professor of surgery. As coroner, he was present when this incident occurred, and he related it to me.

At the college, Harrison, his client, Prof. Conner, and others sought diligently to find the body. They began the search in the cellar and ended it in the top story. Seeing a rope in one corner of the dissecting room, on the top floor, Harrison went over to it and shook it, and calling attention to the fact that evidently there was something heavy attached to it, he asked that it be drawn up. This was done, and as the head of the body, which was fastened at the other end of the rope, appeared above the level of the floor, Harrison started back with an exclamation, "My God, that is my father!"

It would be difficult to imagine a more dramatic situation than such a discovery of the body of one's father, to say nothing of the fact that, in this instance, it involved the son of a past president and the father of a future one.

(I recently have had a confirmation of the truth of this story, from another surgeon who was personally cognizant of the facts.)

When I took charge of the Philadelphia School of Anatomy, in November of 1866, there was no anatomical law. All the medical schools and the two private schools then in existence (in addition to my own) were supplied by (1) the so-called body snatchers, who took bodies from inconspicuous cemeteries; and (2) the unclaimed bodies from the coroner's office. Of course, it was an illegal traffic, and if it had been detected, I could have been arrested and fined, and very probably punished by imprisonment. But there was absolutely no other way of being supplied with cadavers for dissection, and so the practice was winked at, by the authorities, as a necessity.

I gave up the school in 1875, since the United States took the building for part of the site of the new post office, at 9th and Chestnut. In addition to this, the university had moved to West Philadelphia, and the students from the Jefferson alone were not sufficient to make this private school a financial success. (In my *History of the Philadelphia School of Anatomy*, I have given all the facts.)

At any rate, I do not remember the exact date, but a year or more before I discontinued the school, the Pennsylvania legislature passed the very best anatomical law in the country. All unclaimed bodies were delivered to an anatomical board, which consisted of professors and demonstrators of anatomy and surgery of the medical schools throughout the state, as well as representatives of the private schools. We organized the board, and I was the president of it for a good many years. Dr. Mears, the administrative officer, received all the bodies and distributed them in accordance with the data furnished to him by the various schools. This obviated the necessity for encroaching on cemeteries, and the scandalous situation ceased to exist.

The law was drawn up by Dr. William S. Forbes, and curiously enough, when he was a demonstrator of anatomy at the Jefferson, he was the first and only person charged under his own law. The evidence against him was practically complete, and he was arrested. Fortunately for him, on the night before the date fixed for the trial to begin, his father-in-law died. This resulted in his obtaining a postponement of three months (in the next term of the court), by which time the public wrath had subsided. He was finally discharged, though I do not remember on what pretext.

A TRAGIC POST MORTEM

Many years ago, Dr. Weir Mitchell asked me to make a post mortem in the following sorrowful, and even tragic, circumstances. Miss X, perhaps about 20 years of age, a charming young lady from a well-known Philadelphia family, went to Paris to obtain the trousseau for her approaching wedding. For some years, she had been subject to very frequent and severe headaches of unknown origin, and she was attacked by one of them in Paris. Guéneau de Mussy, a very prominent and trustworthy medical man, was called in and gave her a hypodermic injection of a quarter of a grain of morphine, a frequent (if not, indeed, the usual) dosage. She went to sleep and never woke up.

Her body was brought home dressed in her wedding gown. Only the brain was to be examined, and so we did not disturb the body further than to move it far enough over the head of the coffin in order to prevent any soiling of her beautiful dress.

When the top of the skull was removed, the cause of death was visible immediately, but a cause the like of which I have seen but this once in over 50 years of experience. The entire inner surface of the skull was peppered over with perhaps a hundred little bony growths ranging in size from as small as a grain of sand to as large as a small pea. One of them (the only large one) was like a mushroom in shape. There was a slender foot-stalk, about an eighth of an inch high, as I remember it. On this stalk was set an almost circular disk of bone, say a third, or possibly a half, of an inch in diameter. Inflammation of the brain's membranes had caused her death. The bony condition, which had caused her headaches, was absolutely impossible of diagnosis. The fatal result was inevitable, and Guéneau de Mussy was wholly innocent of blame. By breaking down a part of the roof of the orbit, I removed the back half of the two eyeballs, with-

131

out changing in the least the appearance of the features. Examination by Dr. William Thomson, I think it was, showed that the optic disks (i.e., the ends of the optic nerves in the retina) were choked and swollen. Had Guéneau de Mussy examined her eye-grounds by the ophthalmoscope, which I believe he did not do (it was a far less frequent procedure in those days than now), he could have told that there was a very serious disease inside the skull, but he could not have told what it was, nor where it was, nor what to do about it. But it would have led him to make the post mortem in Paris, and that would have exhonorated him entirely, and at once.

HELL HATH NO FURY LIKE A WOMAN SCORNED

Another Sunday, in the afternoon, I was hurriedly sent for to see a woman living not far from my office who had just attempted to commit suicide by swallowing broken and pounded glass. She had pounded a large tumbler in a mortar and drunk it with, as nearly as could be ascertained, almost a pint of whiskey. I found her raving drunk from the whiskey but with as yet no evidence of injury from the glass. As a matter of fact, she had pulverized the glass so fine that under the persuasion of mashed potato (which leaves a considerable residue in the bowel) and a good dose of castor oil, she suffered no damage, and as soon as she got sober, she was as well as ever. She then voluntarily confided to me her story, which after the lapse of very many years, and the death of all the parties to the tragedy, may now not improperly be told.

When I first saw her, she was a woman of perhaps 45 who had at first been engaged by her employer, a well-to-do man, as a housekeeper and attendant upon his sick wife. The latter was hopelessly ill, of a slowly but surely mortal disease. Under promise of a later marriage, after the

132

death of his wife, my patient became his mistress and bore him two children. After the death of his wife, the marriage was deferred by him on
various pretexts, but on the day before the attempted suicide, she read
in a newspaper that he was soon to marry another woman, whose means and
social standing were much above her own. Then she tried to kill herself.

We had more than one conversation over the matter, and as a result,
she promised that she would not repeat the attempt. A few weeks later,
she came to see me again and said that he had married her rival. She was
present at the ceremony and described, with an almost demonic glee, how
she had stood at the very door of the middle aisle, as they walked out of
church to the strains of Mendelssohn's "Wedding March;" how the skirts of
the bride brushed against her own; and how she looked the man direct in
the eye, never glancing aside to the right or left, from the moment when
he could first see her till they passed beyond the door. My only wonder
was that she did not shoot him, then and there.

Her vindictive rage was equal to that, or to any other desperate act
of violence. But a sweeter revenge was in store for her.

I did not see her again until a year or two later. It is so long
since the occurence that many trivial details have faded from memory, but
the main facts are too deeply etched upon my brain ever to be forgotten.

Suddenly, during my afternoon office hour (I was alone, fortunately),
a woman strode into my private consulting room, where I was seated at my
desk. At first, I did not recognize her, as her features were so distort-
ed. Her eyes were all aflame with a hideous joy, and her clenched fists
were raised aloft and then accentuated, with a downward chopping gesture,
every outcry of her now exultant, but sorely-wounded soul. She exclaimed,

again and again (and fiercely), "I've seen him again, Dr. Keen, I've seen him again! Seen him in his coffin, *seen him in his coffin, IN HIS COFFIN!* This last she fairly screamed. And so she passed out of my life.

Then I understood the the adage that Hell hath no fury like a woman scorned. Then I understood also those fearful words of Scripture that refer to the "wrath of the Lamb."

THE MAN WHO COULDN'T SAY "HORSE"

When my present home was building, forty years ago, the chief artisan in the composition of the mortar was an Irishman named Robert. As I was roaming over the building nearly every day, Robert and I became quite chummy. He was an honest, hard-working, and worthy man. At the conclusion of the mortar period, he disappeared, and I did not see him again for perhaps two years.

One day, he and his wife came into my office together. I extended my hand, saying, "Well, Robert, I am glad to see you again. How are you?"

"Ah dochter," said he, "I'm in a bad way." "Indade and he is, Sor," added Mrs. Robert.

"Well, Robert, tell me what is the matter."

"Well Sor," said he, "I can't spake."

"But Robert," said I, laughing, "I don't see just how it is that you are talking and yet say that you can't speak."

"Why dochter," said his wife, "it's *wor-r-ds* that he can't spake." Naturally, I bethought myself of aphasia, and I said, "Oh I see. You mean that you know what words you want to say but can't say them. Is that it?"

"Yes, dochter, that's just it."

"Let me try you then," I replied. "Suppose you say 'horse.'"

"Now dochter dear," said he, putting the back of his hand to his mouth as if to speak very confidentially, "'Horse' is just one of the wor-r-ds that I can't spake."

THE LITTLE "SCRAP OF PAPER" IN MY POCKET

Many years ago, I was called into a neighboring state to operate, in a case of abdominal tumor. When my assistant and I arrived at the farm-house, I found that the patient was a very stout woman of, say, 40. Her husband, when we reached the house, was at work, out ploughing in the field (which I thought was a little strange). While the husband was being called, a careful examination established the existence of a large, but obscure, growth which, if allowed to remain, would be a constant and aug-menting menace to her life. Whether it could safely be removed was un-certain and could be decided only following an abdominal section. What was not doubtful, however, was that by reason of its size, extension, and adhesions--as well as almost certain hemorrhage (with which we could not so successfully cope, in those days, as we do now)--its removal would be both difficult and dangerous. But, balancing present danger against the certainty of a not-far-distant fatal conclusion, I recommended that the operation should be attempted.

I explained the matter fully to the husband and told him that he must be the one to decide the matter. He turned upon me and in a surly--almost savage--tone, demanded, "Will you ensure her recovery?"

"Certainly not," said I. "It is impossible to do more than to prom-ise that I will do all in my power for your wife. What the dangers are I have frankly told you."

"Then I won't have any operation done," was his reply.

"Very well," said I, turning to my assistant. "We will then take the next train back to Philadelphia."

Thereupon the husband began to weaken and ask for further information. After a few minutes' conversation, he finally (and still in a very surly tone) said to me that I might proceed with the operation. "Very well," said I, "but only on the condition that you sign a paper which I am going to write out--if you will find me pen and ink."

Just what made me propose such a paper I do not know. It seemed to be a sudden inspiration. I had never done such a thing before in my life (nor have I ever done it since). But in view of the uncertainties of the case, and of the evident ugly disposition of the husband, I resolved (on the spur of the moment) to protect myself and drew up the following paper:

> I,   , hereby request Dr. W. W. Keen to oper-
> ate upon my wife, and after having heard from him a full expla-
> nation of the difficulties and dangers of the operation, in
> case her death should be the result of it, I will not hold him
> in any way responsible.
>
> [*Signed*]

"Here," said I, "is a paper for you to sign, in the presence of your doctor and my assistant as witnesses. If you sign it, I will operate on your wife. If you do not, I will immediately return to Philadelphia. You are entirely free to sign or not to sign."

After some hesitation, he signed, and we proceeded to operate. All my forebodings came true. I had even by that time seen not a little of hemorrhage, but neither before nor since have I seen a more profuse or uncontrolable loss of blood, and from so many sources. The tumor was finally removed, the hemorrhage controled, and the patient replaced in bed-- but in a terribly precarious condition. Instead of taking the next train, I stayed by her for several hours, doing all in my power to save her, but it was all in vain.

When she was dead, the husband was furious. He almost attacked me physically and proclaimed loudly that he would have the law on me and get the biggest damages he could, that he would pursue me to the ends of the earth, etc.

As may well be imagined, I was glad to escape from such uncomfortable surroundings. I should add, perhaps, that the children were most kind to me and did not show their father's rage. But what comfort that little bit of paper in my inside pocket gave me can hardly be imagined. My conscience cleared me to myself of any moral or professional delinquency, and that little piece of paper would clear me of any legal responsibility.

However, from that day to this, I have never heard from the husband. I have often wondered whether or not, in the eyes of the law, that warrant was worth even the paper on which it was written. Even if not, however, it served as a moral fetter upon one who might have given me a deal of trouble and anxiety.

THE "UMBRELLA STORY" AND THE "$75,000 FEE"

How strangely fictitious stories will appear, and re-appear, is well illustrated in my "umbrella story." I have been introduced, several times, to ladies who have opened the conversation by saying, "I'm very glad to know you, Dr. Keen, for I have often wanted to ask you whether the 'umbrella story' is true." I would suggest, to their amused astonishment, "Yes, certainly, that is just what I was hoping you'd ask."

A man walking down Broadway, so the story goes, slipped on a banana

skin and broke his leg. A crowd collected in a moment, but the only thing
done was a hurried call for an ambulance. While waiting for its arrival,
the crowd gave way to admit a gentleman who seemed to have a clear idea
that something further should be done, and who knew what it was. Slip-
ping his furled umbrella up the man's trouser leg, where it would serve as
a splint, he called for some handkerchiefs and with them secured the broken
bone firmly to the umbrella.

Just as he had finished, the ambulance drove up, and the surgeon,
neatly attired in white, made his way through the crowd. Looking at the
well-splinted leg, he turned to the gentleman and said, "Really, that's
well done. You must have taken some lessons in first aid to the injured."
As the injured man was being lifted into the ambulance, the surgeon asked
the gentleman for his card, saying that he would return the umbrella to
his address.

On looking at the card, he suddenly exclaimed, "Great Scott!" and
added some complimentary remarks which shall be unrecorded here.

Now as a matter of fact, I never saw a man break his leg on Broadway.
I never had an occasion, therefore, to use my umbrella there as described;
nor have I ever met that nice, white-clad surgeon. The inherent improba-
bility of the story is evident (I have always claimed), for I never would
have used my own umbrella so long as I could have borrowed one.

A still more fictitious story, lamentably, is that of the $75,000
fee. As the newspaper had it, a friend entered the office of a Pittsburgh
banker just as he was drawing a check. As soon as he had signed it, he
tore it off and showed it to his friend, saying that it was the "best buy"
of his life. The check was drawn to *my* order, and for $75,000!

The sad truth is that by some error of the post office, neither that check nor any other check representing even a modest fraction of that delightful amount ever reached me. I have longed in vain for that elusive check!

A DISTRESSING NIGHT

One of the most distressing nights of my life was spent at the bedside of the daughter of a medical friend. She was a sweet girl of perhaps fifteen or sixteen who had been ill for a day or two, but not so seriously that the family physician had been called in to see her. Her father, who was purely a specialist, was not familiar with internal medicine and had given her a preparation of opium. I suspect that not only was it a larger dose than was wise, but also that the girl was one of those people who are peculiarly susceptible to opium.

She fell asleep, and after awhile her sleep seemed to be deeper than had been expected. Her father tried to rouse her, but still she slept on. At last, becoming thoroughly alarmed, he called another medical friend and me. It was past midnight, and she had been asleep for several hours. All our efforts to waken her were in vain, and the pupils of her eyes were contracted almost to pinpoints, as is common in opium poisoning. Gradually, her respirations were becoming slower and slower. Distinctly, her life was at stake.

Never can I forget the horrible, dreadful anguish of that father, as he strode up and down the room, into the hall and back, wild with grief and self-accusation, wringing his hands, and groaning, "I've killed my daughter, I've killed my child." Meanwhile, we were so engrossed in our efforts to save the girl's life that we could give little attention to the poor distracted father. We used the stomach pump, though after so long a time it was of doubtful value; we administered various remedies; and in order to sustain the failing breathing, we began artificial respiration and kept it up for hours. At last, signs of more normal breathing and returning consciousness gladdened our hearts, and her recovery was finally assured. The reaction upon her poor father, in the whole episode, was nearly more tragic than had been the hopelessness. He collapsed, under the strain, and I almost feared for his life or his reason.

As I wended my way home, in the cheering rays of the rising sun, how fervently I thanked God that it was not one of my own children that had looked into that open grave. For years afterwards, I never gave one of them a dose of medicine without asking myself, with some anxiety, if it was the proper dose.

WHEN A DOCTOR TRIED TO PROVE TOO MUCH AT A MURDER TRIAL

In a large town not far from Philadelphia lived a German butcher and his wife and children. The wife's sister, a lusty, muscular woman of about twenty, long accustomed to work in the fields at home, had been in America only a few months, I think, when the following tragedy occurred.

The two sisters went to a ball, while the husband remained in his shop. The married sister, after a while, proposed to return and look after the baby, but the umarried sister finally prevailed upon her to stay (as she had many friends there), saying that she would go home instead. When the married woman returned home, about an hour later, she went to her sister's room and found her lying dead, with her throat cut, on the floor. The bed had not been slept in, the furniture was not disordered, and even the little rug (in front of her bureau) upon which her head lay was flat and straight--though covered with blood. In other words, there was no evidence of an attack, or of a struggle such as a strong young woman might be expected to put up. The husband was called from his shop, and he and his wife lifted the body. This accounted for the blood on his clothes and hands.

The police authorities believed that it was a case of suicide. Someone (who, I do not know) suggested that Dr. X, of Philadelphia, be called in, since, as coroner's physician, he had had wide experience in such cases. He suggested that the woman had been murdered. I suppose he was influenced by the rather curious fact of the deep cut in the back of the neck, in addition to the idea that, owing to the sudden and profuse loss of blood (the left carotid artery and the jugular vein had been divided), the seven gashes in the front of the neck could not have been made by the victim herself. *Why* anyone should want to kill her was wholly conjectural. But at all events, the butcher and his wife--there being no other obvious suspects--were arrested, charged with murder, and thrown into jail.

The attorney for the defense asked me to make a second post-mortem examination. This I did with minute care, making, at the time, written notes of every fact observed. Among other things, I noted (1) that the cut in the back of the neck, though deep, had a distinct layer of muscular tissue at the bottom and that the vertebrae were not exposed; (2) that the left carotid artery and jugular vein were both severed; and (3) that the right carotid and jugular were intact.

A few days later, I received from the attorney the typewritten notes of the preliminary hearing before the committing magistrate. The statements made by Dr. X differed materially from the notes I had written at my own post-mortem examination. To cite only one instance, he declared that the cut on the back of the neck not only exposed the bones but also showed the cartilage lining the joints between two of the vertebrae. Any anatomist or surgeon would know that this cartilage could *not* be thus exposed. His statement was calculated, I think, to show that the assailant, attacking her from behind, struck this blow first. Dr. X apparently believed that this blow completely stunned her so that she fell (the fall causing some bruises), whereupon the assailant cut her throat seven times.

I was then face to face with a problem: Dr. X would state certain facts, and I would testify that these statements were not in accordance with what I had found. Dr. X had made perhaps hundreds of *medico-legal* post mortems. I had made none. Whom would the court and jury believe? So I bethought me of a witness that both court and jury would *have* to believe, namely, the neck of the girl herself. On inquiring of the attorney, I learned that the body had not been re-interred, and as it was December, and very cold, there had been no decomposition.

The next day (I remember it was Christmas Day, because we had first distributed our presents), I went by train, met the attorney, secured the girl's neck, took it with me (in a jar of alcohol), and returned to place it safely under lock and key in my own office.

When the trial came on and the defense was to open, there was very great interest (and curiosity), for the attorney for the defendant had stated, in his opening speech at the end of the previous day, that the very body of the girl would be produced as a witness.

While on the train, I read in the newspapers the previous day's testimony and found, to my amazement, that Dr. X had also sworn, in addition to the previous erroneous statements, that *both* carotid arteries and *both* jugular veins had been severed. The only reason I could assign to this wholly wrong statement was the desire to increase the emphasis on the sudden and voluminous loss of blood, thus making an impossibility of the self-infliction of as many as six additional cuts across the neck.

That seven cuts could be self-inflicted after one carotid and one jugular had been divided I knew was possible, for not long before, I had had a case in St. Mary's Hospital where the poor fellow confessed to the self-infliction of his seven exactly similar wounds.

Had I been asked, before this case was seen, whether a person would not immediately collapse and die, when both carotids and both jugulars had been severed, I should surely have answered in the affirmative. But this case led me to carefully look up the recorded literature, and I found, among others, these two surprising but authentic cases. (Unfortunately, the notes I then made have been lost or mislaid, and I cannot give the references, but my memory of the main facts is very clear.)

First: A tramp slept in the hayloft, on the second story of a barn. He had cut his throat, and the post mortem showed that both carotids and both jugulars had been severed. He climbed down the ladder and walked across a small yard and up some steps, then for some distance along an entry-way, before falling exhausted by the loss of blood.

Second: A man (possibly it was a woman) cut his throat on a highway, severing the carotid and the jugular on both sides of the neck (as proved by the post mortem), but managed to climb a fence and walk a considerable distance to a shed, where he succumbed.

But to return to the trial. After the usual preliminary questions as to my name and occupation, etc., the attorney showed me a drawing, something like the following, and asked me to identify and describe it.

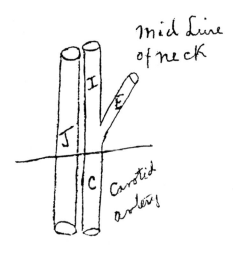

I replied that it illustrated the carotid artery (C) on the right side of the neck, with its division into two branches, the internal carotid (I) going to the brain, and the external (E) going to the face. Also depicted is the jugular vein (J). The attorney stated that the drawing had been placed in evidence by the district attorney (i.e., the prosecution), and that the heavy transverse line represented the place where both of these great blood vessels on the right side had been cut across. (It should be noticed that this line is just below the point where the carotid branches.)

He asked me if the carotid and the jugular on the right side of the neck were divided at any point, to which I replied, "No."

"How do you know that they were not so divided?"

"By my careful post-mortem examination. My notes, made at the time, state expressly that these two great blood vessels were intact."

"Have you any other proof, and if so, what is it?"

"I offer in evidence the woman's neck. Will you please show it to the jury?"

I then demonstrated, by passing glass rods up through them, that
the blood vessels on the left side were completely divided, whereas those
on the right side were not divided at all. (The neck included all of the
blood vessels--carotid and jugular--from a point at the bottom of the
neck to a point well above the division of each carotid into its two
branches.) I also demonstrated to the jury the fact that the deep cut on
the back of the neck had *not* exposed the vertebrae, much less the cartilage.

The case of the prosecution collapsed at once. *Falsus in uno, falsus
in omnibus.*

The poor butcher and his wife were acquitted, but see the injustice
caused by the hasty conclusions of one "expert" witness, an injustice for
which society owed them a debt that would never be paid. The poor man's
business was destroyed, and his wife became a lunatic. What became of
them later I never knew. The mystery of the young woman's death has never
been solved. Whether it was a case of murder (and if so, by whom) or a
case of suicide, I never could even guess.

A SOLDIER OF THE FIRST NAPOLEON

In 1862, while a student at the Jefferson Medical College, I was
taken by my teacher of surgery, Prof. S. D. Gross, to a house where I was
to give chloroform for him (he always used chloroform), for an operation.
The patient, a man of over 70, had been wounded just fifty years before,
in the battle of Borodino, during the disastrous retreat from Moscow, in
1812. The shot had buried itself in the calf of the leg and had not
emerged. A mere flesh wound at Borodino was not of much account. There

145

were other fish to fry. After lying there quietly embedded in the tissues, for half a century, it had at last worked its way to the surface,
finally causing an opening through the skin. One day, the old fellow had
pried it out with a pin. But the wound did not get well. there was a
constant, small (but annoying) discharge of pus, and some sort of hard
substance could be felt deeper in the tissues.

This Prof. Gross proposed to remove. Accordingly, when he had laid
out all his instruments and (as was often his custom) had whetted his
knife on his boot--a fine antiseptic procedure [!] but remember, this was
in 1862--he said to the patient, "Now, my good man, lie down on the sofa,
and my young friend Keen will give you a little chloroform." "Do you suppose," replied the patient, "that a soldier of the first Napoleon wishes
to take chloroform?" At this, he stretched his leg out straight and concluded the discussion with an emphatic, "Go ahead!"

So Prof. Gross went ahead, and never once did the old soldier wince
or budge. The lump was cut out and proved to be a bony mass, cup-shaped
in form, which had been caused by the irritation of the ball, during its
long sojourn. He made an excellent recovery, in spite too of the primitive preparation of knife on boot.

How near to me this incident brought the great emperor!

_____

Note. From *The Outlook*, October 26, 1912, p. 462. "Eight Russian survivors
of the battle of Borodino recently celebrated the hundredth anniversary of
that bloody conflict between the Russians and Napoleon's Grande Armée. This
seems incredible, but the newspaper reports give the names and records of
these hoary veterans. One of them, at the age of 122, has recently been
granted a pension by the Russian government. Another, Peter Laptieff, aged
118, actually met Napoleon face to face, during the campaign, and has a viv-
id recollection of the interview."

146

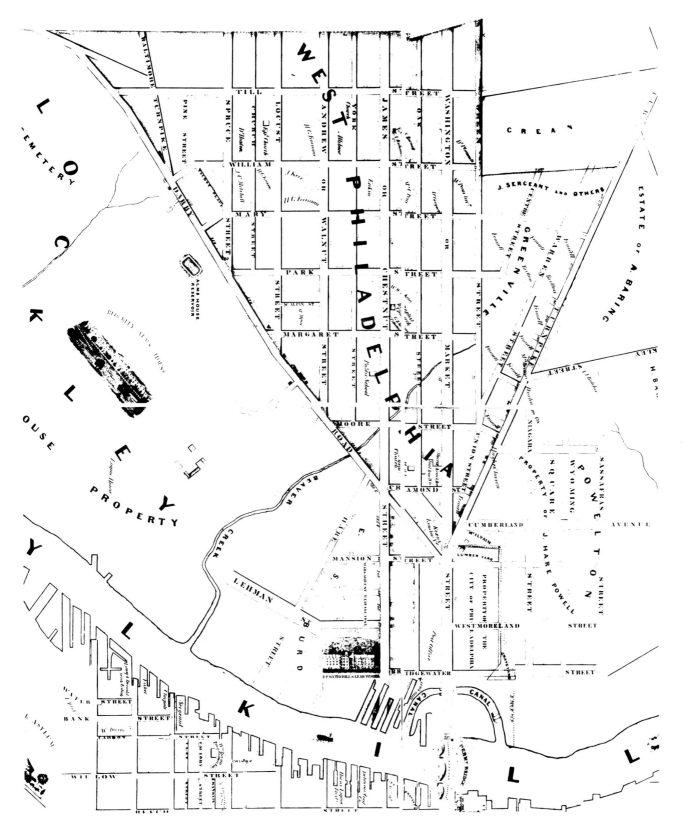

Keen's childhood home, James or Chestnut Street

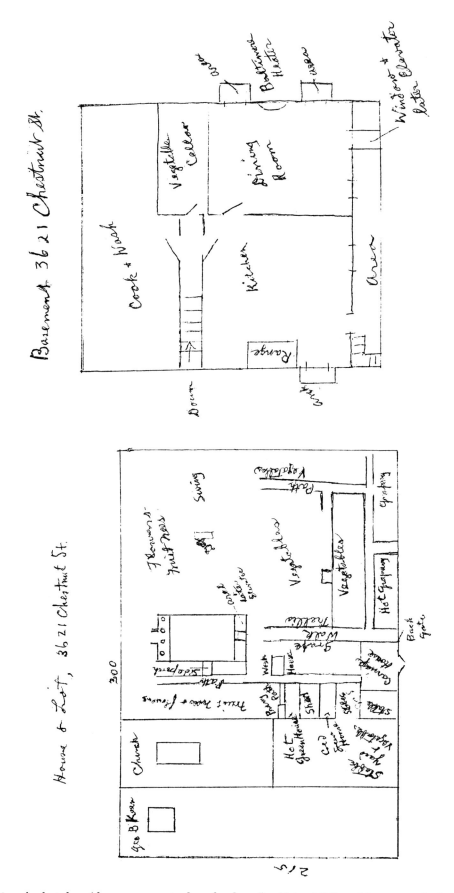

Keen's sketches (drawn some six decades later!) of his childhood home, with the

2nd floor 3621 Chestnut St.

Father & Mother

Bed

Wash stand

Grandmother Later Charley & Mathis

Bed

Buddy

window Later Elevator

closet

10 ft. & Hall

Bed

Bath

closet

my room

Bed

First Floor 3621 Chestnut St.

what not

Chinese

Father's rocking chair

mirror & table

chandelier

Front parlor

garden

Back Parlor

Chandelier

Center table & Festral lamp

area

window Later Poor Elevator

Piazza

Bed

Bed

Hadonis pillars to 2nd story

Table

Little win

Hall

closet

Down to basement

up

up

Later Dining Room

Bench

Baltimore Heater

Slate

Side porch

Bench

Wash House

Grapes

Trellises

layout of the "farm" and the floor plans of the basement and first and second floors

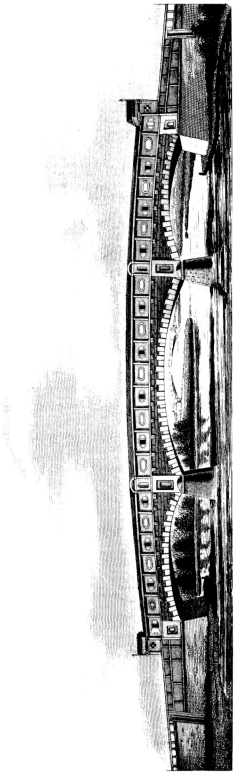

Market Street Bridge with the newer Chestnut Street Bridge visible through the center arch

Weir Mitchell in 1859

Keen at 23

Acting Assistant Surgeon Keen, c. 1863

Keen's field hospital at Bull Run, 1863

Emma Corinna Borden, *left,* and her sister, Eudora, 1863

Left to right, skeleton, cadaver, Keen, and live model, during an anatomy lecture at the Academy

Keen in charge, at his Jefferson clinic, 1893

PHOTO BY
C.B.Weaver

The *Oneida,* the field hospital for Cleveland's operations.

Keen's clinic in 1902

Keen and family, 1906. *Left to right* are daughter Florence, daughter Corinne (with husband Walter Freeman and children, Bill, Walter, Corinne, Jack, and Norman), Keen, daughter Dora, and daughter Margaret (with husband Howard Butcher and children, Howard, Margaret, and Dora)

Weir Mitchell, center front, and Keen, second right, at the Franklin Inn Club, 1907

Caricature of Keen

THE FIRST DIAGNOSTICATION OF A WOUND OF THE SYMPATHETIC NERVE IN MAN

In 1863, when I was executive officer in the Satterlee Military Hospital, in West Philadelphia, it was part of my business to assign new patients to the various wards. One day, as I was writing at my desk, a new patient entered my office and stood waiting beside me, while I signed the letter I had written. I then looked up at him and instantly observed that his left pupil was of normal size while the right one was contracted to a pinpoint. "By George," I said to myself, "He is Dalton's cat."

I must explain. *Dalton's Physiology* was a textbook I had studied at the Jefferson. In the chapter on "The Sympathetic Nerve," he related Brown, Séquard, and Bernard's experimental researches, which included the cutting of this nerve in the neck of cats and rabbits. Up to that time (1851 and 1852), all that was known of this nerve was its anatomy. Little was known of its physiological or pathological functions.

In the neck of both man and animals, it is a slender cord, about as large as medium-weight sewing thread, and it lies just to the outside of the carotid artery and jugular vein, easily accessible for experimental research but never, till then, divided. In cats and rabbits, its division was followed by a great contraction of the corresponding pupil, by a reddening and heat (easily observed in the ear), on the same side as the operation, by a slight falling of the upper eyelid, and by sweating, also on that side.

In spite of the many cases, no doubt, of its division in man, by bullet, sword, or bayonet wound, no observation of the effects of such a division had ever been made--and for very good reason. The missile or weapon which inflicted the wound almost inevitably included a quickly fatal injury, either to the spinal cord in the neck or in the severing of the great blood vessels so close by.

Now Dalton not only described the effects which followed the division of the nerve, but also gave a picture of a cat whose sympathetic nerve had been divided. Had he only stated the phenomena observed, very probably the statement would have been read and soon forgotten. But the picture, with its queer expression, made a strong and distinct impression on my mind which did not fade.

This is a lesson which teachers should not forget. Illustrations, however rude, fix the facts in the mind as mere verbal descriptions can not. Especially is this true of pictures drawn at the moment on the blackboard which students are able to watch evolve before their eyes. Even in my own unskilled hand, a rude sketch growing on the blackboard has often been far more effective than completed, elaborate, or really artistic pictures. The many things seen all at once, and in mass, in a completed picture, often obliterate the memory of details. A picture seen in its genesis and growth is not easily forgotten.

At any rate, this patient, to me, was instantly Dalton's cat. "Where were you wounded?" I asked. "Here," he replied, pointing to his right neck. "Surely," I said to myself, "his sympathetic nerve has been divided!" I transferred him at once to Mitchell and Morehouse's Special Hospital for Injuries and Disorders of the Nervous System, and two or three days later, I was ordered to the same hospital as their junior assistant. There, we studied his case most carefully, recording it fully in our book *Gunshot Wounds and Other Injuries of Nerves*, published in 1864.

When I went to Paris as a student, in the winter of 1864-5, I took a
copy of this book to Claude Bernard and showed him the history of this
patient. It was the first confirmation in man of his experiments on animals. Naturally, his enthusiasm knew no bounds. Only those familiar with
medicine can appreciate how profoundly important has been the discovery
of the function of the sympathetic nerve, in anatomy, physiology, pathology, medicine, surgery, and therapeutics.

1860

My life has covered all of the later phases of the slavery question,
which finally ended in civil war. From, say, 1852, when I was old enough
to take a personal and intelligent interest in public affairs, I was sat-
urated with the debates over the one burning question of the day, human
slavery, the actual ownership of human beings as one owns cattle.

James Ford Rhodes shows, with wonderful clarity, how the slavery
question permeated all levels of society, influenced many discussions,
and considerably affected personal relations; and how it would not
down, even though it again and again was thought to be settled through
compromise. The reason it would not down is that while it was a political
question, it was also far more. For many years, the admission of a slave
state had to be counterbalanced by the admission of a free state, with the
constant threat of having five slave states made out of Texas. A political
question had to be tested by its relation to the slavery issue. If the
slave-owners were not satisfied with a piece of legislation (especially
concerning slavery, of course), they claimed the right to secede. The
South (always following Calhoun and South Carolina) considered that the

United States of America *were* a confederacy, while the North claimed that

the United States of America *was* a nation, one and indivisible.

It was also a huge economic question, hundreds of millions of dollars

in the market of human beings who were bought and sold like cattle. The

South claimed that what was property in Georgia should also be property in

Massachusetts and in every territory. On the floor of the Senate, Robert

Toombs, of Georgia, declared that the day would come when he would call

the roll of his slaves at the foot of Bunker Hill Monument.

But it was, above all, a moral question. This aspect of it was the

source of the tremendous influence of *Uncle Tom's Cabin*. As southerners

now acknowledge, its moral influence was pernicious on the slave-owners,

as was shown by the constantly increasing numbers of mulattos, quadroons,

and octaroons, as well as by the occasional incidents of the same form of

passionate cruelty that leads owners to beat their horses--and how much

more cruel for hired overseers to beat their slaves. By no means were

all overseers cruel, but it was always possible that one, in a moment of

unbridled passion, might become so.

Education of the blacks was prohibited. And if they were freed, they

became liable to arrest as vagrants, from which they might be sold back

into slavery. How hard their life was is well shown in Dr. Booker Wash-

ington's autobiography, *Up From Slavery*.

How far unreasoning passion went, among the abolitionists, is well

shown by an incident in my father's business life. The property of one of

his debtors, in Virginia, was seized, when he became a bankrupt, and sold

by the sheriff, at the insistence of some other creditor. Most of the

man's property consisted of slaves, three or four of which fell to the lot of my father, in settlement of his claim. They were all old and unable to work, to any great extent. My father was bitterly opposed to slavery, but what could he do? He would not sell them; he could not free them, unless he transported them north, but that would break up their families and sever all the other ties of their many years of life. So he simply accepted them, held them as his slaves, and supported them till they died.

One Communion Sunday, he was in Boston and went to the Baptist Church over which his old and cherished friend, Rev. Dr. Nathaniel Colver, was pastor. Between the morning service and the Communion, Dr. Colver, who knew exactly all the facts and motives as to my father's slaves, came to him in the pew and said to him, "Brother Keen, I cannot allow the deacons to serve you with the bread and wine because you are a slave-holder."

In 1856 (while I was in college), "Bully" Brooks, a representative from South Carolina, assaulted Massachusetts Senator Sumner, on the floor of the Senate (though not, I think, while the Senate was in session), and nearly killed him. A wave of horror (in the North) and of rejoicing (in the South) swept over the land. Indignation meetings to denounce the outrage were held all over the North, one, which the entire college attended, in Providence. The earlier speakers were vehement and denunciatory and aroused the crowd to fever heat. Then, Dr. Francis Wayland, the president of the university and easily the first citizen of the state, addressed us. His bulk, his leonine head and shaggy, beetling eyebrows, and his great personality, caused a hush all over the hall. He began in a subdued voice, then proceeded in a calm, clear argumentative speech which convinced every listener. Finally, rising to his full height, with uplifted hand he said, slowly and emphatically, as the impressive conclusion of the matter, "Fellow citizens: I was born a free man and, so help me God, I never will be made a slave!" Then pandemonium broke loose.

Slowly but surely, the forces on both sides of the question girded themselves for the conflict. The great debates, in Illinois, between Lincoln and Douglas were followed with almost breathless interest, all over the country. Then, in November, 1860, the Republican party (which had arisen about five years earlier and, in 1856, had placed Fremont in nomination for the presidency, polling a respectable number) nominated Lincoln. The Democrats were split into two factions, one of which nominated Breckinridge and the other, Douglas. A fourth ticket, backed chiefly by those who would pour oil on the troubled waters and compromise again, named Bell of Tennessee and Everett of Massachusetts.

When Lincoln was elected, the threats of secession grew louder and louder. Such madness was not taken as seriously as (it was later shown) it should have been.

But oh, those *dreadful* days from November of 1860 to March 4th, 1861 (or rather, up to the firing on Fort Sumter, in April), who can describe them! We rushed for the newspapers every morning, to see what new treachery had been perpetrated on the country, and thanked God every evening if the day had passed without an additional traitor. Almost everybody suspected everybody else.

Buchanan, a weakling (though honest), admitted that a state could not legally secede, but if one *did*, he had no right to coerce her to stay.

His cabinet was composed chiefly of southerners who turned traitor. Toucey of Connecticut, Secretary of the Navy, dispersed our ships all over the world; Floyd of Virginia, Secretary of War, divided our petty army into small garrisons all over the South, where most of our arms and munitions were stored; and Cobb of Georgia, Secretary of the Treasury, sent our gold and silver into the South, where it could readily be seized when secession was declared.

General Scott, a Virginian, stood by the Old Flag, but General Lee, another Virginian, went with his state. The army and the navy were disorganized throughout, and nobody knew whom they could trust. Every day, it seemed, this, that, or the other officer, senator, representative, judge, or other well-known man deserted his post under the Union. Every such defection saddened us unutterably. The forces of disunion were all rampant, and Buchanan and his cabinet either declined to do anything to stop the avalanche, or else gave it active support.

Finally, when Cobb resigned, after having done all the harm he could, Buchanan called in John A. Dix, of New York (a "War Democrat," as he and his like were later called). When a treasury official at New Orleans reported that a mob was threatening to pull down the American flag, Dix telegraphed, "If any man pulls down the American flag, shoot him on the spot." "Thank God," we all cried, "we have at last a man in the cabinet." That dispatch went through the nation like an electric shock, and we all took courage.

Along with all others, the medical students at the Jefferson were deeply stirred by the conflict. A very large proportion of the students were southerners, who proceeded to make themselves unpleasant neighbors by trying to bully us northerners. One big chap (from Richmond) who sat near me was particularly offensive and intended, I was told, to do personal violence to me. For some six weeks, therefore, I carried a revolver and let the fact be known, among my fellow students, that I intended to defend myself. No further insults followed.

Finally, the whole body of southern students (perhaps 30 to 50 per cent of our total) left the Jefferson and were received with open arms in the Medical College at Richmond, where they had to pay no additional fees.

From day to day, things went from bad to worse. More defections in Congress, in the army, the navy, and the civil service, in various departments. The gloom deepened daily. Our despairing feeling was expressed in the question, "What will finally happen?"

Mr. Lincoln came to Philadelphia and raised the flag over Independence Hall. As I think I have already written, George Porter and I joined the rather sorry-looking cavalcade, on horseback, as it met the president-elect at the Kensington depot and escorted him to the hall. From there, he went, openly, to Harrisburg, but then, owing to certain threats of assassination while passing through Baltimore, he was sent at night, incognito, to Washington, according to arrangements made by Thomas A. Scott, a vice-president of the Pennsylvania Railroad. When his safe arrival there was announced in the morning papers, what a sigh of relief followed!

His inauguration, on March 4th, 1861, his splendid address, the steps taken to preserve the authority of the United States, and finally, the attack on Fort Sumter (on April 12th) are all matters of public history.

Never shall I forget that excited Sunday of April 14th, when Sumter surrendered. George Porter, my brother Charles, and I walked, after church, in to the Continental Hotel, which was the headquarters for news. The lobby and the streets were filled with an excited mass of people, and personal violence was freely offered to anyone of southern sympathies. I

154

never, in all my long life, have seen such deep feeling, such enthusiasm over the defense of Major Anderson, or such determination as witnessed in the expressed idea that if war was wanted, we were steadfast in our belief that it should *be* war for as long as it took to abolish slavery and save the Union. We did not get home till about 1 A.M. (afoot again), when we found the whole family breathlessly awaiting us.

Then on Monday, April 15th, the papers issued Lincoln's call for 75,000 men, and the community went wild. No business was done. Edition after edition of the papers was issued and devoured. The first troops to go to Washington were a Pennsylvania company (possibly a regiment?), then the Massachusetts 6th and the Massachusetts 5th, then the New York 7th, and so on.

A cloud had been lifted. We felt that, instead of the weak Buchanan, we now had a *man* in the presidency.

The rest is history.*

---

* See also my "Surgical Reminiscences of the Civil War," in my volume of *Addresses and Other Papers*.

U. S. NAVAL HOSPITAL

Washington, D.C.

January 18, 1916

Dr. W. W. Keen

1729 Chestnut St.

Philadelphia, Pa.

Dear Doctor Keen:

Dr. Bell, of the League Island Navy Yard, has just written me concerning your technical capture after Second Bull Run by a Colonel Fauntleroy and asked me if I could identify him. I don't think that there is the slightest doubt that he was my grandfather, who became a general in the Confederate army before the war closed but was badly wounded, about a year before Lee's surrender, and died about one year later. He had two sons on the Confederate side, one who was my father, an assistant surgeon (afterward a medical director of a group of hospitals with headquarters at Danville, Virginia), and another son who was a captain in the navy.

The reason that I am sure it was my grandfather is that there was only one family of that name on the Confederate side, and he was the only one who held the rank of colonel.

I am very glad to know that you received one of my reports on the European war, as I had your name down on my list to send you one as soon as the second installment was received from the Government Printing Office.

With the highest respect and esteem, believe me,

Faithfully yours,

[*Signed*] A. M. Fauntleroy

156

ON ANESTHESIA

One constantly sees, in the antivivisectionist literature, doubts cast
on the absence of pain sensation, in animals, because (according to them)
the anesthesia was incomplete. They also state that so long as the corneal reflex exists, the animal may suffer pain.

Both of these assertions are untrue.

Everybody knows that the eye is exceedingly sensitive to the slightest touch. This is necessary for its protection. The instant that the
cornea is touched, the eyelids close. In fact, we can't keep them open.
Nay more: Even if you tell a person that you will aim a blow at the eye
but will not actually touch him, he can't help closing the eyelids, when
the simulated blow is delivered, even though he may trust you completely
and know that you will not strike him.

This involuntary closing of the eyelids when touched is called the
corneal reflex. When the etherizer wishes to know if the patient is so
entirely anesthetized that he will not move or struggle, while the tissues
are being cut, he lightly touches the cornea, and if the lids do not close,
he knows that the pain of the knife will not be felt. But in many cases,
this test is even too delicate. I have often begun to operate before this
reflex was totally abolished, and yet those patients did not struggle.
After the operation, they always stated, when questioned, that they had
suffered no pain. If this is true of man, whose nervous system is so
much more acute than that of other animals, the retention of the corneal
reflex in animals is quite consistent with the entire absence of pain.

Anesthesia may be incomplete, and the patient may struggle (even
violently), and yet no pain is felt. Very recently, in a case of injury

to the elbow, I was obliged to have nitrous oxide given several times, while I forcibly flexed and extended the patient's forearm in order to prevent a "stiff" elbow. The patient struggled slightly and showed other *apparent* evidence of feeling pain (she groaned loudly, once, and writhed to such a degree as almost to fall out of the chair), yet on no occasion had she suffered any pain.

Such muscular struggles are frequent, while the patient is in the early stage of excitement from ether, so that many surgeons always prepare for them by securing their patients to the operating table, in various ways. Most patients go quietly to sleep; a moderate number struggle, more or less; and a very few are difficult (and it may be *very* difficult) to control. Even those who do not struggle while being etherized will sometimes move when the knife first cuts the skin. They are incompletely etherized, and in order for the surgeon to be able to do careful, exact work, the patient must be anesthetized more deeply, in order that all muscular movement, except respiration and circulation, is abolished.

Yet human patients, when questioned in all the various phases, will say that they never know they are being hurt. Pain causes muscular contractions (that is, a muscular reflex) in the body at large, even under an anesthetic. The corneal reflex, described above, is an example of this protective system.

My friend Dr. Weir, of New York, tells an amusing story of a patient he was once etherizing for the late Dr. Gurdon Buck. Touching the eye and finding no response from the lids, he said, "The patient is ready, Dr. Buck." At the first touch of the knife, the patient drew the leg sharply away. "A little more ether, Dr. Weir," said Buck. Again, after the same test, "The patient is ready now, sir," and again the leg was drawn away.

"Can't you give the patient enough ether so that I can operate, sir?" was

the surgeon's reproach. "But sir, the corneal reflex is entirely gone"

was the excuse tendered. "Which eye did you test?" asked Buck. "The

right eye, sir." "Oh, that's a glass eye."

Sometimes the patient is subject to the wildest delusions. No pru-

dent surgeon will anesthetize a woman patient except in the presence of

others. The same rule should apply in the case of male patients, for the

reason that they sometimes have the delusion that they are being attacked

by the etherizer and will turn furiously upon him.

I never transgressed this rule but once, and early in my professional

life. It was a lesson I never forgot. The patient needed only an instan-

taneous cut of the knife to open an abcess, but I had expected to do it

without an anesthetic, as the discomfort of ether would really be worse

than the pain of the knife. But the patient insisted on having ether,

and as no assistant was available, I gave it to him myself. He had taken

only a few whiffs when he was seized with the delusion that I was going

to do something to him which he didn't want done. He tried to get off the

bed as I tried to keep him there and continue the ether. But as he was

several inches taller than I (and far more muscular), he flung me aside in

a moment. He grabbed a chair, raised it over his head, and threatened to

crush my skull with a single blow. I could not possibly hold him. Agil-

ity had to replace strength, and for a few moments, we had a mighty lively

time of it. Fortunately, he had had only a little ether, and as the vio-

lent muscular exertion quickened his respiration, he blew out the ether

and inhaled enough oxygen to bring him to himself. Had it not been so,

159

these lines easily might never have been written.

On another occasion, at St. Mary's Hospital, Philadelphia, a young, splendidly-developed fireman had been injured. It was needful to etherize him so that a thorough examination could be made to determine the extent of his injuries. There were present two residents, the orderly (a muscular Irishman), the etherizer, and myself.

The patient was perfectly quiet, for a considerable time, so that we were standing to one side and talking together of the possible diagnosis, the etherizer and the orderly being the only ones beside the table. The patient suddenly began to struggle, in an effort to escape from the etherizer. He rose up, flung the ether cone into a corner, brushed aside the etherizer and, seeing me (with blood in his eye), he tried to get at me. Fortunately, the orderly was behind the patient, when he sat up, and was able to grasp him around the waist and hold him--though with difficulty. The man was so intent on reaching and punishing me that he didn't notice how or why he couldn't get off the table. In a moment, all of us were upon him and held him till the ether effects had passed off.

We then sent for four of his fellow firemen and meantime, tied each wrist and ankle to a table leg, passing a broad band around his body and under the table top. The four firemen held his arms and legs, while the orderly held his head. The ether was begun again. The same scene was re-enacted. In spite of the thongs and the strong men holding him, he was so strong that it seemed he would either break his bonds as easily as Sampson broke those of the Philistines or reduce the strong table to firewood. Never before or since have I seen such strength in a man. (The only similar exhibition of strength I have ever seen in a woman was in a case

160

of puerperal convulsions in a rather frail and delicate woman--who almost overcame four ordinary men.) Our fireman finally succumbed and lay as quietly as a child, while we examined him, fortunately finding only a passing injury.

I have often looked at patients in the deep sleep of ether and have wondered at the temerity of Long and Morton, as well as the other early anesthetizers. There lies a patient absolutely motionless. Lift the arm or the leg and it falls like lead. Prick him, pinch him, strike him, or cut him; he shows no evidence of feeling. He seems to be dead, except that he is breathing and his heart has not ceased to beat. But how soon will he wake up? In fact, will he ever even wake up? And if he does not, may I not be adjudged guilty? These and other similar questions must have often thronged the minds of the pioneer anesthetizers, and they have come not seldom into my own mind, even at this late date. Verily, it took enormous courage to give ether and chloroform, in 1846 and 1847. What if the first public case, in the Massachusetts General Hospital, had died on the table?

Today, we would not dare to do as they did then, but would only use anesthesia on human beings after repeated, painstaking (and successful) investigations of the effects, immediate and later, upon animals. Sir James Simpson's first experiments with chloroform, upon himself and his friends, in 1847 (so dramatically described by his daughter, in the January 1894 edition of *Century Magazine*), was a foolhardy experiment which might easily have become a tragedy. Indeed, he even narrowly escaped death, once, when Sir Lyon Playfair refused to give him any of a newly-discovered liquid, which Simpson wished to inhale immediately, until it had been tried first upon two rabbits. These were successfully anesthetized but expired soon afterwards from the after-effects of the poison. (In my *Addresses and Other Papers*, p. 70, is Sir Lyon Playfair's own account of this incident.)

One single, sudden death upon the table delayed the use of ether in Germany for many years, and thus cost many lives, for chloroform is about six times as dangerous as ether. Chloroform is much more agreeable to inhale and is quicker in its effect; it seldom produces excitement; and it requires a far smaller quantity to produce insensibility. Simpson's immense reputation (and the slight esteem in which American science was held, in 1846), together with the virtues just recounted, made chloroform *the* European anesthetic for many years. In some cases, we are still obliged to use it, under certain circumstances, in preference to ether. Only a large body of statistics showing that ether was far less dangerous than chloroform finally induced many German surgeons to use ether as the routine anesthetic.

Concerning that single death: Dr. Sands, a distinguished surgeon from New York, was visiting Prof. Langenbeck in his Berlin clinic, probably in the late '60s. He urged so vigorously the greater safety of ether upon his German friend that Langenbeck finally proposed that his New York friend himself should administer ether at his clinic, the next morning. To the consternation of everybody, and especially of the American, the patient promptly died upon the table. If, even in such skillful hands, it could kill so easily, very naturally the Germans were wary of it.

The danger even of ether has led to the most diligent search for safe, as well as efficient, anesthetics. Several have been introduced but, after extensive trials, have been found to be either as dangerous (or more so) or counterbalanced by other disadvantages, and thus have been either abandoned or used only occasionally. Nitrous oxide is undoubtedly the safest of all, by far, its mortality rate being only about one in 200,000 cases (versus one in 16,000 for ether, and one in 2,500 for chloroform). For very brief operations, it is *the* anesthetic of choice. But until lately, it could be used only for a *very* few minutes without, in turn, becoming a threat to life. Recently, its combination with oxygen has made it far more useful for even very long operations, and it eventually may come to be the most widely used of all.

Local anesthetics, which abolish sensation in the areas into which they are injected, have begun to play an important role in surgery, lately, with patients unable to feel any pain whatsoever (though they are entirely conscious), even during such serious operations as amputations or the removal of tumors.

Spinal anesthesia, by which various anesthetics are injected, by lumbar puncture, within the sheath of the spinal cord, is also a method of great value, in a small proportion of cases in which, for various reasons, neither chloroform nor ether can be safely used. By this method, all nerves below the point of puncture (i.e., the lumbar region--the small of the back) are temporarily deprived of their normal ability to transmit painful sensations; yet the patient remains completely conscious.

But the ideal anesthetic does not yet exist. That it will be found before very long, I certainly hope and believe. But it will not be an agent which produces insensibility to pain and leaves the patient conscious: It will produce unconsciousness, but *without danger to life or later health.* There are few operations done in which sudden emergencies, especially from hemorrhage, do not occur, emergencies (sometimes very grave) which instantly demand all the resources of the most experienced surgeons. Naturally, such emergencies produce some bustle and stir among the assistants, and sharp, quick commands from the operator. For the nervous or timid patient, to be aware of such incidents (even though they be minor emergencies, with which the surgeon deals easily, quickly, and successfully) may be most demoralizing, possibly producing a depressing shock or even sudden, restless apprehensive movements, which could change a minor accident into a most dangerous one.

The controversy over who should have the credit for the discovery of anesthesia was long and bitter. Oliver Wendell Holmes was the only one whose wit enlivened the quarrel. When it was proposed to erect the Ether Monument, in the public gardens in Boston, how to word the inscription was a very embarrassing question. The friends of Morton and Jackson were, each party, clamorous for its own hero. They finally consulted Holmes, whose ready wit never failed. "Nothing is simpler," said he. "Put up your shaft with the name of Morton on one side and of Jackson on the opposite side, and between them, the motto, 'To Ether.'"

I had an amusing incident, in my Jefferson clinic, over the use of cocaine as a local anesthetic. One of the students brought in his father, a clergyman, for an operation on a small cancer of his lower lip. When his turn was near, I told an assistant to inject cocaine into the lip, and while waiting for it to take effect, I went on with another brief operation. The rising seats of the amphitheater allowed space for small rooms under the uppermost seats, and in these rooms, the patients were anesthetized or otherwise prepared for operation. Naturally, any loud noise in these rooms could be heard by the several hundreds of students usually present in the amphitheater.

Just before the prior operation had been terminated, I heard some loud outcries, apparently from my clerical patient. As these continued (and, in fact, increased in vehemence), I asked my assistant to finish the pending operation and went into the room under the seats. I found that the clergyman belonged to the church militant, for he had cleared out the etherizing room and was lord of all he surveyed. He was sensible enough to recognize me, for he shouted, in a loud voice (easily heard in the operating theater), "They have made me drunk, Dr. Keen . . . and . . . I . . . am a . . . *prohibitionist!*" One could sympathize with his indignation, while at the same time not wonder at the shouts of laughter from the benches.

This was only one instance of what is an occasional effect of cocaine (and, indeed, of most anesthetics), the production of a stage of excitement which sometimes is intense, and which may even be dangerous, as I have shown by these various personal experiences. (See my address, "The Dangers of Ether as an Anesthetic," in my *Selected Papers and Addresses*. This was delivered on Ether Day, October 16, 1915, at the Massachusetts General Hospital.)

RISKS THAT DOCTORS, AND ESPECIALLY SURGEONS, CONSTANTLY RUN

Three times I personally have suffered from infection of my fingers, twice during surgical operations and once from a post-mortem prick of a needle. The first two were mild infections, which soon yielded to efficient treatment, but the third very nearly cost me my life.

A patient in my private hospital died from a perforation of the stomach from cancer. He died during the night, between Saturday and Sunday. My assistants did not report for duty on Sunday unless I had foreseen the need and asked them to do so. The family wished to move the body on Sunday afternoon, and as I was very anxious to have a necropsy (and they were perfectly willing), I performed it myself. The abdomen was full of a pus which I knew to be very dangerous, so that I was more than usually careful. I had completed the examination and had almost closed the abdominal incision when, in some unknown way, I pricked my right thumb with the needle. It was no more than many a woman inflicts upon herself when hemming a handkerchief. I barely felt the prick. I at once washed and carefully disinfected my thumb, but I hardly thought it possibly needful to make an incision and make a prolonged and deep disinfection. In fact, I did not give it a second thought.

By about 7 P.M., I began to feel a little creepy and chilly. I lighted the parlor wood fire and decided not to go to church, especially as it was a stormy night, but to toast my toes and read. I went to bed early, feeling rather seedy, but I could not get to sleep. By 1 or 2 in the morning, my thumb had begun to throb, and this recalled to my mind the needle-prick from the post mortem, and I recognized the danger. I partly dressed, slipped quietly down to my office, and called up Dr. William J. Taylor, my first assistant, on the telephone. He lived then on 18th Street, just below Chestnut. While waiting for his arrival, I got out the necessary instruments and dressings, some carbolic acid and bichloride tablets, plus a hypodermic syringe and a solution of cocaine. This last he injected on both sides of my thumb, after which he made a deep incision, scrubbed and disinfected the wound very thoroughly, dressed it, and gave me a quarter of a grain of morphine, hypodermatically.

I went to bed and finally, towards morning, fell asleep for a short time. At 8 A.M., he saw me again and found a temperature of 105 degrees. He called in Dr. J. Chalmers Da Costa and Dr. W. Joseph Hearn. Two days later, or so, they etherized me and disinfected the wound anew. I was desperately ill, for possibly a week, and then gradually mended. It was some weeks before the wound was healed sufficiently for me to resume operating. Never shall I forget the kindness of my friends. Until I was quite well, I knew nothing of it, but they called and inquired and telephoned and left cards, messages, and dainties, almost without number. When I looked over the cards, I was astonished (and, I confess, gratified) to find many from almost entire strangers. Sickness often proves to us how many warm friends we have--often far more than we would expect.

One thing seems to me the most providential. On Monday morning, Dr. Taylor found that his telephone was, for some unknown reason, out of commission. My nocturnal message was the last he had received. Had he not responded to my call, I should almost certainly have waited till morning: The night was very stormy, and only women (my daughters and the servants) were in the house. I should not have wanted to venture out myself, and I should not have asked them to go. Yet had I waited till morning, I am convinced that the result would surely have been fatal.

While this was my only really dangerous illness contracted in the line of duty, I was constantly exposed to such risks, in my earlier professional life, when, from pecuniary necessity, I attended medical--and even a few obstetrical--cases. I suffered several times from a slight infection from diphtheria, especially in the cases which we then operated on by tracheotomy. (Now, thanks to the antitoxin and intubation, we hardly ever even *hear* of a case of diphtheria's being treated by tracheotomy.)

I have been very often exposed to the danger of "professional" syphilis, but fortunately have entirely escaped it. This danger has been a tragedy in not a few of my professional friends and acquaintances.

I have known over a dozen men who for years have suffered the horrible tortures of syphilis and the fear (which is even worse) of communicating the disease to their wives and children. One of my friends told me that he had had several doctors under his care for syphilis who have committed suicide, and I can hardly wonder at it. While I would be the last to do such a deed, I also would be the last to blame them. I am willing also to believe that a merciful God would not judge them too harshly. Two of my own medical friends died, utter wrecks, from cerebral syphilis.

Others also have been under my care who have had wide-spread surgical infections, followed by abscesses in many parts of the body, but who have weathered the gale, finally, and recovered.

In my "Address at the Unveiling of the Statue of the Late Professor Samuel D. Gross, M.D., Washington, D. C., May 5, 1897," as well as in "The Debt of the Public to the Medical Profession" (both in my *Addresses and Other Papers*), I have referred to Gross's splendid example of courage when cholera broke out in New York. I have also referred to the young German bacteriologist who was studying the bubonic plague germ, accidentally became infected, and heroically died; and to the many unknown and unsung heroes who have lost their lives in epidemics of yellow fever.

In *Harper's Magazine* (April 1909), I have recited in some detail the

168

extraordinary and deliberate attempts by doctors at self-inoculation with the germ of yellow fever, in Cuba, and their success in demonstrating the only means by which the contagion is carried (the mosquito, of course), a knowledge attained, alas, by the sacrifice of human lives. Had it been possible to conduct these experiments on animals, it would have been unnecessary to try them on human beings, but unfortunately, man is the only animal liable to this disease.

So too, medical men have gone to Africa to investigate the fatal sleeping sickness, sometimes offering themselves as voluntary victims, for the benefit of mankind. Only a few months ago, Ricketts, one of our most promising young doctors, lost his life while studying typhus fever, in Mexico, well knowing when he went there that his death might be the price of victory. As I write these lines, 17 young men, in Baltimore, have just volunteered for experiments in cancer inoculation, an offer properly declined, since animals can be inoculated as well.

No other profession can show such a record of heroic self-sacrifice. Is it any wonder, then, that I take a just pride in the altruism of the medical profession?

SIDE-TO-SIDE IRRIGATION OF THE INTERIOR OF THE BRAIN

In the *Proceedings of the Philadelphia County Medical Society* for February 13th and 27th, 1889 (pp. 50 and 85), I reported one of the most unusual (and most satisfactory) cases of brain surgery I have ever done. So far as I know, it was the first time in the history of surgery in which the two lateral ventricles of the brain have been both drained and washed out, from side to side, providing evident comfort to the little patient.

He was a four-year-old boy sent to me at the Woman's Hospital by Dr. George Strawbridge, just after Christmas, 1888. The diagnosis was an inoperable tumor of the cerebellum which caused hydrocephalus because it prevented the escape of the cerebrospinal fluid in the lateral ventricles. Since Christmas, he had been totally blind, with a choked disc in each eye, the swelling of the optic nerve being 2.3 millimeters on one side and 1.8 on the other. He suffered greatly from constant and severe headache. After the tapping, this fell to .83 millimeters on each side. His headache was much relieved, though his blindness was unchanged.

On January 4th, 1889, I tapped one lateral ventricle by the method I first devised (*Medical News,* December 1, 1888, p. 603), reaching the ventricle from a small trephine opening, at a depth of one and three-quarters inches, above the ear. I inserted a few strands of horse hair as a drain. From two to four ounces of cerebrospinal fluid escaped daily, into a copious antiseptic dressing. One week later, I substituted a small rubber tube for the horse hairs. The fluid then escaped more freely, from about four to eight ounces a day.

On February 8th, I tapped the opposite ventricle and inserted a drainage tube there also. On two occasions, by a fountain syringe (raised only a very few inches above the level of the boy's head), I washed out the ventricles from side to side, passing eight ounces of a warm boric-acid solution into one ventricle from which it freely escaped by the tube in the opposite ventricle. The moment the warm boric-acid solution began to flow, the boy lost his irritability and settled down into a position of evident comfort.

He lived for 52 days after the first tapping. The first tube was in place for almost that length of time; the other, for two weeks. The first tube was removed, cleansed, and replaced at least 30 times, without discomfort to the child or injury to the brain.

The post-mortem examination disclosed, as diagnosed, a sarcoma of the cerebellum, on the right side. There was no inflammation around the track of the drainage tubes. The septum between the two ventricles had not been injured by the removal and replacement of the tubes. The boy's mental condition was unimpaired until within a week or ten days of his death.

Besides these drainage tubes, the brain was probed six times, in as many different places, in the hope that we might find the tumor and possibly remove it. No evidence of these additional punctures could be found at the post-mortem examination.

OFFERS TO UNDERGO EXPERIMENTS FOR THE GOOD OF THE HUMAN RACE

Among my letters will be found one or more letters from persons who were strangers to me, who offered to undergo surgical experiments, even without anesthesia, if necessary, if there was any possibility thereby of gaining additional knowledge which would further anatomy, physiology, and surgery, etc., in any respect and so be of use to mankind.

I have received, I think, at least four or five such letters. I have always declined, of course, as it was in my opinion wholly unjustifiable, especially since we can learn by similar experiments on the lower animals (and practically always with anesthetics) practically everything we could learn from such experiments on humans.

The most extraordinary offer of this kind I ever had was made to me in Berlin, in April of 1907. A young man of 25 to 30, an American, made two visits to me at my hotel, with the following proposition.

He declared that he was absolutely sound and healthy in mind and body and from head to foot. (Physically, at least, he certainly looked it, but I confess I was a bit doubtful of his entire mental soundness, in view of his insistence on his plan.) He said that we doctors were consulted only by people who were ill, so that we had to observe and deal with only those bodies or organs that were diseased. But he, being in absolutely perfect health, wanted us to open his abdomen (at least; I think he offered his chest as well) so as to have the unique opportunity to study perfectly healthy organs in normal action and learn far more than from diseased organs. I positively declined, showing him how useless such a sacrifice would be, and also how criminal it would be, for I should almost certainly destroy his life. Even so, he replied to this that he was perfectly willing to die if by so doing he could contribute to any lasting good. At his second visit, he was even more insistent than at the first, and I more resolutely refused.

He left me a sadder (I scarcely venture to think wiser) man. That he was seriously convinced that such an experiment would be of great use I have no doubt. What became of him I have never heard.

THE LOST SPONGE

To persons unfamiliar with the actual facts and possibilities of an abdominal section, it would seem both criminal and extremely careless to leave a sponge or an instrument inside the patient. But the published records of well over 100 such cases at the hands of many surgeons (among them, some of the ablest and most careful) should be sufficient evidence to the contrary. My personal experience is that a sponge, and even relatively small instruments, such as forceps or scissors, may easily elude even a careful search at the close of an abdominal operation. Moreover, one of the very best American surgeons had the following experience when we were all using marine sponges. At the close of an operation, instruments and sponges, 12, were all counted and the count found correct. The abdomen was closed. By the third day, it became very evident that something was wrong. The abdomen was reopened and a 13" sponge was found! Though the fact had been forgotten, when recounting the sponges at the time of the operation, it was then remembered that one of the 12 marine sponges had been torn in two, to meet an emergency of hemorrhage, thus making 13 sponges. (The patient recovered without difficulty.)

In 1896, I operated on my sister-in-law, Mrs. George W. Dean, of Fall River, for a very large abdominal tumor. As usual, every small instrument and the gauze sponges, 12, were counted and the numbers entered on a blackboard on the wall of the operating room (as I never trusted to memory). Also, every sponge had a tape, 10 to 12 inches long, sewed on to it, for additional safety, and a pair of forceps was clamped on to the tape whenever its sponge was inserted. At the close of this difficult operation, I told the operating-room nurse to count the instruments and sponges. Though the blackboard recorded 12 sponges, only 11 could be found. The nurse recounted the sponges, and I searched the abdomen with the greatest possible thoroughness. Still only 11. We looked in the folds of the aseptic sheets, over the patient and under the patient; turned out all the contents of the waste bucket and carefully picked them over; and re-searched the abdomen, re-examined the sheets, and recounted the sponges. Still, to my dismay, only 11. It was evident that I could not keep the abdomen open any longer, so I was compelled to close it, trusting that if the errant sponge was really in the abdomen after all, it would declare itself sufficiently early to cause its removal to be not very dangerous.

But my anxiety can readily be imagined. Here was a patient whom I loved, upon whom I had done a highly dangerous operation, for which I had made the most careful, painstaking preparation, planning every step beforehand with scrupulous exactitude. And now, possibly there was a missing sponge in the abdomen! If it should cause her death, could I ever forgive myself? Would her husband and the family ever forgive such carelessness?

The next few nights, I hardly slept at all. The natural (and expected) rise of temperature, after the operation, my fears magnified into certain peritonitis and a possible, if not probable, death. Then, as the days went by and her condition became more and more satisfactory, my dreadful anxiety began to lessen, though the specter of a *late* complication from that missing sponge would not wholly down till weeks, and even months, went by.

Now that 15 years have passed, and the sponge has never been heard from, there is but one explanation: a miscount by the nurses. I so regularly used 12 such sponges that they chalked down 12, although they had really only prepared 11.

But I never want to repeat that unique experience.

THE LOST FORK

One winter evening, I went out to the country home of Mr. T. DeWitt Cuyler, who had kindly invited me there to a reception of the Junior Legal

Club. While we were at supper, I had started to lay the silver fork down on my plate, for a moment, when someone jostled my arm and the fork fell to the floor. As I did not wish it to be trodden on, I looked and looked for it but could not find it. I concluded that it had gone under the table and would be found later, by the waiters.

At the close of the evening, we all went up the stairs together, of course, to take the same train home. As I lifted my right foot, I found, suddenly, that the flexion of my leg was obstructed by something in my pocket, and, inserting my hand, I pulled out the lost fork. All those who were around me immediately began to cry out "Ben Butler!" "Ben Butler!"

The explanation was easy, of course: I had on an evening coat, and the aperture of the pocket gaped, so that when the fork fell, it dropped into the pocket without my observing it.

I venture to think that if any novelist included such an incident in a story, it would be pronounced very incredible. It was another case in which truth is stranger than fiction.

WHEN I FELL UPON BOTH FEET

In December of 1907, when Florence, Dora, and I were passing the winter in Rome, I had occasion to go to Vienna. I was gone about a week, and both in going and returning, I had a noteworthy fellow-traveler.

On the way to Vienna, a husky young fellow of, say, twenty-five occupied the upper berth in our compartment. From the diacritical marks in the book he was reading, I judged him to be a Pole. We fell into conversation, in bad French (I earnestly hope, though I would not be willing to assert, that both my lingo and my pronunciation were not as bad as his).

We soon exchanged cards, and I found that he was a Prince Radziwill, one of the leading and most aristocratic Polish families.

Our passage over the Semmering Alps was at night, and with considerable snow. When we awoke in the morning, the window was frosted over. I rose first, and finding no towels in our little toilet room, I called the porter and asked for four, two for each of us. Just after I emerged from the toilet room, the prince began to yawn, and, finding that he was awake, I told him of my request for towels for him. He stretched and yawned again, and, looking at the window, said, with a shudder, "It's too cold. I shan't wash this morning."

As he had only partially undressed, his dressing was quickly accomplished. He washed neither his face nor his hands, nor even his teeth, but simply put on the few clothes he had taken off, went out into the corridor, and began talking with some ladies! I was glad I was not a Polish prince.

On my return journey, I had really the most extraordinary good fortune to say just the right thing to the right person, and absolutely unconsciously.

A few moments after our train had left Padua, a tall gentleman of about 60 entered my compartment (I had been alone all the way from Vienna) and bowed politely to me. Of course, I bowed in return. After he had arranged his impedimenta, he sat down and opened a conversation in Italian. It was, of course, easy to discern, both by eye and ear, that I was a stranger, and one of the first questions he asked me was if I had ever been in Padua before. To this I replied in the affirmative, but added that in the forty years since my visit to Padua, many of the impressions of the place had faded away. "But," I continued, "I can never forget the fact that Padua is the home--and I put on the proper and customary Italian superlatives--of the *celebrissimo e illustrissimo chirurgo*, Professor Bassini. (Through "Bassini's operation," he is known wherever surgery is practiced. He also is Professor of Surgery in the University of Padua.) He half rose and, putting his hand to his heart, replied, "Thank you. I am Professor Bassini."

The arrow, shot at a venture, hit an unexpected bull's eye.

We then exchanged cards and mutually recalled the fact that, at the celebration of the Royal College of Surgeons of England, in 1900, when we both had been made honorary fellows, we had met before, but only casually, of course, and in the over seven years that had passed since then, the face of each had been forgotten by the other.

We chatted, on and off, all the way to Rome, and he dined with us, very pleasantly, the next evening.

TWO FAMILY CALAMITIES

In the middle of the night, many years ago, my night-bell rang violently. I found my nocturnal caller to be an old medical friend, with whom I had been a fellow student in Berlin, in 1865-6. He was greatly excited, as he told me his tale of woe. He had just come from Washington, where he held an important position in government service. He was engaged to Miss X, who was one of two (or possibly three) sisters of a family widely known in literature and in public life. His fiancée had fallen ill with peritonitis and was under the care of a physician who was also her near relative. For some unaccountable reason, this physician had actually given her three (or it may have been four) drops of croton oil. This is a violent purgative, which is rarely used, and then cautiously, in doses of one drop or less. As we drove to the house, he explained the situation and said to me, "Now remember, you are to take command of the case. Spare the doctor, her relative, if you can, but if possible, save her life at all hazards, no matter what the consequences to him."

As soon as I saw her, it took but a glance to know that her case was absolutely hopeless. All I could possibly do was to soothe her suffering. I stayed by her all the rest of the night and saw her several times during the following day. The second night was a distressing admixture of sorrow and joy. The wedding reception of a young friend was held that evening. I left the house of mourning and, with my dear wife, went to the house of joy, afterwards spending the rest of the night with the dying girl and my desolate friend.

I had never been in that house before and had no occasion to go there again until some years later, when I was a witness to an even greater calamity. A sister of the first patient had been sought in marriage by two young men, A and B. She really loved A, but, having had some quarrel with him, she turned around and, almost on the instant, married B. This was at noon. By 7 o'clock she had become insane! When I saw her, some days later, I found her unwilling to talk, or even to answer any questions. But she was never still, save for short intervals of sleep. Walking, walking, walking the entire day, upstairs, downstairs, wandering into room after room, and seizing food from the table when the family was at meals. She *never* sat down her entire waking day, so I was told. She must have walked, I judged, not less than twenty miles a day, and it might well have been more.

Only exhaustion made her tramp, tramp, tramp to cease. I advised that she should be placed under the care of an alienist. I never saw her again.

Some time afterwards, her husband sought me, stated that her condition was unchanged, and asked me to give him a certificate to be presented in court in proceedings for divorce. This I refused to do. I pointed out that he had married her, promising to cleave to her alone "in sickness and in health, till death us do part," and that I could not and would not aid him to violate this vow. I have often discussed with myself the question of whether this was a righteous and just decision. It was a very hard case to decide. On the one side, his solemn vow "in the presence of God and these witnesses;" on the other side, his ruined life. But on the whole, I still think I was right. I never heard the later history of either the man or the woman.

WHEN I SAT IN THE SEATS OF THE MIGHTY

In 1900, I was appointed one of the seven official government delegates to the International Medical Congress, which met in Paris. Also in Paris, that year, was the International Exposition, or World's Fair. I had Florence, Dora, and Margaret with me.

We agreed, one day, to separate after breakfast and meet for dinner. I went to the congress, Florence and Dora went to the exposition, and Margaret stayed at home. In the morning, Margaret received an invitation, addressed to me, to which a reply was requested. It was signed "Jacques," though written in English, and conveyed an invitation from the president of the republic to occupy his box at the opera that evening. Margaret at once accepted, hoping that my daughters were included! At the congress,

I met Dr. Jacobs, of Baltimore, the secretary of our government delegation--
and the "Jacques" of the invitation. He explained to me that the president had courteously placed his box at the opera at the disposition of the
seven official delegates. Accordingly, I went to our rooms rather early,
explained the facts to the girls, and arranged that we should dine at the
hotel where Dwight Merrick (one of their friends) was staying, ask him
to dine with us, and then go along to the opera. All went auspiciously.
I had bought four tickets in the orchestra for them. I left the dinner
table a little early, so as to be in my place promptly.

No ticket had been given me, so I presented my visiting card at the
ticket office and explained the invitation I had received. Without any
hesitation, I was handed over to a much be-medaled man who conducted me to
the president's box (formerly that of Napoleon III). After a few minutes,
Dr. Robert F. Weir, another government delegate (and an old friend from
the Antietam-Frederick, Md., days in 1862) joined me. We sat there looking around in a superior way, as if we were accustomed to sitting in imperial and presidential boxes every week or so, and condescending, from
time to time, to cast a benevolent look down upon my daughters and Merrick.

The opera was *Les Huguenots*. We sat through the first act, but none
of the other American delegates arrived. We thought this very odd and
finally decided to explore. We searched the corridors and foyer, but all
in vain. Finally, we went out upon the large terrace in front of the opera
house, and there we spied them in close consultation. They beckoned us to
join them, and then Weir and I learned, to our consternation, of our error:
The invitation was not for the Grand Opéra but the Opéra Comique! We flew
to our places, gathered up our belongings, and fled, along with the others,

180

to the Opéra Comique. What a complication it would have been if another guest (possibly even the president himself) had appeared in our loge at the Grand Opéra while we were there! How embarrassing, and even inexplicable it would have been! Happy indeed were we to have been spared such a humiliation!

I have often thought it extraordinary that we two could have penetrated to the president's loge without tickets and without authority. We always have said that it was owing to our own honest and handsome faces.

The Opéra Comique performance was poor, and we soon left. We picked up Florence, Dora, and Margaret en route and went to the home of Prof. Lannelongue (the president of the congress), who gave a reception for the foreign delegates, that evening, and I presented "Monsieur Jacques" to Margaret. Ever since then, Jacobs has been our "M. Jacques."

This last reminds me of a photograph of *"Jacob Wrestling with the Angel,"* which I bought in 1865, in Berlin. The legend is printed in German, French, and alleged English, as follows:

> *Jacob mit dem Engel ringend*
>
> *Jacques luttant avec l'Ange*
>
> *Jack wringing with the Angel*

A VERY INTELLIGENT HORSE

Of the several horses I have had, "George" certainly was the most remarkable. His judgment, memory, and reasoning power were astonishing.

He was a swift bay, whom I had to drive, as a rule, with my feet on the cross bar and with the lines taut. He served me for years, therefore, as a gymnasium. He never needed a whip. In fact, my friends said I must have been a descendant of Jehu the son of Nimshi, and that when they saw (or, often, heard) us coming, they were wary till I had passed. They also said that when I turned a corner, it was usually on two wheels only. I drove him for, I think, well on to ten years, and then when he failed physically, probably around the age of sixteen, I sent him to the zoo. He was useful even in death, for he was shot and fed to the lions.

I always drove a buggy, and never a pair, because this was the swiftest method of locomotion. If I took along my boy or man, it was only to hold the lines, but for a number of years, I drove a good part of the time alone. Very commonly, I left "George" unhitched. As soon as he saw me coming out of a patient's house, he would turn either left or right, but always away from the curb for me to get in the more readily.

Twice, he stood unusual tests. In one, he was standing, fortunately unhitched, facing west on Green Street, west of 19th. I happened to be looking out of the window and saw a hack driving westward. The careless driver caught my hind wheel with his front wheel and turned my buggy completely around so that it was facing east. "George" turned with it and calmly waited for me to drive to my next patient.

At another time, when the Centennial buildings were under construction, I had occasion to go out there for an interview with one of the officials. I left "George" facing a railroad track, not fifty feet away. In spite of the length of my call (fully half an hour), and the backing and filling and whistling of a switching locomotive in front of him, he never budged.

While standing facing east on Pine Street near 21st, one time, he played me a trick. My call was unexpectedly prolonged, and I was not able to leave till around 8 o'clock, after dark, on that autumn or winter day.

When I opened the door, no horse and buggy were to be seen. He evidently disapproved of my late hour and wanted *his* supper, however careless I might be about my own. I went at once to the stable at the northeast corner of 17th & Sansom Streets, and there he was, safe and sound. Later, I learned from a friend that he had trotted east on Pine to 17th, turned north on 17th, and gone straight to the stable. The cars on both streets ran in the opposite direction to his own, but he avoided every car and all other vehicles. The only damage done was that, in turning in to the stable (according to the ostlers, who were startled at his arrival without his master), the hub of the front wheel barely grazed the brick doorway.

When nearing a cross street, he watched for the horsecars, when he heard the bells on the horses, and could almost always judge at once whether he ought to hasten and cross in front of the car, or slow down and allow the car to pass in front of him.

His memory was well shown by this incident. I drove up 5th Street to Thompson, turned west on Thompson, and stopped on the north side of the street near the middle of a row of houses, all alike, from 5th to 6th. This was a part of the city to which I was rarely called in consultation, and I had never been called to this particular block. A year or more later, during which time I had never visited anywhere on Thompson Street, I had a consultation on a street some blocks further north than Thompson. I was driving again up 5th Street, and when I got to the corner of Thompson, "George" evidently thought I was going a second time to the house where I had been before and began to turn west on Thompson Street. My former consultation instantly flashed upon my mind. I slackened the reins, and "George" stopped on the north side of the street, within one door of the house where I had stopped a year or more before. Could there be a clearer indication of memory?

I have never had but one "George." His successor was a light-spirited sorrel named "Colonel." Once, while passing the Union League (going south) on the way to a post mortem, I had a very ugly accident. The front axle on my side broke, and the buggy toppled over, throwing Fuller, my faithful colored man, and me out onto the cobblestones. In the buggy, I had a large, two-gallon glass jar, half-filled with a solution of bichromate of potash, and a case of post-mortem instruments. It was winter, and I had had a gray fur robe over our knees. Everything was spilled into the street, and either the glass jar was broken or the top came off (I am not sure which). None of the acid touched either of us. One spot, as large as a hand, on the robe was stained yellow when a little of the acid spilled on it. The instruments were all right. We were not struck by the buggy nor injured on striking the cobbles, though our clothes were soiled, of course, with dust and dirt. I gathered up the impedimenta and went into the League to get washed and brushed up, but sent Fuller after the horse and buggy, for "Colonel" had not stopped for a moment. "George" would have stopped, as he did on two occasions following much less serious accidents. This horse ran down Broad to Spruce (a block and a half), turned east on Spruce, and stopped. The reason for his stopping was unexpected. The buckle fastening together the ends of the two reins fell, fortunately, into the apex of the V between two spokes and was caught there. The revolving wheel gradually wound up the reins around the hub, finally stopping the horse. I called a cab and got to my post mortem in time, minus only my jar.

THE GREATEST TRIUMPHS OF THE HUMAN VOICE I KNOW OF

In 1867, after the war had closed, Gilmore, the well-known conductor, organized a mammoth "Peace Festival," in Boston. A very large (but temporary) building was erected to seat 50,000 auditors. The stage held a chorus of 10,000 voices, 1200 musicians, and an immense organ. Several great oratorios, as well as patriotic and other musical productions (both vocal and instrumental), were heard.

In one chorus (I forget which), Parepa-Rosa was the prima donna. Never shall I forget how she thrilled everyone. Above the orchestra, chorus, and organ combined, her voice was heard by everybody, in that vast audience, like that of a lark soaring up into the clouds. She accomplished the seemingly impossible.

On May 10th, 1876, the opening day of the Centennial Exhibition, a prominent part was assigned to the Centennial Choir, which numbered, I think, four or five hundred voices, in addition to a large orchestra and a number of soloists. President Grant initiated the program, which was held in the open, but his address could be heard by only a few. It was estimated that the audience numbered 100,000 people, or more. Myron W. Whitney rendered a splendid bass solo, heard by practically the entire audience, even in the open air. It was a glorious triumph.

My dear wife and I were both in the chorus. After the opening exercises, we went to the Southern Restaurant for dinner. It was crowded to the utmost--as, in fact, was every restaurant on the grounds. After waiting for some time, we obtained places at a table. Then the problem was to catch a waiter. In time, we seized the coattail of one and had him take our order. Then followed a still longer interval. Our waiter had apparently forgotten us. Finally, I caught another one, again by the coattail, rounded him up, and re-ordered our dinner, recounting the woes of our delays. But very frankly, and with perfect good humor, he replied, "Well, de fact is, boss, dat de grub's give out."

THE HARDEST QUESTION I EVER WAS ASKED

One of my very early patrons (in the days when another patient was as welcome as the cry "A sail!" to shipwrecked mariners) was the family of Mr. Y. There were several sons. One of them was a passionate young man who indulged, from time to time, in a wild spree. In due time, he married a fine young woman. His means were limited (he was only a clerk); yet he persisted in his earlier habits, from time to time, freely spending money, in his dissipations, that was needed for the household. When he sobered up, he almost invariably appeared, the picture of despair, in my office. His one fear was that he had contracted syphilis and might communicate it to his wife, to whom, in spite of his unfaithfulness, he was most deeply attached. He threatened again and again to commit suicide and seemed so much in earnest that I felt it my duty to warn his wife to take possession of his pistol and knife, as well as any poison he might have obtained. It was hardly needful for me to lecture him. He saved me all that trouble: No one could blame, warn, entreat, or caution him more seriously--or more fiercely--than he did himself.

He lost one position after another and was unable to support his wife and child, scarcely supporting himself with the necessities of life. Finally, her father practically compelled her to leave him and return to her parental home. Mr. Y drifted about the country, for a while, till one day the news came that, in despair, he had at last carried out his threat and hanged himself. His body was brought home, and I had the unwelcome, sad duty of idtentifying it.

A year or so later, his widow called to see me. In the course of the conversation, she asked me the hardest question I ever have had propounded to me. Suddenly, she looked me straight in the eye and said, "Dr. Keen, do you think George went to heaven?" I was startled, dumb-founded, speechless. Happily for me, she went on to answer the question for me. After a pause, during which one could have heard a pin drop, she said, "Dr. Keen, I loved George devotedly. I knew of his bad habits, his intoxication, his remorse, and even of his unfaithfulness to me. I'll tell you how it seems to me. If I, with my little heart, could forgive him again and again, I think that God, with His great heart, could also forgive him."

Reason as we may, theologically, I believe she was right.

But what a vast depth of a woman's love is revealed, by that question and that answer! Only divine love surpasses it.

MY DEBT TO FLORENCE AND DORA, IN THE "DREADFUL" SUMMER OF 1910

(I feel such admiration and gratitude for and to Florence and Dora, for their splendid conduct in the summer of 1910, that I want especially to record it here.)

On July 2nd, 1910, Florence and I sailed for Glasgow. Dora had gone to Switzerland, a little earlier, to climb in the Alps. I took my auto and my chauffeur with me, and it was arranged that Florence would stay with me till the end of August, when she wished to return, via Montreal, to attend the conservation congress in St. Paul; and that Dora would join me, a few days before Florence sailed, and continue with me till I sailed home from Bremen, on October 18th. Our more complete itinerary included a visit to Edinburgh, where we were to stay with Dr. George A. Gibson; then a visit with Dr. P. H. MacLaren, in the Highlands, followed by a leisurely motor trip down to London. After a visit with Herbert and Hattie, we then had planned a trip through Somersetshire in search of relics of my mother's family, the Budds. After that, on to Penzance and Land's End; then Wales, Holland, and Germany, where I wanted to visit Göttingen, Jena, Halle, and Leipzig (which universities I had never seen), reaching Berlin by the first of October, in advance of the celebration (October 12th to 15th) of the centenary of the founding of the University of Berlin, to which celebration I was the American Philosophical Society delegate.

Prior to the trip, I attended the commencement at Brown (and the meeting of the corporation) and then, with Florence, went to Weekapaug to visit Margaret's camp. I had intended to stay there till Florence and I sailed, in July, with the auto. But early in June, I began to suffer from diarrhoea, without any apparent cause. It did not yield to the usual remedies. I had no pain and did not feel sick; I had my usual appetite and had no rise of temperature. But the diarrhoea persisted, especially at night.

I left Weekapaug and consulted Fitz, in Boston, and later, just before we sailed, Janeway, in New York. Neither of them (naturally enough) made any physical examination, but both prescribed medicines, which I took, but without benefit. On the ship, Dr. Collins, of Providence, was my roommate, but he could throw no light on my continuing trouble.

In Edinburgh, I asked Dr. Gibson to make a physical examination. He

188

discovered a tumor in the lower left abdomen, or upper pelvis. I gave up our planned visit to Dr. MacLaren and, by Dr. Gibson's advice, motored directly to London, where I consulted Dr. W. Hale White, to whom Dr. Gibson had written. He too discovered the obscure tumor and said frankly that, at my age (74½), such a tumor might be very serious, adding that he would like to have a surgeon in consultation and a sigmoidoscope examination, under ether, if necessary. Of course, I consented at once, and a Mr. Mummery was called in. The examination was made on the next day, at a nursing home (and without ether, as the pain was bearable). They both declared to me that they had discovered nothing wrong. Dr. White then left the room to tell Florence, while Mr. Mummery continued the examination with the sigmoidoscope, in which Dr. White again took part, when he returned to the room. They made no further comment or explanation to me, but I learned later that after the conclusion of Mr. Mummery's examination, they told Florence that I had an inoperable cancer of the bowel.

Naturally, the first question she asked was whether or not her father should be told the truth. They advised against undeceiving me, for to tell me then would spoil my whole summer (it was early August by then) and cause me either to give up my Berlin trip and go home, or to lose all heart in the celebration in Berlin. And even if I had wished to go home at once, it would have been difficult, if not impossible, to get berths, as the steamers were all full. Moreover, I would, in time, spontaneously and inevitably discover the truth.

All of this rather long story I have told in order to explain the splendid self-effacement of my two noble daughters. When put to such a critical test, they were not found wanting, but proved themselves pure

189

gold through and through.

But Florence and Dr. White, at her suggestion, wrote to Dr. William
J. Mayo (without a word to me), explaining the exact facts as they understood them. Florence also wrote fully to Dora and the two at home. Dr.
White and Mr. Mummery were kindness itself, and I appreciated their good
intentions. But as a surgeon, I feel that no man, in the presence of such
an obscure tumor (and by only a sigmoidoscopic and a digital examination),
can--or ought to--say positively that a case is inoperable. There is only
one way, an abdominal section, to reach a positive and correct opinion, as
was later proved. Any surgeon, no matter how skillful or experienced, can
easily make a mistake in diagnosis, in such an obscure case, but to avoid
a mistake in treatment, it is absolutely necessary to open the abdomen.

Florence and I left London and, as we had planned, motored down to
Penzance, where Dora joined us. Shortly afterwards, Florence left for St.
Paul, and Dora and I continued our tour, including the celebration in Ber-
lin, and sailed for home, on schedule.

All through this period, for nearly two months, my two dear girls
never once, by word or deed, by silence or by unusual sympathy, by a tear,
or even a sad face, betrayed that they were conscious of the fact that I
was fatally ill and should be spared to them probably only for a few
months. I went along as gay as a bird, free from pain and anxiety, sup-
posing that the obscure tumor had disappeared as a result of the free pur-
gation I had had, and that, in fact, the supposed "tumor" had been only an
accumulation of feces. How their hearts must have ached, and how constantly the joyous face was a mask hiding an anxious heart! Never can I be
grateful enough to them, or too appreciative of their self-effacement. I

often think, however, of their lonely hours of grief. "It was a hideous nightmare. Let us forget all about it," said Florence, a few days ago.

To finish the story, I add a few words. At the beginning of October, von Eiselsberg, of Vienna (who, by good fortune, was in Berlin), examined me, as a result of a secret conversation with Dora. Even up to the point of this examination, I did not suspect the truth. He found the same tumor as the others and said, frankly but cautiously, that "at your age, one must be suspicious as to its character." With this I entirely agreed and was quite convinced that 95% of the chances were that it was cancer.

What, then, was my decision, as a surgeon and as a man? Within an hour after von Eiselsberg had left me, I was writing to Mayo, asking for an exploratory operation, as soon as I possibly could get to Rochester. I reached home on October 25th, made some changes in my will, and set my house in order, in all earthly matters, and, I confess, with a coolness and absence of fear or distress which surprised even me. Never did I feel so completely as then that God was my support--and was so very near to me. I felt that I was, in truth, walking in the valley of the shadow of death, but I feared no evil.

Before the operation, I told Mayo that I had only two things to say: first, that when he opened my abdomen, he had carte blanche to do any- and everything that he thought needful; and second, that unless the removal of the tumor involved a risk that no prudent surgeon would take, that tumor was to be *removed*. If the possibility of removal was in doubt, I wanted him to make the attempt, for I would far rather die from the operation than to die after months of suffering, a burden to myself and my children.

With Florence and Dora, I left for Rochester on November 5th, arrived on the 7th, and was operated on two days later. The tumor proved to be caused by a diverticulitis and was removed. When I awoke from the blessed sleep of ether, my dear Corinne was beside me (and Maragaret was in Rochester, also). They could not stay away, and rightly. They too had shown the same self-control as Florence and Dora, for they also had believed, during the week I was at home before the operation, that I was fatally ill, and yet never once flinched, or by their anxious sympathy tended to unnerve me. What a proud and happy father I am to have four such splendid daughters!

After three days of bearable, though disagreeable, pain, I was free from any further pain; was sitting up, out of bed, in twelve days; left the hospital in three weeks; and have been entirely well ever since. As the tumor was not malignant, there is no fear of its return. The rarity of such cases is shown by the fact that mine was only the 16th case that the Mayos had ever operated on.

We are all most grateful to our heavenly Father and sing a thankful Te Deum.

MY SEVENTY-FIFTH BIRTHDAY

On January 19th, 1912, I attained my 75th birthday. On the 18th, I had had to go to New York, where I spent the night, leaving at noon for my return, and reaching the house at about 2:30. As soon as I came in, the girls said I "must go upstairs and spruce up a bit, for you know that at three, the whole family, including all the grandchildren, are coming in to greet you." I got downstairs at just about three.

Soon, to my surprise, not only the whole family but also many others began to assemble. There were flowers on all sides, in the parlor and the library, and there were many presents, not only from family but also from friends. Before long, there were, I suppose,   hundred who had come to greet me. I learned later that Florence had sent out cards to a number of friends, including the Philadelphia members of the American Philosophical Society and members of the Franklin Inn Club, inviting them to a surprise party, from 3 to 6, on my birthday.

Prof. and Mrs. Newbold sent a "debutant" bouquet, with long ribbons, which I carried all the afternoon. We had scarcely enough vases (gathered from all over the house) to hold the cut flowers, to say nothing of the baskets upon baskets, all of which made the house into a veritable conservatory. And the greetings were all so cordial and sincere.

To say that I prized and enjoyed such a friendly tribute is saying little. It touched my heart and made me feel how far more generous and kind my friends were than ever I had deserved.

At 4:30, Mr. Rosengarten read a round robin, hastily got up by the members of the American Philosophical Society, congratulating me upon my birthday and inviting me to sit for my portrait for the society. I accepted, in a very informal speech (for I could hardly express myself), later sending a more formal written acceptance. Robert Vonnoh was selected by the committee to paint the portrait, and with the approval of the committee, he selected my Saint Andrews robe as the costume. There was a certain propriety in this choice: I was to be seated in Franklin's chair (the president's chair at the society's meetings), with a bust of Franklin (the one in New York's Metropolitan Museum) behind me, and Franklin received his first honorary degree from Saint Andrews (in recognition of his

distinguished service to science. Yet its brilliant scarlet made me almost self-conscious to wear it. (The LL.D., *causâ honoris*, was awarded
me by Saint Andrews, in September, 1911, when they were celebrating the
500th anniversary of the founding of the university.)

It is a wonderful portrait, and Mr. Vonnoh considered it his very
best work. It was presented to the American Philosophical Society, at the
general meeting, in April, 1913.

One underlying note of the whole celebration for me, however (and a
diapason of sorrow), is the deep regret that my dear wife had not lived to
see that happy day.

A SOLDIER'S ALTERNATIVE

On May 27th, 1915, I went to Allentown to give an address at the conferring of diplomas on a class of nurses at the Allentown Hospital. Seeing
in the newspaper the notice that I was to be there, one of my old patients
(whose name I neglected to get, unfortunately) hunted up Dr. Schaeffer to
learn where and when he could see me.

When we reached the hospital, at about 4 o'clock, I encountered a man
who was pretty nearly my own age, but looking hale and hardy, who reminded
me that he had been a patient in the Christian Street Hospital (where Drs.
Mitchell and Morehouse, and I, had established a hospital for diseases of
the nerves). When he had recovered, he told me (for I had quite forgotten
the incident, very naturally), he was placed on duty as an orderly in the
ward. Among our patients were a number of epileptics, and it was no uncommon thing to have as many as 200 fits in a night. He stood it for a few
days but then asked to be returned to the front because he couldn't stand

194

the fits. He preferred to face the bullets of the enemy, rather than the contortions of our unfortunate patients.

MY LITTLE ITALIAN SPEECH AND HOW IT GREW

While spending the winter of 1907-8 in Italy, we took Italian lessons, in Florence and Rome. Persuaded that the ability to speak a language is attained only by practice from the very start (just as a child learns to walk by reason of--and in spite of--its many falls), I began to speak, or rather, try to speak, Italian when I attended the Italian Surgical Society, even after I had had only a few lessons, and I had, of course, many grammatical and verbal stumbles and falls.

After one of the meetings, I was kindly invited to luncheon by Prof. Durante, its president. His two daughters were the only ladies present. After the luncheon, both of them joined the gentlemen in the drawing room, where cigars and cigarettes were served along with the coffee. I stumbled along in Italian as best I could, with one of the daughters kindly aiding my unsteady steps with gladly welcomed suggestions, and without betraying the least amusement at my many mistakes. Finally, I wholly upset her gravity, and the humor of my mistake (which I immediately recognized and instantly corrected) made me join in her hearty laughter, which was not at me but with me.

I wanted to ask her if she smoked, but instead of using the verb *fumare* ("to smoke"), which is linked with the noun *fumo* ("smoke"), I coined the verb *fuocare* (which doesn't exist) from the noun *fuoco* ("fire") for my inquiry. That blunder made us at once the best of friends.

While in Rome, Dora, Florence, and I had three teachers who gave us each a daily lesson. We changed around each day but with each teacher had a continuous course. This had some advantages, as one teacher would insist more on grammar, another on pronunciation, and the third on style, while the three, with slightly different voices, accustomed our ears to the subtle variations of spoken Italian. We wrote exercises daily and, like schoolchildren, had them returned to us after correction by the teacher, usually in red ink. But how bloody some of mine were! One day, I must have reached the acme of inaccuracy: My teacher handed my exercise back to me and said, "Really, Dr. Keen, this is so bad that you must write it over again," which I did, with great meekness and some success.

When I described my misfortune to Miss Pierce and Miss Lawrence, they were not a little amused by my seeming apprehension that if I again had such a bad exercise, I was afraid that my teacher would keep me in.

While I was one of the managers of the American Baptist Publication Society, I became familiar with the self-sacrificing and successful work of the Italian Mission Church, in Rome, and I frequently attended service there on Sunday morning. One morning, fortunately after I had been studying Italian daily for over two months, the minister asked me to say a few words of encouragement to the little congregation, adding that he would be glad to act as interpreter. I had the hardihood (I can call it by no milder name) to say that I would like to attempt to speak in Italian, for I was sure that I would never have a more sympathetic or forgiving audience than this one, and that if I broke down, he could come to the rescue. This seemed to please him. I spoke for perhaps three or four minutes, telling them in the simplest (and, I suspect, the boldest) Italian how and what I had known of their early trials, congratulating them on their success, and conveying to them the best wishes of their American friends for a rich blessing from Heaven. I was very sure that my intentions were better than my Italian, but they understood me, at least, and I did not break down.

On returning to the hotel, I said not a word to Florence or Dora (who had not gone with me). Three or four days later, Florence was a patient of Dr. Webb, the American dentist, who congratulated her on the very successful speech her father had made, in Italian, at the Baptist church on Sunday. To this she naively replied, "Oh no! He didn't make any such speech. He couldn't." And so was the Scripture fulfilled that a "prophet is not without honor, save . . . within his own house."

But the echoes of that squib of a speech were most remarkable. Not long afterwards, Miss Lily Frishmuth (our opposite neighbor in Philadelphia) wrote to Florence from Switzerland and asked her to congratulate me on my success in giving a lecture in Italian. A month or so later, Mr. Penniman wrote to me from Philadelphia and said that it was currently reported that I was giving lectures in Italian. And at the June meeting of the board of fellows of Brown, in 1911, Col. Robert Goddard alluded to those lectures, describing me as an accomplished Italian scholar. "How great a fire a little matter kindleth!"

I have told my friends, when the subject has arisen, that if they were to hear that I had been offered the chair of Italian language and literature at the University of Rome, they were authorized to say that I had declined it.

Since the above was dictated, I have heard two further exaggerations which much amused us.

Miss Mollie Coles followed me, in my Italian lessons with Signora X, and reported that the signora declared that after my hour was over, she was quite exhausted.

The second was still worse. The report ran that, after she had received Florence, Dora, and me, during which we had conversed with her for a few minutes (especially about her children), Queen Helena said she had never met Americans who spoke such excellent Italian.

Such exaggeration reminds me of a report I had from Dr. George W. Spencer, one time. In Burma, in December of 1901, I broke my left collarbone by a fall from my horse. (I rolled downhill until stopped by a tree, and as I was rolling over and over, I bethought myself of the learned butler who, as he was falling downstairs, replied to his master's inquiry as to what was going on, "'Tis I, sir, rolling rapidly.") I was able to discard my bandages and splint only upon leaving Bombay. Twelve days later, in Cairo, I operated on Miss Margaretta Taylor for appendicitis. Someone telegraphed the news to America and reported that I had operated with one arm in a sling. And Spencer told me that he saw the operation announced in an Indianapolis paper, including the news that I had operated with *both* arms in slings.

YELLOW JOURNALISM

One Wednesday evening, I read a paper on the "Massage of the Heart," in which I had collected all of the then-reported cases and added two new ones, one of my own (fatal), and one of Dr. Igelsrud (successful), of Tromsö, Norway.

The next morning, I was called up on the telephone by the editorial office of the *New York Evening Journal*, one of Hearst's papers. The speaker said that they had understood that I had made a great discovery and had "brought the dead back to life," and that they wanted the full particulars for their paper. I replied that they were quite right, except that I had made no great discovery and had not brought the dead back to life, for my patient had not recovered.

Moreover, I added that I could not give them any information whatever, as I was averse to the publication of professional cases in lay journals, and that when my paper was published, it would then be public property and they could get the exact facts and make any comments they saw fit. I also requested that nothing should be published about the case.

About an hour or so later, the editorial office of the same paper called me again and said that they had not quite understood whether my patient had died or recovered. I replied that he had died two years ago and was still dead.

In that very afternoon's *Journal*, in spite of my twice having stated that the patient had not recovered, they published about a third of a column (with display headlines) as to Dr. Keen's wonderful discovery and his bringing back to life a man who had died. Worst of all, they proceeded to report an "interview" with this man (who they *knew* had been dead for two years) in which he described his sensations, etc.

I was mad all over at such obviously conscious mendacity and wrote to Mr. Hearst himself a letter as indignant as I could make it, including the comment that he could hardly have learned to lie so outrageously while a student at Harvard. The managing editor replied, most blandly, that Mr. Hearst was attending to his congressional duties in Washington (which I believed was an additional lie); that they were extremely sorry to have mis-stated the facts; and that their columns were open to any communication I might wish to make. I replied that I had never even bought a copy of a Hearst paper, much less printed anything in one, and that I declined to do so now.

In 1907 or 1908, while in Rome, I saw that Hearst, in order to influence the New York election, had written (on a Tuesday) a long telegram to the *Times*, accusing his political opponent of lying. (I forget who the opponent was, but it can be found in my collection of newspaper clippings in my office desk.) The telegram was timed so that it could be re-telegraphed to New York without the possibility of a reply in the New York papers before the election. I could not resist the temptation: I wrote to the *Times* and described Hearst's lying, in my own case, and they published my letter.

Another good illustration of the persistence of a newspaper in spreading false news comes from the following incident.

In May of 1912, while I was abed with an injured knee, Dora was climbing Mt. Blackburn, in Alaska, and at about 8 o'clock, one evening, a reporter of the *Philadelphia Press* called to see me. I sent word that I was in bed for an injury and asked to be excused. He sent up word that he wanted to talk with me about a dispatch they had just received stating that two men (fellow climbers) had left Dora and returned to Kennecott, reporting that my daughter was marooned on Mt. Blackburn and in danger of starvation. I had him come up at once, of course. The dispatch proved to be in inquiry from the Western Press Association, in Seattle, asking if this was true. I told him that it evidently was false, for I had had a letter from Dora, only two days before (written just as she was starting for the climb), in which she stated that she was taking five weeks' provisions, so that the date when the men "left" Dora was only two weeks from the time she had started; that if these two men could get back, so could she, thus she could not be "marooned;" and that if the Seattle people wanted to ascertain the facts as to what was going on in Alaska, the proper place to inquire was Kennecott, and not Philadelphia. Therefore, I especially requested that he *not* publish the dispatch, which was evidently false, and he promised to suppress it.

The next morning, there was the printed dispatch in full, without a word of my explanation, and from all sides I began to have inquiries and letters of sympathy and alarm.

I wrote the editor, complaining of the breach of faith, and he replied that a reporter had no authority to suppress dispatches, and that these decisions rested with his superiors. He made no excuse for printing false news, nor any apology for the anxiety and pain which such an occurrence could not but give me.

TRANS-CONTINENTAL TELEPHONING

About the first of February, 1915, I was requested by Mr. Crosman, one of the officers of the Bell Telephone Company here, to give him the name of the most prominent surgeon in San Francisco. His object was to arrange that that surgeon should be present at the Bell Telephone headquarters in San Francisco, on a certain day and hour, in order that he and I might telephone to each other entirely across the continent, a distance of 3400 miles.

Accordingly, I gave the name of Dr. Thomas W. Huntington, and Mr.

201

Crosman made an appointment with him for the day and hour. On February 11th, I went to the Bell Telephone headquarters, at 12th and Arch Streets, and at 5 o'clock found probably two hundred gentlemen gathered for the inauguration of this wonderful feat. It was very dramatically staged. We were all seated on rows of chairs. To each chair was attached, by a cord, a little, watch-size telephone receiver. In front of us, on a platform, were Mayor Blankenburg, Mr. Stotesbury, ex-Governor Stuart, John Wanamaker, and three or four other prominent citizens and officials. In front of the mayor was a small replica of the Liberty Bell (perhaps six or eight inches high), with a small hammer lying beside it. When we were notified that everything was ready, complete silence reigned in the room, and every man held his little receiver to his ear. The mayor struck the little bell three times with his hammer. This sound was carried by telephone to the custodian of the Liberty Bell in Independence Hall. He, in turn, struck *his* bell three moderate blows with three separate wooden hammers, which I presume were to serve as souvenirs.

In front of the Liberty Bell was a large receiver, very much like a megaphone. This carried the sound to a telephone, which transmitted it to San Francisco. The moment it was heard there, a bugler began "The Star-Spangled Banner." All of us stood up, on the instant, until he had finished the whole verse, which was heard as clearly as if it had been only a block away, and then all of us burst into a wild cheer.

Following this, the mayor and several other gentlemen at the table talked over the wire to corresponding officials and citizens with ease.

After these official conversations were finished, I talked with Dr. Huntington for perhaps three or four minutes and heard him with the same ease as with an ordinary city telephone, and all the other gentlemen who were present (and who, I presume, had made similar appointments with other friends in San Francisco) took part in similar conversations.

One other item should be recalled. In 1876, Mr. Alexander Graham Bell called his assistant, Mr. Watson by name, I think, for the first time over a wire. This assistant was in the same building, in a room below that occupied by Mr. Bell. When Mr. Bell called, "Mr. Watson, come here. I want to see you," his assistant rushed in, in a minute, with his eyes almost starting out of his head, and said, "I heard every word you said, as distinctly as if we were talking in the same room."

A few days before our long-distance conversation in Philadelphia, Mr. Watson (in Francisco) was again called by Mr. Bell (in New York or Washington, I am not quite sure which), and the two conversed with greater ease and efficiency than they had thirty-nine years before. Mr. Bell even used the first original receiver that he had used in 1876 and found it still available for conversation.

ORATORS I HAVE HEARD

I have been more fortunate, perhaps, than most in having heard a considerable number of distinguished orators, both American and foreign. Unfortunately, I never heard Webster or Clay; nor Henry Ward Beecher, either in the pulpit or on the platform. Wendell Phillips and George William Curtis were the earliest two I can remember. I never heard Phillips in one of his fiery philippics against slavery, but only in his lectures on Toussaint L'Ouverture and "The Lost Art." Hence, I can judge only his powers of description, his broad knowledge, and his powerful delineation of character.

Curtis had the most charming, mellifluous voice I have ever heard. I first saw him when I was an undergraduate at Brown, when we initiated him as a brother in our chapter of Alpha Delta Phi. He gave the oration before the Phi Beta Kappa (or it may have been the alumni), at Commencement, on "The Scholar in Politics." It was the most charming oration I ever heard. Never shall I forget with what soul-stirring effect he quoted Mrs. Hemans's "New England Hymn." We were almost lifted from the pews, in the old First Baptist meeting house, which was dedicated in 1770 (as the cornerstone records) "for the public worship of Almighty God and to hold Commencement in." The night before, we had initiated him, and he had spoken to us as brothers. With what pride we shook his hand and claimed him as our own.

The story by which he will always be known among Brunonians is his celebrated toast at one Commencement dinner. We always wanted him at these dinners and several times prevailed upon him to preside, for he was a past master in the difficult art of introducing the various speakers, gracefully and with an apt quotation or reference for each. His memorable toast was, "The Brown-bred boys make the best-bred men."

I once heard Edward Everett deliver his celebrated address on Washington, which was prepared to aid in the founding of Washington University in St. Louis. He delivered this address, it was said, two or three hundred times, all over the United States. It was most carefully prepared and as carefully memorized, but after he had delivered it over a hundred times, so the story runs, his memory failed him, and he had to re-memorize it. One sentence, and one gesture, I remember. This sentence described the Mississippi River, beginning with its origin at Lake Itasca, in Minnesota, following it downstream, receiving its several tributaries, and debouching, finally, into the Gulf of Mexico. The sentence was almost as long as the river, very possibly intentionally so. If I remember rightly, it covered two or three printed pages and contained over three hundred words, before the final period at last gave us breath. His gesture was an elevated and long, trembling hand, which he shook as if from intense emotion, but it was too frequently repeated and at last became wearisome. Probably this repetition and his too-florid style, as contrasted with Lincoln's immortal speech at Gettysburg, were responsible for the reduced effect. I write this with some reserve, however, since I have never read Everett's speech after first reading it in the papers, while I have often read Lincoln's address.

While in college, I heard Thackeray deliver his lectures on "The Four Georges." The one thing I remember of this series was his gradual disclosure of the mean figure of the real George IV, as he divested him of one garment after another, till he stood before us a poor manikin.

Charles Kingsley I heard, and my impression is that his lectures were, on the whole, a failure. If this impression is accurate, I do not wonder at it, for I have a very clear recollection of his tall, gawky figure standing up a few paces from the desk on the platform, striding up to a nearby table, every few moments, taking a sip of water, and then striding back again. I wondered why he didn't stay at the desk.

I had the great pleasure of hearing Tyndall's course of scientific lectures, and they were a treat. But while his distinguished reputation made them a treat, I do not think that he was the equal of Prof. George F. Barker, as a popular lecturer on any scientific subject. Barker's descriptions were models of lucidity and his experiments always striking and (what is often lacking in scientific lectures) brilliantly successful.

For side-splitting laughter and charming literary excellence, let me commend the joint readings of George W. Cable and Mark Twain. Both read from their own works. Cable not only read most charmingly, but also interspersed his reading with the most melodious singing of old Creole songs. I had read, and merely smiled at, some of the works of Twain, but when *he* read them, with his drawl and his expressive face, I nearly "burst the buttons off my vest and fell in a fit." At the end of the evening, I was actually exhausted, tired, and sore from the uproarious and continuous laughter. My facial muscles scarcely regained their normal condition until 24 hours had passed.

In foreign politics, I have been most fortunate, for I have heard Virchow and Bismarck, in addition to Gladstone, Disraeli, and Roseberry.

In 1865-6, while in Virchow's laboratory (and he was a leader among the liberals, as well as in science), I asked him if he could provide me with a ticket to the Prussian Landtag (there was no Reichstag, as yet), when there was to be an interesting debate. He very kindly gave me one for a session when he and Bismarck were to speak. Bismarck was just then becoming (one might even say had become) the leading figure in Prussia. The Austro-Prussian War (1866) made him the foremost statesman in Prussia, just as the Franco-Prussian War (1870) was to make him the foremost states- man of, not only Germany but, all Europe.

Virchow, slight of figure and under, rather than over, medium height, was a very quiet, but usually convincing, speaker. He spoke politically in the parliament much as he spoke to us students on science. Bismarck, by contrast, was large and burly, as became the "man of blood and iron," and was most emphatic. As I remember the debate between them (and certainly as history has recorded), Bismarck won the battle over the more logical--but perhaps more legalistic--and progressive Virchow, though whether by force of character, manner, and circumstances or not, I do not remember.

In the spring of 1866, on my way home, after nearly two years of study in Europe, I stopped in London. Mr. Charles Francis Adams, our minister (it was before we had any ambassador), gave me a ticket to the House of Commons. The evening was a memorable one, for Mr. Gladstone was to move the second reading of his Reform Bill of 1866. (I have often wondered at my good fortune, but I suppose it was because there were few Americans in Europe so soon after the close of the Civil War.) Lord Morley, in his *Life of Gladstone*, says that this speech was one of his best efforts. Certain it was that, with his flashing eyes, his earnest manner, and his wonderful voice, he held us all spellbound to the very end. Meantime, "Dizzy" had sat, or one might almost say slouched, in his seat on the front Opposition bench, with his arms crossed and his top hat drawn down over his forehead. He scarcely moved and did not make a note. But the moment that Gladstone had finished, Disraeli's hat was off, and he was on his feet and speaking. He dealt in short, pithy sentences which seemed like thrusts of a stiletto. His speech, as I remember it, was short, perhaps not over 15 or 20 minutes, but it was brilliant.

The general impression upon my mind, very possibly largely tinged with my later knowledge of their careers, was that Gladstone was a man convinced of the righteousness of his cause, dead in earnest, and determined that he could, and would, convince his listeners. Disraeli was an opportunist and a political gambler, adroit, resourceful, and often successful. His ability as a phrase-maker is best illustrated, perhaps, by his allusion to Gladstone as a "sophisticated rhetorician, intoxicated by the exuberance of his own verbosity." His often splendid retorts included this reply to an opponent in the House of Commons who had twitted him with being a Jew (in itself a wonderful testimony to his ambition, pertinacity, and ability, that he should be premier of England). In his loftiest tone, he said, "When, sir, your ancestors were barbarians, *mine* were priests in the temple of the everliving God." Nothing could be finer than that.

Last summer (1911), I heard Lord Roseberry for the first time, and with the greatest delight. His rectoral address at Saint Andrews was a splendid effort, and his lighter, after-dinner speeches were perfectly charming specimens of lambent wit suited to their several occasions.

Of medical speakers, there are few who are eminent. I do not think I can well estimate French or German speakers, as a foreigner scarcely appreciates the full flavor of what is said. As a clinical teacher and speaker, Nélaton was, by far, the best I ever heard in France, and Langenbeck in Germany.

Two among the British and two Americans far excel the others I have heard. Sir James Paget, in his address as president of the International Medical Congress, in London (1881), was perfectly charming. At present, Mr. Moynihan, of Leeds, has no peer in a surgical debate, either in matter or style or manner.

In America, J. M. Da Costa was the easiest, clearest, most charming and scholarly speaker, both as a clinical teacher and in occasional addresses. Dr. J. Chalmers Da Costa and Dr. George E. de Schweinitz I would place in the front rank among living Americans.

I have heard only three from the pulpit whom I would place in the very front rank, Edwards A. Park, Phillips Brooks, and Francis Wayland (with Theodore Cuyler right behind). Never can I forget a sermon at a Commencement at Brown which Dr. Park delivered before the Missionary Society. His text was, "I shall be satisfied when I awake in Thy likeness," and though the substance of the sermon is gone from memory, the effect, the uplifting effect, can never pass away.

Phillips Brooks was the most rapid speaker I ever heard and was the despair of all but the most rapid reporters. His sermons were read, as well as heard, a severe test of their merit. They are full of meat. But as a speaker, he was an educational and uplifting force by the substance of his sermons, rather than by his manner. He was no orator. He spoke too fast to be impressive. The minds of his hearers were, all the while, on tension.

(He was a warm friend of Dr. George Dana Boardman and preached in our pulpit at Broad and Arch Streets more than once. I always remember his personal kindness to me, in August of 1886, when I was in the Massachusetts General Hospital with a broken collarbone. In spite of the weather, with temperatures in the 90s, on hearing that I was there, he came to see me, and most cordially. So, too, did dear Professor Bigelow. They both heartened me not a little.)

Dr. Wayland I was so fortunate as to hear every Sunday, after he had retired from the presidency of the university and was filling in the long vacancy between the death of Rev. Dr. Grainger and the coming of Rev. Dr.

S. L. Caldwell to the old First Baptist Church, in Providence, whose corporate name was (and still is) the Baptist Charitable Society.

Dr. Wayland was no orator, in the sense of rhetorical flights of description or imagination, but he was eminently a logician, one who, having set forth the facts, drove them home and compelled his hearers to apply them to their own lives and consciences. It was a treat to hear him.

On one memorable occasion, also, I heard him on the platform. "Bully" Brooks, as one of the congressmen from South Carolina came to be called, had struck down Senator Charles Sumner, on the floor of the Senate, and nearly killed him. The attack grew out of one of the many ante-bellum debates on slavery. Instantly, all over the North, indignation meetings were held and protests made against this invasion of the right of free speech, especially in Congress. At the meeting in Providence, the earlier speakers had appealed to the passions of the audience and wrought them up to fever heat. Then, the big, burly figure of ex-president Wayland, easily the first citizen of all Rhode Island, was seen to mount the platform and was received with tumultuous applause. When, at last, this had subsided, Dr. Wayland began (as usual, in a very quiet manner) to set forth the logical results of such attacks, if they were allowed to be repeated. His audience was, with difficulty, held in leash, but at the last, he raised himself to his full height and in a slow and most impressive and earnest manner said, "Fellow citizens, I was born a free man, and, so help me God, I never will be made a slave." Then the waters of enthusiasm broke all bounds. Every one shouted himself hoarse, hats and caps filled the air, and for a long time, nothing was to be heard but the repeated cheers of approval. The words were simple, but the sentiment was

210

one that appealed to every man present. Moreover, they had been spoken by Dr. Wayland, the calm, cool reasoner, who was not given to appealing to passion, but when he did, as in this sentence on this occasion, his appeal went to the deepest depths of every man's heart and soul. It was the finest effect I have ever seen or heard, similar, it has always seemed to me, to that splendid appeal of Wendell Phillips to those "pictured lips," on the walls of Faneuil Hall.

Two of my pastors at the old First Baptist Church, Drs. George Dana Boardman and George H. Harris, have also been notable preachers. Dr. Boardman was the greater master of language, of imagery, of simile--in a word, the greater orator. He was simple of taste and almost timid in physical matters, but of the stuff martyrs are made, in spiritual affairs.

Dr. Ferris is rather awkward of gesture and emphasizes his sentences too much by postures that are sometimes uncouth (sometimes bordering on contortions), but his views are large and wide, his convictions sincere, his knowledge extensive, and his diction admirable. He is one of the best preachers I have ever heard. He makes one think. He wears well, Sunday after Sunday.

PRESIDENTS I HAVE KNOWN

I saw President Lincoln only once, when George Porter and I, while students of medicine, rode in the procession which escorted him from the old Pennsylvania Railroad station, in Kensington, to the State House. In the carriage with him was John Hay, his assistant private secretary (and our old college friend).

I met President Grant only once, at one of the Saturday-night receptions at the home of Mr. A. J. Drexel, and barely exchanged greetings.

President Cleveland and his charming wife I knew well, as a result of our operations upon him (described in the recollection that follows).

President McKinley I also knew well. Mrs. McKinley had been a patient of Weir Mitchell's, while her husband was a representative, and I had done a minor operation upon her, for Dr. Mitchell. At that time, and during a later visit to Washington, with my dear wife, I saw the president frequently and formed a high opinion of his ability and personality.

The summer of the Spanish-American War (1898) I spent in Europe, sailing for home from Antwerp in the autumn. The very day I left Antwerp, Dr. George W. Spencer, my assistant, received a long telegram from President McKinley, naming me to a commission to investigate the alleged misconduct of the war, especially as to unsatisfactory food, unnecessary mortality, and general inefficiency. Not knowing what to do, Dr. Spencer took the dispatch to my brother Charles, and together they went to the Red Star Line office to see if it would be possible to reach me, but I was a few hours out to sea, fortunately. Had I received the dispatch, I should have been in a serious quandry. On the one hand, I could not keep the president of the United States waiting, for ten days, until I reached New York; on the other, I knew nothing of the reasons for the appointment of the commission, of its scope or personnel, or of the time that probably would be required for the investigation, and so forth.

My first knowledge of the matter came on landing at the dock. I bought all the New York and Philadelphia papers and, on the train to Philadelphia, read everything about the commission, to post myself as much as possible. On reaching home, I talked with Charles, and at 7 o'clock, I called up the president's secretary to say that I was obliged to decline

212

on account of other engagements. At 9, I was asked by him to come to

Washington for a conference with the president. I went early the next

morning and spent an hour with President McKinley.

He begged me to accept the appointment. I told him about our church

history (of which not one word had been written), which had to be ready

by December 11th, only two months away. He promised me all the stenogra-

phers and other help I needed. He said that he wanted one medical man on

the commission; a man of good sound judgment, one who would bring in a

verdict absolutely free from bias or prejudice in favor of or against any

person, high or low, who had been guilty of neglect; and a man who would

be governed only by the facts elicited and fearless enough to state his

honest conclusions. He was kind enough to add that, from his previous

knowledge of me, he believed I was the person eminently fitted for this

purpose. I finally agreed to think over the matter, to sleep on it, and

to let him know the next day of my final decision. In the end, I de-

clined the appointment, and I have always been very glad that I did so:

The church history could not have been properly written by anyone else.*

Moreover, the commission had to work for some months and was much abused

for its report. (Had it brought in a different report, it would have

been abused just the same, although by the opposite side.)

---

* The reason no one else could have written this history was that, by vir-
tue of nearly two years' work, I had made myself familiar with the details
of the history. This involved familiarity with many large volumes of minutes, and other church documents, covering 200 years, reading of the lives
of our ministers and some notable members, in addition to the histories of
all the various churches, institutions, and religious movements with which
our church had been in contact, for these two centuries. No one else could
do this, and also write the history, in the remaining two months.

What struck me most was the very evident growth of Mr. McKinley. I had not seen him for several years. I found him a much larger, broader man. Great responsibilities, especially those of the war, had developed his powers, and he was a far stronger man. I respected him most highly and deplored his death.

Several times, I lunched at the White House en famille, with President McKinley, and on one most embarrassing occasion, Florence and Dora were with me. The president sat at the end of the table, and on his right was Mrs. McKinley. I was placed next to her, with another guest, a lady, on my right. In the midst of an interesting conversation, fortunately with my right-hand neighbor, Mrs. McKinley was suddenly seized with an epileptic fit. She did not fall from her chair; nor were her convulsions so general or violent as to require her removal to a lounge or to the floor, and she was in no danger of biting her tongue. She trembled rather violently and convulsively all over. In an instant, the president rose, threw his napkin over her head and face, and drew her body and head tenderly to his breast. He thus supported her, for two or three minutes (which seemed an hour), and when the attack subsided, she was able to keep her erect position without help. Her face was deeply flushed, and she was quite dazed. The president resumed his seat. Meanwhile, as Mrs. McKinley evidently did not need my professional assistance, I tried to continue the conversation with the neighbor on the right. Never did I find it so hard to continue a conversation, without cessation, embarrassment, or seeming to notice what was going on at my left elbow. Florence and Dora also did the same, and the incident was never alluded to.

President McKinley was a beautiful instance of a loyal and devoted husband. Mrs. McKinley's malady was the result of the birth of one of her two children (who did not survive). Never did he miss writing to her at least one letter a day, when they were unavoidably separated. Sometimes he wrote two, and occasionally even three, letters a day. This she told me herself. When one remembers the exigencies of his public life, this is remarkable. While he was a candidate for the first time, his wife had a similar attack, in a large department store in Cleveland. Mark Hanna, the manager of his campaign, was said to have advocated secluding Mrs. McKinley until after the election. "Mark Hanna," Mr. McKinley replied, if to become the president of the United States I must shut up my wife, I will never be president of the United States." A splendid, loyal rebuke.

When in Manila, in October, 1901, we were invited to lunch with Mr. Taft, then the governor-general of the Philippines. It was my first meeting with him, and he impressed me most favorably. I was his most enthusiastic supporter in the 1908 contest for the presidency.

Soon after his inauguration, he consulted me about the health of his daughter Helen, then a student at Bryn Mawr. As she evidently needed orthopedic treatment, I placed her under the care of Dr. J. T. Rugh, who did admirably for her.

Several times since then, in connection with the annual dinners of the American Philosophical Society, with the proposed establishment of a National Seismological Bureau, and with the re-establishment of the army canteen, I have met him, and always with pleasure and heightened esteem.

The most important subject which brought me in touch with him was the International Humane Congress, which met in Washington, in September of 1910. President Taft was the honorary president of the congress. Knowing that the antivivisectionists would endeavor to secure a pronouncement for their cause, I wrote to the president, calling his attention to this and expressing the hope that he would not take such an anti-scientific (and also anti-humane) attitude. He wrote me at once, enclosing a copy of the letter which he had written to Dr. Stillman, president of the American Humane Association. In this letter he stated that if the antivivisectionists were to attempt any such maneuver, he could not countenance it by continuing to act as honorary president. (This letter is in the drawer of my office desk.) Dr. Stillman replied at once, giving a pledge that no discussion of vivisection would be permitted at the congress. Thus, fortunately, I was able to block their game. Dr. Stillman was true to his promise. But in their journals, the antivivisectionists fumed and frothed at being thus muzzled.

One of the finest instances of noble and patriotic altruism I have ever known was when, on two occasions, Mr. Taft was offered the blue ribbon of his profession, a seat on the Supreme Court of the United States, he declined it for the reason that his duty to his wards, the Filipinos, was not yet completed. A man who could do that is made of the finest clay.

And now (October, 1912), the next president will certainly be either Mr. Taft, again, or Gov. Woodrow Wilson. Should either be elected, I should know him well. In the case of the latter, I should again be in close touch with him: Only this last spring, I operated on Mrs. Wilson, and a few years ago, I operated on two of their three daughters. The operation on one of them was *very* dangerous, as the hemorrhage was furious and almost uncontrollable. I feared a recurrence and had Dr. Spencer sit up all night with her, lest it should recur and be quickly fatal, unless

216

skillful help was at hand on the instant. Such an emergency brings the surgeon and the family *very* closely together.

I am sincerely puzzled to know whom to vote for. Mr. Roosevelt has forfeited my confidence by his deceiving the people, by breaking his pledge "under no circumstances" to accept another nomination, and by his wild vagaries as to the recall of judges and of judicial decisions. Governor Wilson I would trust personally, but I do not like the platform and the tendency of his party.

I shall probably vote for Mr. Taft because he has been a very careful and conservative, and yet progressive, president. I think he is entitled to a re-election as an endorsement of his course. He and the Republican Party have undoubtedly learned some wisdom and will be willing to institute the reforms which are greatly needed.

THE OPERATIONS ON PRESIDENT CLEVELAND

About June 16th, 1893, I received a letter from my old friend, Dr. Joseph D. Bryant of New York, saying that he wished to consult me about a very important private matter. As I was going on to the Commencement at Brown, on June 21st, leaving home on the afternoon of the 19th, I wrote him that I would leave early in the afternoon and that we could talk over the matter in entire secrecy on the Fall River boat. Accordingly, he met me on the boat, at about 4 o'clock, and we had the deck to ourselves. He informed me that Mr. Cleveland, who had just been inaugurated for the second time, on March 4th, was suffering from a serious disease of his upper left jaw, that he intended to operate upon it shortly afterwards, and that he wished me to assist him. This I agreed to do, holding myself in readiness for the moment when he should need me.

About ten days later, he wrote me full instructions as to the course to be followed so as to ensure complete secrecy. These I followed to the letter. The political and financial condition of the country made such secrecy an absolute necessity.

The country was passing through a severe financial panic. The Democratic (and not a few in the Republican) Party were thoroughly possessed by the silver craze, and the country was rapidly drifting toward a silver standard. Vice President Adlai Stevenson was known to be an advocate of free silver. Only Grover Cleveland, a sturdy champion of the gold standard, stood between us and wide-spread (one might say almost universal) bankruptcy. He wished to secure the repeal of the Sherman Silver Purchase Act, and it would require all of his energies to bear down on the congress with this issue.

The only persons to whom I confided the facts were my brother Charles and my assistant, Dr. William J. Taylor, in both of whom I could place the most absolute reliance. (Charles, as a broker, was profoundly interested and might be most adversely affected in his finances, should Mr. Cleveland die--or even should a hint of a serious malady become public.)

If it had been suspected that the president was suffering from cancer or a sarcoma (the latter being the probability), the possibility that his life might be shortened, or his considerable influence diminished, would cause the politicians to desert Mr. Cleveland (as the setting sun) and flock to the support of Mr. Stevenson (the rising sun), the Silver Act would never be repealed, and the direst possible consequences to the country would follow. Even to my children I did not disclose my errand, but simply told them that I had been called to New York for an important consultation and operation and might be absent several days. With character-

istic good sense, they did not even ask for further information.

Mr. Cleveland left Washington, openly, on the afternoon of Friday,

June 30th, stating (as he often did) that he was going on a cruise on the

Oneida, the steam yacht of his intimate friend Mr. E. C. Benedict, a New

York banker. He reached the city after dark, repaired to one of the piers

on the East River, and was rowed out to the yacht. With him was the Sec-

retary of War, his friend Daniel Lamont. Before leaving Washington, the

president had issued a call for a special session of Congress, three weeks

later, for the purpose of relieving the financial panic by the expedient

of repealing the Silver Act.

Dr. Bryant and his assistant, Dr. John F. Erdmann, rowed to the

yacht from one or two other piers, and Dr. Edward G. Janeway and Dr. Has-

brouck (a dentist), and I rowed from still other piers, all reaching the

Oneida between 9 and 10 o'clock. A large operating chair, all of the

necessary instruments, anesthetics (nitrous oxide and oxygen), dressings,

and so forth, had already been put aboard.

Mr. Cleveland and I sat on the deck for some time, smoking and chat-

ting. I had never met him before and was greatly interested in and im-

pressed by his personality, especially by his high ideals concerning his

personal duty to his country. As his own administration had followed a

term of Republicans, he was sorely beset by a horde of office-seekers, to

whom he referred in terms of the utmost abhorrence. "They always follow

me," he said, "and even assault me in my dreams." The yacht soon got

under way, and all went to bed.

On Saturday, July 1st, we were cruising slowly eastward, in Long

Island Sound. The weather (as I remember it--I am writing in February, 1912) was bright and the water smooth. Immediately after breakfast, all our surgical preparations were made, in the cabin where the surgeons and Dr. Hasbrouck were assembled. The chief steward was the only other person there. Col. Lamont and Mr. Benedict were on deck.

The best and safest method of anesthesia was a question of the utmost importance. The president was 56 years of age, a very corpulent man, with a very short, thick neck. His skin showed many warts and moles. I do not remember, at this late date, what the reports were as to his heart and kidneys, but I am fairly sure that they were in "good" condition, though it may have been only "fair." He had been through several periods of stress, as an attorney at law, as the mayor of Buffalo and the governor of New York, and, in a prior term, as the president of the United States. Such strains would almost certainly have seriously taxed, and possibly impaired, the condition of these vital organs. Hence, Dr. Bryant had asked Dr. Hasbrouck, the dentist, to be ready to use nitrous oxide. It was soon evident, however, that this could not be administered so as to keep the patient well under its influence, inasmuch as the operation was within the mouth, and, accordingly, chloroform was substituted for the nitrous oxide. This was chosen because we would certainly be obliged to use the Paquelin cautery. (Although we had ether at hand, we did not even try to use it, as I remember, because of the danger of its taking fire.) I am quite clear in my recollection that Dr. Hasbrouck was wrong in describing, in later newspaper interviews, nitrous oxide as the only anesthetic used. On the contrary, it was quickly found to be unsatisfactory and was definitely abandoned.

220

Dr. Erdmann, I think, gave the chloroform. Dr. Janeway carefully

watched the pulse, while Dr. Bryant did the operation, I acting as his

assistant. We used my own silver mouth retractor

to draw back the cheek and expose the jaw. The

entire operation was done within the mouth, with

The cheek retractor bought in Paris from Luer in 1866 by W. W. Keen. By its means the operation was done wholly within the mouth thus avoiding any external scar.

no external incision whatever. The retractor

served admirably and gave a wide and most satisfactory access to the jaw.

The malignancy was situated on the upper left jaw, involving the

alveolar border and extending some distance beyond. Two or three teeth

were removed. Then, with the rongeur forceps, considerable portions of

the upper jaw, on its anterior and palatine surfaces in the roof of the

mouth, were removed, as far as, and somewhat beyond, the visible limits

of the disease. The excision extended nearly to the orbital plate and for

a moderate distance on the palatine surface, though not so far as to reach

the attachment of the soft palate. The antrum was very widely opened, of

course. The hemorrhage was considerable, but not at all alarming. Pres-

sure, and later, an iodoform gauze plug, controlled it. I do not think a

single ligature was used, but in this I may be in error. The raw surface

was then seared by the Paquelin cautery, the wound re-packed, and the op-

eration was ended.

What the relief was to the surgeons no one can ever realize. Not

only was a serious surgical operation completed on the chief magistrate of

the land, but the patient had not collapsed, or even died, under the an-

esthetic (a possibility we had considered).

For the country, the result was too momentous to be imagined. The

fortunes of hundreds, nay of thousands, were saved; the panic then in progress would be stopped, a stable currency (based on gold, the only proper standard) would probably be assured, and the prosperity of the nation would be certain.

Never did I feel such a deep, almost overwhelming, sense of responsibility as during that operation. In itself, it was as nothing, as compared with many others I have done of greater difficulty and danger; but in its possible consequences for good or evil, none I ever was concerned in would compare with it.

Mr. Cleveland was placed in bed, in a short time revived from the anesthetic, and soon became himself. Of course, he could talk only with great difficulty, as the wound had been packed with gauze to arrest the hemorrhage. When the packing was taken out, so much of the bone had been removed that his speech was entirely unintelligible, resembling that of a child with a very bad cleft palate.

As we had no communication with the shore for several days, the yellow newspapers spread the wildest reports as to the spree he was supposed to be on, reports which even today, so many years after the event, make me almost fiercely indignant. For a large part of July 1st and 2nd, I sat at his bedside and, to occupy his mind, read to him. He had almost no stimulant. What little he did take (only two or three tablespoonfuls, as I remember) was necessary after so considerable an operation. Even that he would have preferred not to take. But he was one of the most docile and easily managed patients I ever cared for.

Dr. Hasbrouck was landed at New London on the 2nd. I landed at Sag Harbor on the 4th, I believe, and returned at once to my home. We all kept the matter absolutely secret.

222

This operation later became known (see below), but it has never been known that we did a second operation, some ten days later. Dr. Bryant wrote me that he was not satisfied that we had removed all of the diseased tissue and thought it best, therefore, to take away some more. It can be easily understood that one cannot apply a tourniquet about the mouth, as one can to the arm or leg, and how difficult it is, therefore, when the blood is flowing rather freely, to judge the exact limits of the disease.

At any rate, on the evening of July 14th, we all (except for Dr. Hasbrouck, whose services were not needed this time) were again conveyed from various docks to the *Oneida*, at anchor in New York harbor, and we again steamed out into the sound. The next morning, Mr. Cleveland was again chloroformed, and in a few minutes, the second operation was over. The same routine was followed as before, and everything went well. This time, I was landed at Newport, on the evening of July 18th, just before the Fall River boat arrived, on its way to New York. Then a very funny incident occurred.

In order not to betray my presence to my friends, I intended to get my stateroom at once, to go and stay there. But as I reached the head of the main stairway, whom should I meet but my brother-in-law, Spencer Borden, who was on his way from Fall River to New York. "Hello, Billy Keen, what are you doing here?" he asked. "Well, Spen," I replied, "the simple fact is that I reached Newport from a consultation nearby only a few minutes ago and had just enough time to catch the boat, but no time to visit the family in Fall River." This entirely satisfied him, but there was no stateroom for me till bedtime.

Meantime, Mr. Cleveland had returned to "Gray Gables" and had been fitted with an artificial jaw by a very skillful dentist. With it in place, his voice was perfect. Without it, his speech was unintelligible. He received public deputations, very shortly after his operation, and made speeches to them; he went fishing; and in all ways resumed his usual life. No one suspected the truth.

Though the story of the operation got out, the president's evidently vigorous health, and Dr. Bryant's equally vigorous denials quieted all public apprehension. (The scandalous stories of Mr. Cleveland's sprees on the *Oneida* also died down.)

On August 4th, with Florence, Dora, and Margaret, I went to the World's Columbian Exposition, in Chicago, and then to Lake Minnewaska, where I stayed until the 12th of September. The explosion came on August 29th, but too late, fortunately, to prevent or undo the action of Congress, which had met the third week in July. The House of Representatives repealed the Sherman Silver Purchase Act, and the Senate followed suit in October. In the *Philadelphia Press* of August 29th, 1893, "Holland" (E. J. Edwards), their New York correspondent, published a long dispatch giving what was, to all intents and purposes, a full and fairly accurate account of the first operation (neither he nor anyone else, apparently, caught on to the second), with dates, places, and names (excepting that Dr. Janeway's name was never mentioned). It was a great newspaper scoop. How the story got out, I do not know, but I think Dr. Bryant does. I have always suspected Hasbrouck, who was at the first, but not the second, operation, but I could be wrong. He certainly talked a great deal more than he should have, after Holland's piece appeared. Whether he also talked before then I do not know.

All the papers were then agog. Reporters flocked to see everyone whose name was given, but especially Bryant. I have always thought that the steward and the crew of the *Oneida* received scant credit for their silence.

Only one reporter found me. A number of them came to my house, but Dr. Taylor met them with the statement that I was somewhere in the woods and he could not give them my address. One man, however, a reporter for the *World*, returned to the house after Dr. Taylor had left and tried to find out from the servants where I was. As they were unsuspicious, they told him that they thought I was in Fall River. He took the Fall River boat that night and learned from the men at the wharf in Fall River, the next morning, that Mrs. George W. Dean was my sister-in-law (I had been going to Fall River every year for over 30 years); so he immediately went there. Dora (Mrs. Dean) met him in the parlor, and he told her this touching, but fictitious, tale. According to him, I had done him a great service, many years before, for which he had been able to thank me only by letter. But on hearing, in Warren, R.I., where he was spending a short holiday, that I was in Fall River, he had called and wished to thank me in person. She, in guileless sincerity, told him that I was at Lake Minne-waska. He took the same boat back to New York and hastened, the next morn-ing, to New Paltz, where he learned that no trains were running and, as it was a Sunday, the Smileys did not allow the back-and-forth shuttle of the stages. Nothing daunted, he hired a team and drove some thirty miles, I think, across country. After supper, I was in the lobby, reading, when his card was handed to me, and he told me his errand. I said that I was very sorry to have to deny him any information, but all of us had agreed that only Dr. Bryant should make any official statement. The only thing

I did was to admit (as already published) that there had been an operation

on Mr. Cleveland and that I had assisted Dr. Bryant. Out of this, how-

ever, he wove quite a little story--chiefly fiction. I knew nothing of

his perigrinations here or to Fall River until later. The dispatch in the

World in no way represented what I told him but enlarged and embroidered it.

When Holland's dispatch appeared in the New York papers, Spen read

the account, at home in Fall River. One can imagine his saying, "Effie,

I'll bet a dollar that was where Billy Keen had been when I met him on the

Fall River boat." As a matter of fact, he did not remember the exact date,

for when he and I met in Newport, I was returning from the *second* operation,

which even today, after 19 years, is practically unknown.

(The newspaper clippings I have saved are only those which happened

to come my way and were not systematically collected. A complete collec-

tion would have filled a very large scrapbook, for practically every paper

in the land published dispatches and editorials.)

Dr. Bryant's policy to say nothing was undoubtedly the wisest, but

I'm afraid that he bent the 10th Commandment rather badly. He had made

careful notes of the operations, and all of their incidents, as or soon

after they occurred. My own account may be inaccurate in some details,

and thus should be corrected by his account, but the main incidents I have

cited are certainly correct.

I often shudder, to this day, when I think of the heavy risk we ran

and of the terrible disaster which would have followed either Mr. Cleve-

land's death or even the premature disclosure of the extent and character

of the operations. (After the repeal of the Silver Act, the gold standard

226

was finally inserted in the Republican--possibly even the Democratic--platform of 1896.)

For the next few months, I went to Washington, at varying intervals, to examine Mr. Cleveland's mouth. In spite of the fact that the microscopist made a diagnosis of, I believe, sarcoma, never was there any return or the slightest suspicion of it. (Certainly that was the clinical diagnosis.) In these visits, I usually lunched with the family and saw Mrs. Cleveland and the children, who were charming young girls. I was angered almost beyond endurance at the villainous reports, in some of the yellow papers, that one or more of them were feeble-minded. Whatever opinion the paper (reporter or editor) held, as to the president's acts or policies, why strike a woman in the tenderest spot of her heart, her love for her children? Only a beast could do so.

Twice after that, I saw Mr. Cleveland, in consultation with Dr. Bryant. He was then living in Princeton. He complained of attacks, sometimes very severe, of abdominal pain. Owing to his excessively fat belly walls, it was impossible to examine the abdominal viscera with accuracy. The first consultation was early in 1905, the second, at the end of the year. The symptoms seemed to point to recurring intestinal obstruction. Palliative, rather than radical, treatment was recommended, for to do an abdominal section, at his age and in his condition, both Bryant and I thought very injudicious. His death did not occur until 1908. I have never learned the results of a necropsy, if indeed one was performed (as I believe), but I have always suspected that it would have disclosed a malignant growth. But that he had no local recurrence for over thirteen years was indeed a triumph.

Twice lately, in 1911 and 1912, I have met Mrs. Cleveland in Dr. de Schweinitz's office, and she greeted me most cordially, as usual. On the second occasion, one of her daughters was with her, and curiously enough, Mrs. Cleveland told me that only the night before she had told her daughters, for the first time, of the operations above described.

ELEVEN CENTENARY CELEBRATIONS

It has been my good fortune to take part, either as beneficiary, active participant, or spectator, in eleven celebrations of centenaries, ranging from one century to five centuries. In one of the drawers of my office desk are a number of memoranda, relating to several of these centenaries, which will show more in detail some of their features. I have also medals and other mementos, in addition to a number of diplomas, from some of these celebrations. Diplomas from the Royal College of Surgeons of England and the German Surgical Society, as they were of especial interest surgically, I have given to the library of the College of Physicians of Philadelphia.

1. My first centenial celebration was at Brown, in 1864, when we commemorated the first 100 years of the university. (A full account of this celebration was published by the university, and I need not refer to it further.) We are now, in 1911, engaged in planning for the sesquicentennial, in 1914, and I hope to be present and enjoy that function.

2. In 1887, I attended the first centenary of the College of Physicains of Philadelphia (of which a full account has also been published).

3. In 1900, the Royal College of Surgeons of England celebrated the first centenary of their new charter, and with great pomp and success.

The original college charter had been granted by Henry VIII, in 1540, but in 1799, by some legal action (or want of action, I do not recall which), that charter was forfeited. The new charter was obtained, under George III, in the following year. At the time of the centenary, they were authorized to create as many as 50 honorary fellows. Up to 1900, they had had only fellows, members, and licentiates. The Prince of Wales (afterwards, Edward VII) was privately made their first honorary fellow. At the public function, in July of 1900, Lord Salisbury and Lord Roseberry (the leaders of the Conservative and Liberal parties) and about 35 surgeons, from various countries, were made honorary fellows. The four Americans so honored were Prof. J. Collins Warren, of Harvard; Prof. Robert F. Weir, of Columbia; Prof. William S. Halsted, of Johns Hopkins; and myself. The full account of this very notable function I have published in a pamphlet entitled "The Graduation Ceremony, with an Account of Some Modern Surgical Celebrations," in *Medical Library and Historical Journal*, March 1906. Florence, Dora, and Margaret were with me. Margaret will not forget, I am sure, how Dr. Osler (now Sir William Osler, Bart.) mystified a lot of English ladies by introducing her·as "Mrs. Osler."

4. In 1910, the University of Berlin celebrated their first century. Dora only was with me. I was not a little disappointed at the very meager attention paid to the ladies of the delegates, who were invited to only minor functions, and not to either of the two principal ones (although the ladies of the faculty, all Germans, were present in force).

The two main functions were held in the aulic (royal court). The Kaiser was present at the first; the imperial family, at both. As a delegate of the American Philosophical Society, I had a seat between Lord

Reay*, president of the British Academy, and Prof. Alex. Lappo-Danilevski, the "wirklicher Mitglied der Kaiserlich Akademie der Wissenschaften," St. Petersburg, with both of whom I had pleasant and interesting conversations.

During the ceremony, the Kaiser announced the gift of a large sum of money for research, amid much applause.

5. In 1893, I attended the sesquicentennial of the American Philosophical Society. The chief recollection I have of it is the delightful way in which Mr. Frederick Fraley, the president for many years, presided at the dinner. Though he was then 88 years old, his incisive wit and his easy, gentle, and charming remarks, in introducing the speakers, was very notable, especially as coming from one so aged, and one whose occupation was not that of a scholar or a scientist, but a businessman.

The proceedings appear in print, in the records of the society.

6. In 1898 occurred the bicentenary of the First Baptist Church, in Philadelphia. All the proceedings appear in the history of the church,** a volume which I edited and to which I contributed, in some detail, an account of the first 200 years. It was impossible for me to read personally all of the many volumes of the minutes of the church, the deacons, and the trustees. This was undertaken by a Committee of Six, who made notes of the important matters, with references to volume and page. All of these references I read (and the records of the period of strife or contention, with the Spruce Street Baptist Church, I read and re-read two

---

* For the interesting and curious career of Lord Reay, upon whom the LL.D. degree was conferred by Saint Andrews, see the list of their honorary graduates in September, 1911.
** Full title: *The Bi-Centennial Celebration of the Founding of the First Baptist Church of the City of Philadelphia, 1698-1898.*

230

or three times. I made an honest and, I believe, successful effort to write with entire impartiality and accuracy.

This history of the church saved me from a very disagreeable task, as I have chronicled (above) among my recollections of presidents I have known. Mr. McKinley had nominated me to serve on a commission to investigate abuses connected with the Spanish-American War, but I explained to him that I could not accept, in that, while I had made many notes for the bicentennial history, not one word was yet written, and the day of the celebration, December 11th, was only two months away. No other member of the church could possibly make himself familiar with all the facts, in that time, much less write a worthy history for the very important occasion. I declined the president's offer and recommended, as a substitute, my old friend from college days, Prof. Phineas S. Conner, of Cincinnati.

My refusal was fortunate. The commission lasted for several months, travelled extensively, heard many witnes es, and published their report. They were harried and grossly abused by those whom they condemned. (Had their verdict been the reverse of what it was, they would have been attacked in the same way, but by the other side.) I could not have written the proposed history; nor could anyone else. The celebration would have been a failure. My time would have been wasted, and my practice would have suffered greatly. I should have been belabored by either one side or the other and have obtained little, if any, credit with the general public, however much my conscience (and those whose judgment I really cared for) had approved.

Had I been free, I should certainly have accepted the appointment as a public duty, accepting the abuse as an inevitable aspect of that duty.

7. In 1906, the American Philosophical Society celebrated the bicentenary of Franklin's birth, with distinguished success. The state made an appropriation of $20,000 towards the expenses. Congress voted that a commemorative medal be struck, in bronze, and I have one of the many that were distributed. A replica, in solid gold, was presented to the French government through the ambassador, M. Jusserand, himself one of our members.

A very striking and pleasant episode, during the celebration, was the conferring of the LL.D. degree of Saint Andrews upon Miss Agnes Irwin, the head of Radcliffe College. She ascended the platform of Witherspoon Hall clad in a black academic robe. She was supported on the one side by Dr. Horace Howard Furness, in his scarlet Oxford robe, and on the other by Dr. S. Weir Mitchell, in his scarlet Edinburgh robe. The contrast of colors was picturesque indeed.

The degree was conferred upon her by Dr. Andrew Carnegie, as the lord rector of Saint Andrews. His own purple robe added still further to the mise en scène. The awarding of this degree was appropriate to a celebration of Franklin, as Miss Irwin is the great-granddaughter of Benjamin Franklin, and, moreover, Saint Andrews was the first university to recognize Franklin's eminence by giving him an honorary degree.

The addresses by Secretary of State Root, President Eliot, and especially Dr. Furness, and others, were all delightful and made the occasion a very distinguished function.

8. In 1907, the University of Uppsala celebrated the 200th anniversary of the birth of their most distinguished alumnus, Carl Linné (or, in its Latin form, Carolus Linnaeus). As he was a member of the American Philosophical Society, we were invited to send a delegate, Harvard being

the only other American institution so honored. Prof. Farlow, the Professor of Botany at Harvard, was one delegate, and I was the other. Florence and Dora went with me. I have published a description of this ceremony: "An Account of the Festival Held at Uppsala and Stockholm, May, 1907, in Commemoration of the 200th Anniversary of the Birth of Carolus Linnaeus," in *The Aesculapian,* December 1908. I have also one of their medals; the wreath of laurel, which was placed upon my brow (!); the diploma; and the beautiful ring placed upon my finger, at the function in the cathedral, when I received the Ph.D., their highest degree. One incident, previously described, I did not include in my printed account, as it was too personal, it seemed to me. Our young Swedish guide pointed out, in one of the side chapels of the cathedral, the coat of arms of his ancestor. "What was his name?" I asked. "Oxenstierna, the great chancellor of Gustavus Adolphus," was the reply. "Well," said I, "I do not believe that any other student and any other guest of the university can say what you and I can, that your ancestor sent my ancestor to America, in 1642!"

9. My list is gradually including celebrations of older and older foundations and now reaches a quattro-centenary (400 years), with the commemoration, in 1905, of the founding of the Royal College of Surgeons of Edinburgh. (I have referred to this 1505 foundation, in my "Early History of Practical Anatomy," in my *Addresses and Other Papers.*) To this celebration, as to that of the Royal College of Surgeons of England, I received a personal invitation. I was doubly honored, on this occasion, as I was not only made an honorary fellow of the college, but also awarded the LL.D. degree by the University of Edinburgh. I have published an account of this celebration and having nothing to add here.

10. In 1906, the University of Greifswald celebrated the 450th anniversary of its foundation. I was travelling in Europe, that summer, when I received some letters from America, congratulating me on my new German degree. I had heard of none and supposed it to be a false report. On my return, however, I found that this venerable institution had given me the degree of Doctor of Medicine *causâ honoris*, at their celebration. I knew no one of its faculty, but I acknowledged the diploma to Professor Friedrich, who was the dean of the medical faculty (and is now at Marburg).

11. September 12 to 15, 1911, the University of Saint Andrews celebrated, with great distinction, the 500th anniversary of its foundation. I was not a little surprised on receiving, at the end of May, a formidable document, in Latin, setting forth this fact and inviting me personally to be present. As I had intended to go to Brussels anyway, for the Congress of the International Surgical Society, the last week in September, I at once accepted and left, with Florence, for London on the 27th of August. Meantime, in July, while at Weekapaug, R.I., I received a notification that the honorary degree of LL.D. would be conferred upon me. This was done, on September 14th, by Lord Balfour, the chancellor, following the rectorial address by Lord Roseberry, who was the new lord rector. This address, and two other speeches, were fine specimens of Lord Roseberry's learning, graceful wit, and charming English diction. Everyone was amused when, during the rectorial address, he looked down straight at Mr. Asquith, the premier (who sat in the front row awaiting, too, his honorary LL.D.), and referred to the "ruins of the House of Lords." I suspect that Mr. Asquith rather chuckled, since he had successfully carried his bill for the reform of the House of Lords, and in a moment would be given his honorary

degree. Mr. Balfour, the former premier, spoke at the dinner, but his speech was a great disappointment. It was worthy neither of the occasion nor of the man.

The most striking thing about the anniversary dinner, apart from the very distinguished company present (including the gaikwar of Baroda, the American ambassador, Mr. Whitelaw Reid, President Butler, of Columbia, Lord Reay--the principal--and Sir William Turner, among others), was the number of toasts. Besides the two loyal toasts, there were 25 speakers. As Florence and I were staying at Mr. A. Sinclair Henderson's in Dundee, we had to take the special train at 11:40. When I left, there were still 14 speakers to be heard. (It reminded me greatly of the dinner of the British Medical Association, in 1897, in Montreal: I was the last of 32 speakers and arose to speak at 2:30 A.M.)

I spoke very briefly at the luncheon in Dundee. I repeated my old chestnut about the man who was challenged for any proof of the truth of the doctrine of the survival of the fittest and, pointing to himself, replied, "I am here." I also cited the quotation from Psalms in saying that we were like the Hebrews going up to Jerusalem, "chanting our Songs of Degrees." A few caught on, but only a few. When I had used the same quotation at a Commencement at Brown, at the semi-centenary of the Class of 1859, it was greeted by an instant and loud outburst of laughter (just as it had been, when offered by Bishop Clarke, at a Commencement dinner years ago).

I may add to this list the one centenary that I did not "bag." In 1901, the University of Glasgow celebrated its 450th anniversary. I received a personal invitation but was unable to attend. Also, in 1912, I was invited to attend the 300th anniversary of Trinity College, Dublin, but was unable to go.

The next centenary I am already planning to attend is my own. Since I have attended so many others, it would surely be amiss (or a miss, if your prefer) if I were to omit this. After all, "Moons" (i.e., Moses) Keen, a collateral ancestor, lived to be 106.

Post Script:

In October, 1914, Brown celebrated, with great pomp and circumstance, the 150th anniversary of its founding. A new and worthy history of the university (by Prof. Bronson), a new historical catalog, and later, a volume containing the addresses, etc., were published. It was a notable success in every way.

My own address, as representative of the First Baptist Church of Philadelphia, as well as of the alumni and the corporation, was on "The Early Years of Brown University, 1764-1770" and is published in this *Sesquicentenary Celebration of Brown University*. I also presided at the dinner. The proceedings at the dinner are included in this volume. Condensation was necessary, and hence the cruel editor killed my favorite "baby": In introducing Ambassador Naón, I referred to the conference of the representatives of the A B C powers of South America (Argentina, Brazil, and Chile) and expressed the hope that the E F G nations of Europe (England, France, and Germany) might soon complete the entire alphabet of peace.

ON THE BULGARIAN FRONTIER

We left Constantinople for Genoa, by way of Budapest and Venice, to take our steamer for home. (There were six of us: three of my daughters,

236

Dr. D, of Providence, a friend, and myself.) We had exactly one extra
day to catch our boat. We left in the evening, by the Orient Express,
and were due at the Bulgarian frontier at 7 the next morning. As I always
woke up early, I took all the trunk keys, so that my daughters could
sleep as long as they wished. We had had a pretty strenuous time in Con-
stantinople--and, in fact, during the whole summer. The only other first-
class passengers in the wagon-lit (sleeper) were a family of three from
Wilmington. The son was a young businessman who had spent three years,
or so, in St. Petersburg and, most fortunately for me, as it proved, was
able to speak Russian.

We stopped, at the frontier, at what could only by courtesy be called
a station. It consisted of two small, wooden buildings, one for disinfection and the other for the storage of disinfected baggage. About a
quarter of a mile away, on a hillside, were some barracks for passengers
who might have to be quarantined. About three miles away, beyond what,
in Illinois, should be called a prairie, lay the little town, or rather,
village of Hebibchevo, which, we found out later, was made up of a small
number of mean-looking, two-story houses, at irregular intervals, all resembling each other, fringing both sides of its one street.

I had given our passports to the conductor, and soon after the train
stopped, I heard an official calling for me. I found that he was a quarantine officer who had just arrived the day before from Sofia (the capital), where he was a professor of Bacteriology in the university. "You
have come from Russia?" he inquired. "Yes," I replied, "from Moscow to
the Crimea, and thence to Constantinople." To my consternation, he then
said that we would have to be quarantined for two weeks. "For what reason?"

I inquired. "Because the plague exists in Russia." "But my dear sir," said I, "the plague exists only at Astrakhan, on the Caspian Sea, and we have not been within 500 miles of Astrakhan." "My orders are the quarantine everybody coming from Russia," was his uncompromising reply. Finally, after much expostulation and debate, he agreed to allow all of our party, and the H family from Wilmington, to proceed to Budapest, on condition that all of our baggage be left for 24 hours for disinfection. Neither the young Mr. H nor I was willing to turn over all of our possessions, unguarded, to strangers; so at last, the impatient officials and other passengers (the train had been delayed 15 or 20 minutes, by this time) departed for Budapest, almost a two-day journey, while Mr. H and I stayed behind. The members of our party had absolutely no baggage save for toilet articles; they told us later that when they got to Budapest, tired and dusty, the first thing they did was to go to bed, while their clothing was being washed, for they had not a single change.

Meantime, Mr. H and I had more than a dozen trunks, in addition to as many more pieces of hand baggage. All this baggage the doctor then proceeded to disinfect by unpacking and placing everything in large, deep drawers of what might be called a huge bureau. The bottoms of the drawers were pierced by large auger holes, and sulphur was burned below the "bureau," the fumes being supposed to reach and thus disinfect everything in the drawers. Fortunately (but almost by force), we were able to rescue some ladies' hats, gloves, and photographs from impending destruction. There being so much baggage, the "bureau" had to be filled three times.

As to the trunks themselves, they were sprayed inside and out (and most inefficiently) with a little carbolic-acid solution and then dried

in the sun. How to get everything back in the proper trunk and handbag,
and to the proper owner, was a problem. Finally, I made a list: The
things from A's handbag were in the top drawer, front, to the right; those
from B's, in the second drawer, rear, to the right; and so on. When we
came to re-packing the trunks, and especially the ladies' hats, I said to
Mr. H, "As soon as we turn these trunks over to the ladies, at Budapest,
you and I had better take to the woods." To our credit, be it said, that
the ladies all declared that they couldn't have done it better themselves,
though I have always esteemed this a bit of very polite flattery.

The tedious process of unpacking, labeling, disinfecting, and re-
packing occupied the whole morning. Meantime, we had not had a mouthful
to eat. But now, the doctor took us in a canvas-covered wagon, with no
springs, over the stony three miles to Hebibchevo. Here, a steak and some
potatoes (which were cooked--and also burnt and smoked--over an open wood
fire) and black bread were set before us, with nothing but two-pronged
iron forks with which to eat this unappetizing meal. Calling for a knife
to carve the steak, I was provided with what might be called a cutlass,
or even a scimitar, but at a pinch it served its purpose. The doctor
warned us against the water as unwholesome, and the wine was bad, so we
had to be content with poor beer. The sun was fiercely hot, the temperature being, we judged, in the 90s, and we were hungry, thirsty, tired,
and in no very placid state of mind.

We passed the afternoon in a short nap, on the straw in the wagon;
inspection of the industries of the town, including blacksmithing by one
of the women; and a tiresome, hot walk to see some neighboring gypsies,
said to be camped two miles away, but they had vanished before we reached

their encampment. We also conversed with the doctor, whose French was distressing but comprehensible, with constant effort. I was greatly amused, when I recalled the spendidly complete bacteriological laboratory of the Jefferson Medical College, at his calm assumption that in America we were entirely ignorant, of course, of so scientific a branch of medicine as Bacteriology. But he was a self-satisfied and very superior person, and this was a good example of his knowledge of America.

After supper, which was a repetition of dinner (including the cutlass), the doctor offered to take us, in the wagon, back to the station, but, remembering the testimony of our aching bones from the morning drive, and noting that the moon was bright, we thought that the road would be marked well enough for us to follow; so Mr. H and I lingered, for an hour, and then started. We had not been on our way for more than ten minutes, however, before we confessed to each other that we had lost our way and decided to return to the village. With some difficulty, we found it, only to discover another problem: The houses were so alike that we could not tell which our "hotel" was, and, moreover, not a light was to be seen, as everybody had gone to bed.

We finally roused the people in one house (whether the right or the wrong one, I have never been sure), and a head protruding from the second-story window asked, evidently, what we wanted. How fortunate it was, now, that Mr. H could speak Russian, for, using a kindred slavic tongue, they understood him and provided us with a small boy as a guide. We reached the station, with his help, but en route, we were suddenly halted by a soldier, who only reluctantly let us pass after the boy explained to him who and what we were.

240

I then asked the doctor for my suitcase, to get out my toilet articles, but he shrugged his shoulders and, pointing to the storehouse, said
that it was locked inside, and that the guardian was back in Hebibchevo
and had the only key. That settled the question of nightclothes, toothbrush, soap, and hairbrush, finally and conclusively.

The doctor then led us to the barracks where we were to spend the
night. Just after we started, I noticed a soldier following closely on
our heels. He was carrying a rifle and was possibly armed to the teeth
(whatever that means). I asked the doctor why we had this guard. "My
dear sir," he said brusquely, "you don't seem to realize that we are on
the frontier between Bulgaria and Turkey, and that at any moment, but especially at night, we may be attacked by the Turks." This was a soothing
nightcap, indeed.

Mr. H and I only half undressed, but we soon fell asleep and slept
soundly till six o'clock, when we were roused to our very brief and limited toilet. At seven, we started out for Budapest. Fortunately, we
now could, at last, obtain a good breakfast in the restaurant car, and we
did full justice to it.

The wagon-lit was not quite full, there being two unoccupied berths.
But per contra, we were out of luck, for our sleeper tickets were valid
only for berths in yesterday's train. In spite of elaborate explanations,
the conductor would not accept them for *his* train, so we had to buy new
tickets. It is only just to add that, on our arrival in Budapest, we
sent a reclamation to the chief officer of the sleeping-car company, in
Brussels, and after some weeks, the cost of our extra tickets was refunded
to us, an unexpected but just restitution.

If the porters had been astonished at the paucity (or rather, the absence) of baggage, when the rest of our two parties arrived the day before, their surprise must have been even greater at the excessive amount of baggage apparently required by two mere men, unadorned with an entourage of valets and other such luxuries.

We just caught our steamer at Genoa, after a most uncomfortable night on an accommodation train with no wagon-lits, the only train we could take, for there were no through express trains on that route. But we were thankful to have started out with one day's leeway and grateful that our Bulgarian Professor of Bacteriology was lenient enough to keep us only one day, instead of two weeks.

Evidently, his ideas of disinfection were as imperfect as was his knowledge of the state of medical progress in America. But we forgave him and hope that he has won distinction in the present Balkan War.

I'm not sure but that, in the long run, we have had so much fun in recounting our experiences that we are almost glad we were quarantined.

AN AUDIENCE BY THE KAISERIN

Berlin, April 7th, 1907

Dear Walter and Corinne:

I shall write to you and to Ardmore on alternate Sundays, to catch Wednesday's steamers. Please exchange letters.

On arrival, we came here, just across the street from the Friedrich Str. Bahnhof. Dora and I have rooms on the street side, but it is so quiet that we would never know there was a station 100 yards away.

We very soon learned that we were in Deutschland, for alles ist "verboten." In the cars, besides a map of the road, there were *18* other signs, such as *Warnung*; *Notbremse*; *Nicht hinauslehnen, es ist lebensgefährlich,* etc. Surely one is cared for almost to death. Self-reliance and personal initiative are almost at a discount, except in the streets, where the autos and autobuses whiz by, and you must look out for yourself and step lively.

The imperial family have *white* autos with a special *flag* and a specially-toned *horn*, and when *they* go by, Donner und Blitzen! everybody and every carriage has to get out of the way.

Prof. Trendelenburg (Howard's friend, "Trundle bed") is sick and can't come; nor can we visit them in Leipzig, as arranged. His son, Paul, came on Sunday at noon and was with us till Tuesday night and was most kind.

We made our calls Monday and Tuesday, on Frau Kausch (née Mikulicz), the Ewalds, the Krauses, Prof. Riedel (president of the surgical society) of Jena, the Hoffas, the Körtes, and some others to whom the girls had letters.

At one, I lunched with Riedel and about 30--a sort of preliminary canter. As I sat between Braun, of Göttingen, and Hildebrand (König's successor at the Charité Hospital here, and the "other" Kliniker--von Bergmann being the first), and they knew not a word of English, I was pitched headfirst into the waters of German and *had* to swim. It was very good for my German, but a bit hard on *me*, and I fancy on them too, in spite of their good-natured fibs as to my *ausgezeichnete* German.

Wednesday, the congress opened. Von Bergmann's portrait was draped, and at the conclusion of Riedel's presidential address, all rose in respect to his memory.

We all lunched with the Ewalds and with Prof. and Frau Virchow (he is the Professor of Anatomy and the son of *the* Virchow) and our old friends (whom Margaret will remember as our hosts, in '99, at their villa on the Elbe, near Hamburg), Prof. and Frau Krause. We *like* the Ewalds more than any other of our Berlin friends. They are simply charming, and Frau E's English is faultless!

In the evening (5:30!), I dined with Prof. and Frau Olshausen, at a delightful dinner for about 20. Again, Frau O's English was excellent. They know many of my friends at home, tho' they have never been in the United States, but he has had many pupils from there. The Ewalds were at the Washington congress, in 1903, and were delightfully entertained.

Thursday, Hoffa called. He is just back from St. Petersburg, whither he had gone to see the little tsarevich, who is a little pigeon-toed. I spent the day at the congress (800 members present, out of 1600 members!) and in the evening went to the Fest Dinner at the Savoy, 200-250 present. We were bidden at 5:30 and sat down at 6. By 8:30 (there were only six courses, besides cheese, fruit, and coffee) we were through, speeches and all, and by 9, nearly everybody had gone--most sensible.

The speeches were made in between the courses, and the waiters then waited. After the soup, Riedel gave the first toast, to the Kaiser, and he was followed by König, Küster, Czerny, von Eiselsberg, Rovsing (of Copenhagen), and myself! I knew I never would have a more friendly and more lenient audience, so I plunged in headfirst and spoke in *German*, begging them to excuse my "zerbrochen Deutsch." I did better than I had feared, tho' not so well as I had hoped. They seemed, at least, to understand me and even applauded a joke or two.

Friday, I was at the congress all day. Von Eiselsberg was elected president for the next year--a capital choice. Some say that he *may* be appointed in von Bergmann's place, for they all recognize him as now the leading operator in Germany, including, in that term, German Austria. But they fear that he made a mistake in going from Königsberg to Vienna. Had he stayed on German soil, his election would have been *sure*. He is, however, an Austrian by birth, and all his family live in Vienna.

In the evening, I dined at Körte's. Frau Körte gave me her arm and placed me on her left, which I suppose is the place of honor. Many old friends (there were 30 in all) were there, among them, Küster (of Marburg), whose son Margaret will remember (Paris, 1900), as she nearly knocked his nose off. He (the son) is a lawyer and in the Ministry of the Interior here. This dinner was at 6:30, the usual hour, I think, and we left at 10.

The family is blossoming out in German! Last night, Florence and Dora went to dinner at Frau Kausch's (Mikulicz's 2nd daughter), and Prof. K. clinked his glass and said that, as I was not present, Fräulein Dora would respond for me, which, following my example of the night before, she did in German. There's no telling to what we may come before we return!

I will send you the invitations. Lay them aside for me for when I return. I shall send other similar documents later.

Saturday, the congress adjourned. At 1 o'clock, 10 of us were asked to meet the president, who then gave us instructions as to an audience of the kaiserin: Meet at the Schloss at 5:15 in full evening dress, including white tie and white gloves, orders and all. I went with von Eiselsberg, in an ordinary fiacre. I was in "grand tenue," as described, but I did not wear my orders.

We were present 15 minutes before the appointed time, and after leaving our wraps (but, by instruction, carrying our hats--mine was an opera hat), we were ushered from one room to another, and finally to one on the second floor--all handsome but not especially noteworthy. We ended in a room about the size of our parlor and were placed in a semicircle, in the order in which our names had been handed in on the official list. The court chamberlain placed us, I being No. 1 (!), as the only *Ehren Mitglied*. Then came Picqué (of Paris), Mr. Barker (of London), Rovsing, Eiselsberg, Braun, Kümmell, Rehn, Madelung, and Körte. The kaiserin entered, in a few minutes, first talked to the president, then came to me, and then went to each one, in turn talking with equal ease in English, French, or German, for probably three minutes each, so that we really had quite a nice little conversation.

I watched Riedel and, in turn, when she held out her hand, I took it, bowed over and kissed it (more Germanico), as if I were accustomed to do so every day. Of course, I waited for her to speak first, and, naturally, her opening question was whether this was my first visit to Berlin. I told her that I had been an old student, with Langenbeck, Virchow, etc., in '65-6; that I knew many of the German surgeons; and that I had the honor to know, among others, the Princess Henrietta and Prof. von Esmarch. Whereupon, she instantly said, "Oh! Yes, I remember their speaking of you and of the very pleasant dinner they attended at your home, in Philadelphia." This broke the ice, and we talked very pleasantly about the von Esmarches, the German Surgical Society, etc., till she bowed and passed on to Picqué. I confess I was surprised at her remembering such a detail as a dinner about 13 years ago. I think your ball dresses must have so impressed the Princess Henrietta that she passed them on to her niece, the

kaiserin.   I wanted dreadfully to tell her I would like to call on her

distinguished and, I might say, well-known husband, but as she said noth-

ing about him, I forbore.

Now as a model father, I carefully studied her dress and will try to

describe it in detail.   She wore a broad black hat with black ostrich

feathers.   Her dress was a high-neck, light blue-green satin (or silk?),

and she evidently had been sitting down, for the skirt was creased trans-

versely in several folds.   She wore a lace collar and a string of pearls

that reached to her waist.   Her dress was adjusted to the bust, not by

plaits but rather by being narrowed from the shoulders to the waist by

seams pretty close together.   It then was expanded from the waist to the

hips by widening seams.   Below, it was bordered by greenish velvet, say 4

to 5 inches wide, and had a short house train.   The sleeves were puffed

and slashed, and into the slashings were interpolated some figured thin

stuff like velours.   The sleeves stopped at the elbow and were trimmed

with a brownish lace.   The same kind of lace trimmed the dress all over,

converging from the shoulders to the center of the waist, front and back,

and continued from the waistband (of the same lace) in a long

streak down the front and back of the skirt.   Where the back

streak joined the waistband was a bow of the same lace.   The

lace also went parallel to and a little above the velvet border of the

skirt and rose in two or three points on each side half-way to the hips.

She wore light-gray long gloves with two or three bracelets outside

the gloves.   She carried a fan (closed) but no prayer book.

Voilà!   Now if you can't reproduce this dress in all its details, it will not be my fault.

Her gray hair, I forgot. It was done up in a roll (knot)
like this. I think that it must have been a true lover's knot,
at the back, but it was so shaded by the hat that I am a bit in
doubt.

She is a little inclined to stoutness, but she has a very pleasing
face and Shakespeare's proper woman's voice, low and sweet. In her charm
of manner, she reminded me not a little of Mrs. Cleveland.

In the evening, I went to the Anglo-American Medical Association,
formed, some years ago, by Dr. Honan, a Chicago man in practice here for
10 years. It is a most useful club (as is its counterpart in Vienna) in
giving help of all sorts, professional and personal, to English and American students. It has usually 50 to 80 members and meets every Saturday
night at 7:30, for an à la carte dinner, and at 8:30, for a lecture by
some German professor or docent. Last night's was by Schleich--him of
the "fluid." If Walter will keep his eye on the Journal of the American
Medical Association, he will see a letter from me, describing the meetings here and this club. The boys appreciated most *heartily* my going,
and I was *very* glad I went. It encouraged them very much to see that I
took a timely interest in their welfare and wanted to help them. Of
course, I had to make a little speech.

We expect Hilde Mikulicz (Frau Willy Anschütz) and Dr. A. to lunch
with us, and at 3:30, we go by Krause's auto out to Krause's summer villa,
40 minutes away. The Anschützes have a *Sprössling*, a girl a year old.

In order to let Dora see something of the schools here (they re-open
on Tuesday), we shall not leave till Thursday morning at 8, reaching Vienna

at 9:30 in the evening, and probably leaving on Saturday morning for Trieste. On our way back, we shall probably stop for two or three days in Vienna, and for one or two days in Berlin, where we shall leave our storage trunks. After May 1st, these rascally Germans abolish *all* free baggage, as in Holland and Italy.

Margaret's letters of the 23rd and 24th came, to our delight, three days ago, and we were greatly pleased to hear once more from home (how good that word sounds, so far away!) and to know that all are well.

Now you see, like St. Paul, how long a letter I have written to you with mine own hand (how I long for the typewriter!) and told you all our doings. Repay me by others. No detail is too familiar or too petty to be without interest.

Most affectionately,

Your loving father,

W. W. Keen

P. S. I have received here a letter from the florist in New York. The beautiful flowers came from a patient from Wheeling, W. Va.

PERSONAL INCIDENTS OF TRAVEL IN PERSIA, BUKHARA, AND THE CAUCASUS

I. How We Escaped from a Persian Prison

In 1902, Florence, Dora, and I were traveling in Persia. Shortly before this, a Mme. Humbert, along with her brother and sister, M. and Mlle. d'Aurignac, had perpetrated an enormous swindle, amounting to millions, and were being sought all over the world. The French government heard that they had been seen in Persia and telegraphed their minister to arrest them on sight. As there are less than half a dozen places of entry and

exit in Persia, the minister telegraphed to each of these, and among them,
to Enzeli. The consul there replied that the three persons wanted had escaped on a steamer the night before, *We* were the three suspects! I always said that we had two ample means of disproof: 1, our three passports;
and, 2, if they heard us speak French, the proof would at once be convincing. It was bad enough to travel in Persia outside a prison. What it
would have been inside a Persian prison one could only imagine. Doubtless
we should have had abundant reason to long for Persian "insect powder,"
most appropriately named. Of all these facts we were blissfully ignorant
until told of them by Mr. Lloyd C. Griscom, who was the minister to Persia
when we were there and who mentioned them to me while en route, in 1903,
to his new mission as ambassador to Japan.

II. A Persian Play

While in Teheran, we visited the palace and lovely gardens of the
shah's brother. Being tired, I sat down, in the shade in front of the
palace, while the girls (Florence and Dora) walked around it. They were
gone quite a long time, and I went to find them. Very shortly, I found
them in conversation with a lady whom they introduced to me as Mme. X,
a Parisienne and governess to the children of the shah's brother. As
soon as they told her that they were from Philadelphia, she fell upon
their necks, in her joy, and said that her daughter had married an American dentist practicing in Baku, and that her grandson was a draughtsman
in Cramps' shipyard.

In a few minutes, she went to her apartment and brought us a large
diamond ring, which she asked us to carry to him (how confiding!), which
we very faithfully did. Nothing was a trouble to her, and she laid her-

self out to please us. Just then, it was Bairam (the Mussulman Lent), and the chief of police was giving a play to his friends (no tickets were on sale) to which Mme. X said she would try to get us admitted. The same play was repeated elsewhere, and even Mrs. Griscom herself, the minister's wife, was refused admittance in Isfahan. The play lasted ten afternoons and cost the chief $10,000.

She got permission from the chief's wife, a special friend, to admit Florence and Dora (to what, I did not know, except that it was some sort of show), and I was left outside. But in a half-hour, or so, I also was asked to enter, with my Armenian servant. 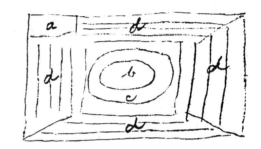 We entered a tent about as large as a circus. At "a" was a latticed enclosure, where the wife of the chief, Florence, Dora, and some other women were watching the play unveiled; "b" was an oval stage, say 3 feet high and about 12 to 15 feet long by 10 feet wide; "c" was a passageway, 10 to 12 feet wide, for soldiers, camels, and others in processions; and "d" indicates rising seats, as in an amphitheater.

When I entered, at the top (and I was the only infidel present), I saw a high pole in the middle of the stage and a boy with a rope around his neck suspended from the pole. My first thought was that we were witnesses to a Persian execution-by-hanging. In a moment, however, he began to make a speech, reading from a slip of paper, and my fears for his life were appeased.

Then followed different actors, on the stage, each of them furnished, by an old man, with a slip of paper with his speaking part. There was much banging of shields by ineffective swords, and some other action, intermingled with various recitatives, some hideous music (?) by a band, and marching and counter-marching, in the "c" space.

Finally, the crowd seemed overcome with what I thought, at first, was laughter, but I found that they were sobbing and weeping profusely. Even my Armenian servant was wiping his eyes and gulping down his sobs. Never have I seen such universal passion and religious fervor. I verily believe that if I had exhibited any disdain or unbelief, this crowd of excited, fanatical Mohammedans would have readily attacked me, if, indeed, they had not torn me to pieces, in their wrath.

The play was, it seems, the tragedy of "The Life and Death of Hassan and Hussein," the sons of Mohammed.

Florence and Dora were in the women's box and witnessed everything through the lattice. They can relate their experience with coffee beans and other spices, with the narghile (through which each took a whiff), the mouthpiece of which was not even wiped clean, when handed to them by the hostess, much less a fresh narghile offered to each.

They also had a new experience on our return by boat from Enzeli to Baku. Their stateroom (the only first-class one) was invaded, willy-nilly, in the middle of the night, by a Belgian woman who carried only one small bag. She rose first, in the morning, and Dora found, to her astonishment, that the woman had borrowed her hairbrush and comb. Later, in the presence of the woman, she carefully washed them, as a hint, and stowed them, the next night, under her pillow. Florence, thinking the rebuke had been sufficient, did not take the same precaution and in the morning was furious, naturally, on finding that the woman had used *her* toilet articles, including even her *toothbrush*!

252

III. The Russian Railroad from Krasnovodsk to Samarkand

Returning from Persia to Baku, we next crossed the Caspian, directly eastwards, to Krasnovodsk and took the railroad to Bukhara and Samarkand, a distance of nearly 1000 miles. In that whole journey, except for a few points such as Kizyl-Arvat, Ashkhabad, Mary, Bukhara, and Samarkand, the country was a continuous sandy desert, the sand being thrown up in billows, by the wind, and engulfing everything in its way. Yet, in the time of Alexander, it must have been well-watered and fertile, for he led his vast army the entire distance, all the way to Samarkand.

At Geok-Tepe, the train halted for 20 minutes, while we visited the fort (a mile or so square) which had immensely thick mud walls, in which the Turkomans for so long resisted Skobelev before they were practically *all* slaughtered, men, women, and children indiscriminately. That so cowed the Turkomans that they have never lifted a finger in revolt against the Russians since then. Opposite the fort is a small museum, with many relics of the fight--and a large equestrian portrait of Skobelev.

We were met, at Bukhara, by a Swedish missionary speaking excellent English, whose acquaintance we owed to Mr. Koop. He spent two days (of great interest) with us and then refused, not only for himself but also for his work, a contribution that I tried, in vain, to get him to accept.

By permission of the Russian governor, we visited old Bukhara, some five or six miles from the new city, which has grown up around the railroad station. The bazaars were a never-ending delight, and I remember seeing a hair clipper made by Brown & Sharpe, of Providence, R.I.

The ark, or citadel, is a spacious and quite imposing mud fort, the residence of the finance minister (the emir always resides in a town some

253

20 miles away), who is also--and this seems to be his primary function--
the chief falconer. Our guide obtained an audience for me. The girls
were not allowed to enter but watched a snake charmer outside, for the 20
minutes, or so, of my audience.

The room in which I was received was 15 by 20 feet, more or less,
with a mud floor, but the mud walls were covered by exquisite silk rugs.
There were European chairs and a table on which was served sweetmeats and
other courses, ending with boiled mutton. The falconer/finance minister
was a large man of about 60, with a large snow-white turban and a robe
stretching from his neck to his heels. It was light pea-green, of satin,
with large stars all over it, so woven as to show a sheen which was absent
in the rest of the robe. He looked every inch a king and was dignified,
courteous, and kind. I am quite sure that when he had heard that I was
an American, he had no more idea of what America is, and where it is situated, than the man in the moon.

Next, we visited the nearby dungeons of the prison. Through a small
door, the only avenue for any light, we saw a score or more of filthy,
abject-looking, poor wretches, with fetters on wrists and ankles. They
looked half-famished and devoured voraciously some long Persian loaves of
bread we gave them. (A loaf was about 6 feet long, 6 inches broad, and
an inch thick.) Below their prison, reached by a hole in the floor, was
a second dungeon, of inexpressable horror, the same in which the two English officers, in the '40s, or thereabouts (see *All the Russias*, by Henry
Norman), were eaten alive by vermin and finally died. It was perfectly
horrible.

In Bukhara, the men are the birds of fine plumage. The colors of their long robes, white, yellow, purple, red, green, are astonishing. Great splashes of color on a white, or other-colored, background. I have some samples to show what they are like.

Samarkand, the furthest point reached by Alexander, has some remains, nearby, of his palace, almost entirely buried in the sand. The bazaars here too were a delight. But the chief object of interest was the tomb of Tamerlane.

The mosque is surrounded by a square wall with minarets at the four corners. Two of them had already fallen; a third was leaning over badly and has since fallen; and the fourth will doubtless follow. The mosque proper has a beautifully fluted dome, and the dome and walls were once covered with beautiful blue Persian tiles. A very large percent of the tiles had fallen off, and there were many fragments on the ground. (I have always been vexed that I did not appropriate two or three of them.) Among the Mohammedans, by *building* a mosque, one "acquires merit." But repairing one is a work of supererogation.

Our journey back to Krasnovodsk and Baku was marked by amusing--and annoying--incidents. From Krasnovodsk to Tashkent, then the terminus of the railroad, is 1200 miles. The year we were there (1902) was the first year that the train had a first-class car on a daily basis. (Prior to that, a first-class car--and a restaurant car--were included only three times a week.) The first-class car had three compartments with four berths each. Florence and Dora occupied half of one compartment; I took a lower berth in another.

I had as one of my companions a Russian officer, who was resplendant in his overcoat of gray with scarlet facings. But when he removed the overcoat (and the thermometer was up to about 103), his once-white uniform was dirty, to a degree. When he went to bed, I understood the reason for the notice which had puzzled me the very first time I rode in a Russian car, namely, "Please remove your boots when you go to bed," a superfluous injunction, as it seemed to me. But my officer, making a pillow of his overcoat, and not even hiring a sheet or pillowcase, threw himself on the bed with his boots, and even his spurs, on.

In the middle of the night, I was awakened by an altercation in which I heard Florence and Dora's voices, so I got up to take a hand in the game. I found that, the other two compartments being full, the conductor was insisting on giving a third berth in their compartment to a man, a proceeding to which they vehemently objected, in English, French, and German, but in vain. So I concluded that if any man was to go into their compartment, it should be I; so I gave the intruder my berth and took a lower in their compartment. Later still, another woman was assigned the remaining berth. We lived in harmony for three days.

IV. How I Broke the Imperial Bank of Persia

When we reached Rasht, I wanted to draw enough money to take us into Teheran and out again; so I took my letter of credit on Brown, Shipley & Company to the Imperial Bank of Persia and asked for fifty pounds, forty pounds in notes and ten pounds in currency. The Indian babu at the desk told me that he could not cash the draft. I asked him why not, and he said that the manager of the bank had gone to Enzeli with the British ambassador on the way to the coronation of Edward VII. "When would he be back?" "In three days." "But I want to start tomorrow morning for Teheran." He shrugged his shoulders and said it would be impossible to let me have the money. I bethought myself that, just before leaving Baku, on the eastbound trek, I had drawn considerable Russian gold and asked if he could change that, to which he promptly replied, "with pleasure." I then gave him 500 rubles and asked him to let me have the amount as indicated above. He was gone a long while and finally came back with $40 in Persian notes, which he said was all that the bank had, and $210 in currency.

Now the currency of the country, for all practical purposes, consists of krans (i.e., crowns), of about the value of 10 cents, and tomans, worth about 10 krans. (In theory, the tomans are struck in gold, and the krans in silver, but the gold is never seen and the silver only rarely.) The krans were coins about the size of our nickels, but so debased that the handling of a few of them made the fingers black, and also so debased that the tenacity of the metal was lost, so that when the die came down, it not only made a very poor impression, but at the margin of the coins, they were often split radially. (I have two or three of the coins in a little coin box in the parlor.)

He brought me, therefore, 2100 of these vile krans, in two great linen bags which filled the pockets of my sack coat and so weighted it down that I was afraid the fabric of the coat might give way. I had to hold them up with my hands. The counting of them was not only laborious but also soiled my hands very badly. Fortunately, I got rid of about 1000 of them at the posting station, where I paid for a landau into Teheran and back. When we reached Teheran, I immediately went to the posting station to see if we could not get a better landau, for this one was so bad that we declared we would never go back in it, fearing we should break down at any moment, and a breakdown, in that desolate country, would be a very serious business. But when we saw the array of dilapidated coaches that could be had, we gladly re-engaged the one in which we had come. Fortunately, it did not break down before we had returned to Rasht.

THE OPENING OF THE KIEL CANAL

In the summer of 1895, I went to Europe about a month or six weeks in advance of my three younger daughters, who came over later to meet me. I utilized this time in a round of visits to different surgical clinics in order to study German methods. I had arrived in Hamburg a few days before the opening of the Kiel Canal, which took place on a Thursday, Friday, and Saturday. From Hamburg I went to Kiel, on Monday morning, and spent that day and the two following in von Esmarch's clinic. I had written to him, some weeks in advance, asking him (as I was entirely ignorant about the hotels, etc.) if he would kindly engage for me suitable quarters. I received in reply a letter from the Princess Henrietta von Schleswig-Holstein Gemahlin von Esmarch. She herself had gone to see a friend, Frau Peterson, who, with her two daughters, kept a very nice small boarding house. There I had a bedroom and a salon and was made very comfortable. The entire week through, I was invited to von Esmarch's home to one meal every day. During the three *Feiertagen* at the end of the week, we had Prince Henry's band under the window, during mealtime. Von Esmarch also had obtained for me fine seats on the tribune, where I could see everything.

I learned a great deal, during the three days when I was in his clinic. Bier, now the successor of Langenbeck and von Bergmann, in Berlin, was then his first assistant. All the court was in Kiel, during the last three days of the week, and I met at mealtime several of those in the court circle. I particularly remember a very bright and entertaining young countess, a bride of perhaps 24 or 25, whom I took out to dinner, on one occasion. Never were my ears on more tension than during that meal. She spoke, in German, with the rapidity of a racehorse, and I am very sure that my *ja wohl, gewiss*, etc., every now and then came in at the wrong place. It was a comfort to me to turn to the princess, on whose right I sat, and have a little conversation in respectable English.

The celebration was wonderfully well organized. Each had directions as to his toilette, as well as to the boat on which he was to go to the end of the canal (which was some distance from Kiel itself)--and where the boat was to be found. No more spectators were placed on any one boat than could be accommodated with seats. When the opening proper took place, the Hohenzollern boat came first. On her deck were many colorful-ly costumed and distinguished-looking people. On the bridge were perhaps a dozen of the highest ranking admirals and generals, etc., and on the *Überbrücke* stood one alone, the Kaiser, who was eminently IT. He was dressed in the white uniform of the corps de garde, with a bright red sash across his chest and his silver helmet, surmounted by the Prussian eagle, on his head. He looked every inch a king. From time to time, he saluted with his hand, and as he passed through the canal into the open water, salvos of artillery (3000 guns in all) greeted him, to which were added innumerable bands and lusty cheers from the great multitude. It was a most inspiring sight.

THE MULTIPLIED MISHAPS OF A TRIP TO PANAMA

In January, 1905, the Pan-American Medical Congress was to be held in Panama, followed, a few days later, by an American Congress of Hygiene, in Havana. A doctor from Washington (who did not himself finally go with

259

us) organized a party of over 40 doctors (and members of their families) and inspected and arranged for an Italian ship, the *Athos* (which was engaged in the banana trade between Baltimore and Jamaica), to take us to Panama and Cuba for the two congresses, then return us to Baltimore via Jamaica--for a cargo of bananas. We were to leave Baltimore at 11 A.M. on December 26th. Dora and I engaged passage and left Philadelphia at 7 o'clock, not an agreeable hour of a dark winter's day. On arrival in Baltimore, at 9, we drove quickly to the pier, as it behooved us not to miss our steamer. When we arrived, there was no *Athos* to be seen. But some earlier arrivals pointed her out, coming up the bay from the ship-yard, where she had been undergoing renovation. She arrived about noon. The day was cold, a drizzling rain was falling, and soon a fog fell like a blanket, so that one could only dimly see anything 100 feet away. The ship had narrow decks and only one saloon, which was to serve as dining room, social hall, smoking room, reading room, writing room, and conversation room. The door, of necessity, was constantly open, and there was no steam in the pipes. This cheerless room was surpassed only by the dreary, disheartened passengers themselves.

We soon sat down to lunch, and that meal augured so ill that we made a combined raid upon the best grocery store in the city and supplied ourselves with coffee, canned milk, canned meats, sardines, biscuits, preserves, and other comestibles. Also, fortunately, Dora bought a good coffeepot. Investigation of the ship showed but two bathrooms, and each tub was so repulsive that a deputation visited the captain and were promised two new ones. Only one arrived.

Meantime, other troubles arose, with the cook's wife and the engineer's wife: One fell ill, and the other committed suicide. A new cook and a new engineer had to be procured. We had time for all of these emergencies, as the captain announced that, owing to the fog, we could not leave till the next day. Some of us spent the evening in town, with friends, or at a hotel, or in various places of amusement; but some were discouraged and gave up the trip entirely. About forty set sail the next morning, however, and then the troubles came thick and fast.

On the second day out, the electric-light apparatus gave out, and we had only candles, lamps, and lanterns. There was no electrician on board, but one of our stewards knew a good deal about electricity, fortunately, and he was excused from dining-room duty in order to repair the dynamo. As we had only two stewards to begin with, this left only one man to look after the forty of us. We looked after ourselves, in fact, and didn't mind doing our own "reaching."

In the corridors and other places, kerosene lamps were set on the floor. If a storm arose, a very likely event at the season, this seemed to expose us to danger from fire. On looking around us, we found no fire buckets, no reels of hose, no lists posted, giving the names and places assigned to the crew in case of fire or other emergency, and no provision for a fire drill. As the son of one of the owners was on board, we called his attention to these facts. He took us to the roof of our composite living room, where he assured us there were a dozen fire buckets. This we found to be true. There were twelve buckets. One of them was partly full of water, and the others absolutely empty.

We then called upon the captain. In broken English, he naively objected to ringing an alarm of fire for a fire drill because, said he, "nobody would know what to do." (!) Both the humor and the danger of such a reply were evident to us, if not to him, but he finally promised to have such a drill, post up such notices, etc. The notices were soon posted, but as they were in English, while the crew knew only Italian, their usefulness was not very apparent. The fire buckets, though fairly inaccessible, were at least filled, and the next day, we had a fire drill. The bell rang, and the crew ran; an ancient hose lying on the deck was screwed to the pump; and an attempt was made to turn on the water by an iron lever with a square hole in the middle. This lever promptly broke in two, and it was ten or fifteen minutes before another was found. How long it would have taken had there been a panic from a *real* fire was not clear. Even when the water was turned on, the hose leaked so badly that the captain started the crew sewing on a new canvas cover.

These many shortcomings suggested to us that an examination of the lifeboats would not be amiss. Of these there were three, in addition to an ordinary, large rowboat. Not one of these boats had *any* water aboard; two of them had *no* food. On a third we found a large square can, the lid of which was rusted off, and the contents of which, once presumably hardtack, had compacted into a sodden, pasty mass resembling Gorgonzola cheese in looks and surpassing it in odor. In one boat was an unmounted compass; in the others, none at all. I cleaned out an empty sardine can and filled it with the Gorgonzola biscuit paste for later use.

By this time, the electric light was going again, and we had two stewards once more, but in two or three days, it broke down a second time, and the electrical steward had to be excused once again for auxiliary duty.

Our misfortunes, by this time, had become a daily joke, instead of an annoyance. Our fellow-passengers were very pleasant companions and full

of merry jests and quick repartee. But by the time we had passed Cuba,

on our way to the Isthmus of Panama, the blower broke down, and our speed

(if our rate of progress could be described by such a misnomer) fell to

4 or 5 knots, under natural instead of forced draught. It was evident

that by the time the blower was repaired, we should be late to the con-

gress, or possibly miss it entirely; so we resolved upon a mock congress

of our own. The official Mexican delegate represented Dr. Amador, the

president of the Republic of Panama, and welcomed us in perfervid Spanish.

To this, Dr. Ramon Guiteras, as president of the congress, responded, also

in Spanish, if I remember rightly (it is over six years since these events).

We were all dressed fantastically. I made a chapeau out of some stiff

paper and stuck a borrowed feather in it. I borrowed also a green sash,

from one of the ladies, and fiercely flourished a table knife as a sword.

I represented the chief medical officer on the Isthmus. One of the ladies

had carved a medal in wood, with "A" on the obverse and "K" on the reverse.

This, by vote, was hung around my neck on a ribbon as a decoration of

honor, the speaker declaring that "A" was for *Athos*, that swift and re-

nowned vessel, and "K" for the worthy recipient. Dr. McDonald declared

later, in a very witty speech, that this interpretation of the symbols

was wholly wrong and that "A" and "K" stood for "Anti-Kamnia."

After the effervescence of the dinner and the speeches, we really

settled down to work and read and discussed our papers. These papers, by

a generous laxity, were later included in the printed proceedings of the

congress.

Before we reached Colón, our indignation at the danger from the inadequate appointments of the ship caused us to draw up and sign a protest. This, together with a statement in full of the dangerous conditions found (and with my sardine tin of Gorgonzola paste), we signed and mailed, in Panama, to Mr. Metcalf, the Secretary of Commerce and Labor. We accused the inspectors of gross laxity in allowing a ship so badly equipped to sail from any port of the United States. After our return, Mr. Metcalf sent a paper of each signer upholding his inspectors! I confess that it was a double (though a rather grim) satisfaction when I sent him a letter, a year later, announcing the fatal loss of the *Athos*, and in the following June, when we sat on the same platform at Yale, he received only an honorary A.M., while I received an LL.D.

But we reached Colón at last. We were so long delayed that they were anxious for our safety, and a revenue cutter was to start to hunt for us that very morning. Here again, more trouble arose. Nobody had notified anyone at Colón that we would need a berth at the dock and a special train to Panama (since the regular train had already gone). The captain rowed ashore, finally, and arranged for the train; we left about noon. On the way, we stopped at Gatun, the Culebra Cut, and possibly one or two other places, and reached Panama just as the congress had closed. The only part at which we assisted was the final dinner. President and Mrs. Amador also received us. The next day, we returned to Colón and left for Havana.

We reached Havana just as the Hygienic Congress was adjourning, but we assisted at the ball, that evening, at the palace of the president, and went on the excursion to Matanzas the following day. There we visited a large sugar mill and were greatly interested in sugar-making.

In view of the very poor equipment, and even (as I believed) the unseaworthiness of the *Athos*, we abandoned her, not being willing to trust Dora and myself in a possible storm off Hatteras. We waited three or four days and returned to New York on a Ward liner.

Only four of the original forty passengers continued on the *Athos*. She went to Jamaica, and misfortunes still followed her. When they dropped anchor in the harbor of Kingston, the anchor chain was so weak and rusted that it parted, and they left a $250 anchor at the bottom of the sea. Finally, they started home. Off Hatteras, a severe winter storm set in. They were driven far out to sea, as the wind, fortunately, was offshore. Had it been onshore, she would undoubtedly have been wrecked. They had to shut off the steam from all the cabins and the "living" room, as it was all needed for the engine. Even then, they were able to make only 3 knots. For two or three nights, the four nearly-frozen passengers dared not go to bed for fear of foundering. The voyage being prolonged by the storm, and provisions running low, the crew broke into the stores, and for some time, possibly two or three days, the bananas of the cargo were their principal diet. Many of these also were wet by the sea and rotted, producing an extremely disagreeable and nauseating odor. They reached Baltimore, at long last, cold, starved, and disgusted. The passengers all united in employing counsel to prosecute the lessees of the vessel for obtaining money under false pretenses: Even had no accident befallen us, the best rate of the ship was wholly insufficient to have landed us at Colón and Havana in time for our congresses. But we were informed that, during our absence, the firm had been merged into the Fruit Trust, and we could get no damages, by suing either the owners of the vessel or the firm that had leased the vessel and made the contract with us.

The later history of the ship was just such a tragedy as I had feared when we abandoned her at Havana. Just one year later, she sailed from Cape Breton, and from that day to this, she has never been heard from! Doubtless, she foundered during some storm and carried down with her some thirty human beings comprising the passengers and crew!

I have often wondered how Secretary Metcalf felt, when he received my letter stating this fact and calling to his attention that our protest, sent from Colón, had been, unfortunately, more than vindicated.

THE WOMAN'S MEDICAL COLLEGE

From 1884 to 1888, I was Professor of Surgery in The Woman's Medical College. For several years before that, I had been a lecturer on regional surgery. I found the students in dead earnest, hard workers and diligent. They were careful and exact dissectors and very soon overcame their natural repugnance to handling a dead body. Their emotional nature was at once a help and a hindrance. It gave them enthusiasm, but at the same time, it made inroads upon their sleep and mental poise, especially at examination time. As I once said to them, not a little to their amusement, during the examinations, one half of them were taking black coffee to keep themselves awake while cramming, and the other half were taking bromides to put them-selves to sleep.

When I was asked to accept the chair of surgery, women doctors were decidedly at a discount. A very few men (among them the only prominent ones were Dr. Ellwood Wilson and his first assistant, at the Lying-in-Charity, Dr. Albert H. Smith) were friendly to them and warmly advocated their admission to the county medical society. The large majority were partly neutral or, more commonly, actively hostile. I, therefore, advised

266

with several clear-headed friends as to whether I should accept the appointment. They were doubtful, as a rule, but not averse to my accepting
the place. For myself, I felt that the stage had passed when only strong-
minded freaks constituted the major part of the students, and that a
goodly number of young women, who had to earn their own living and who
were, therefore, in earnest, had a right to study and practice medicine,
and if so, they should have the best possible instruction. If I could
give them such instruction, I felt it my duty to do so, and so, despite
the certain unpopularity of the position, I accepted the chair--and never
regretted my action. In fact, it enabled me to try my wings in surgery,
and in clinical extemporaneous teaching, and in operating before a body
of critical students, all of which fitted me for the more important place
at the Jefferson.

In the sketch of my medical career, I have recorded some of my surgical work at the Woman's Medical College, and the influence it had in my
success. Two little additional incidents are all that it seems worth
while to record. At Commencement, the students usually took with them
photographs of the college and hospital buildings and of the faculty. One
year, the photographer who took a picture of the college building made a
curious and fatal mistake. The hospital and the college were placed thus:

x

Hospital [   ] y [   ] College

The photographer placed his camera at x, and the wall of the hospital, at
y, appeared in the left-hand margin of the photograph. Now on this wall,
in large letters, appeared the full name of the hospital:

WOMEN'S HOSPITAL
for
WOMEN & CHILDREN

Without observing the fact, his camera was so placed that the resulting picture had neatly amputated the "WO" on each line, leaving the name

                        MEN'S HOSPITAL
                             for
                        MEN & CHILDREN

The students would have none of it, and he had to take another.

The other was a most embarrassing incident.* I have always lectured extemporaneously, having before me only a few notes, as a skeleton of the lecture, so as to be sure to preserve a logical order, and also so as not to omit or repeat. But on more formal occasions, I wrote my address and read it. In writing such addresses (and my scientific papers) I have always followed a regular routine. First, I made brief notes of the topics and facts and arranged these in order. I had all my books and authorities at hand, with bookmarks at the desired pages, and after mulling over the matter for some days, or even weeks, I dictated a rough copy to my secretary. (In an evening, from 8 to 10, I could dictate, usually, about 3000 words, the equivalent of four pages of *Harper's Magazine*.) My secretary then wrote out this copy, with about double the usual space between the lines. This I went over one, two, or even three times, erasing, adding, transposing, etc. Then she made a fair copy, in duplicate. I next read over the carbon copy with great care, only for the purpose of correcting the English, since the arguments and facts had already been criticized and corrected in the rough copy. When this carbon copy was satisfactory, I then embodied the corrections in the original copy, which I would use the formal reading. This was on sheets of rather stiff paper, the size

_____

* This incident is partially alluded to at pp. 103-4.

of letter paper, and on one side only. As I read each page, I slipped it behind the last page, and so was never annoyed by having a MS which would easily bend over and thus be difficult to read.

At the opening of the winter session at the college, when the corporators and friends of the college, as well as the students, were present in full force, one of the faculty, in turn, delivered an "introductory" lecture. On the occasion when it was my turn, I picked up my MS from my office desk and went on my way in peace. In consequence of the method above described, I was, of course, very familiar both with the substance of the lecture (including, to a large extent, its exact wording) and with the sequence of thought. I read very freely; i.e., I was not bound to my text. Being nearsighted, I used spectacles with the lower half cut away. By looking through the upper half, I could look at my audience, a very important means of keeping in touch with them; and by looking underneath the lenses, I could glance at my MS and, by catching a word or phrase, could immediately look up and into the eyes of my auditors.

After I had read a number of pages of my address, on this occasion, I partly displaced the sheet from which I was reading, so as to slip it behind the others and thus be able quickly to fully expose the next sheet, I saw, to my consternation, that the next sheet was page one! In picking up my MS from the desk, I evidently had taken only part of it, some four or five sheets being left lying on the desk--without my having noticed it, strange to say! I had only four or five lines yet to read till I would reach the missing pages. That the human mind *can* do two things at once, I then found to be both true and *very* useful. While reading these last four or five lines, I debated what I should do. Only two courses were open to me: first, to confess the fault and stop abruptly; or second, to continue extemporaneously. I decided promptly on the latter course. Never was I more glad that my method of preparing an address had made me so familiar with its text.

I turned the last sheet to the back and proceeded extemporaneously, deceptively glancing at my MS, from time to time. When I had spoken, as I judged, about the amount that would occupy a page, I slipped the uppermost sheet to the back and so continued, sheet by sheet, till I reached my conclusion. But that hot sweat covered my face, and that my mental tension and activity were most strenuous, for those few minutes, were mild statements of fact. That I succeeded in my venial fraud is evident from the fact that only one person caught me at it, a friend who sat directly behind me and, happening to glance at my MS, observed the re-appearance of page one!

I have spoken, above, of the usefulness of a carbon copy of addresses and papers. On one occasion, I had good reason to deplore my not having had such a duplicate copy.*

In 1890, the International Medical Congress was held in Berlin. Cerebral surgery was then a very new field, of which many parts had been imperfectly explored, or even not explored at all. Accordingly, I spent all my spare time, for a whole year, on an elaborate paper on "The Surgery of the Lateral Ventricles." I searched systematically, with the invaluable help of the index catalog of the surgeon general's library and the *Index Medicus*, for every recorded case, from the Middle Ages down, involving

---

* This incident is partially alluded to at p. 97.

these ventricles. After exhausting the library of the College of Physicians of Philadelphia, I went to Washington and investigated the older literature, in many quartos and Latin folios. As a result, my paper was a very complete and, I may say without vanity, a most valuable résumé of the whole subject. It covered probably 50 or 60 pages of MS and was far too long, therefore, to be read in extenso at the congress. Accordingly, I had made an abstract, covering only 3 or 4 typewritten pages, which was all that I read at the congress. At the conclusion of my reading, I placed both the full MS and the short résumé in the hands of Dr. (now Prof.) Sonnenberg, of Berlin, who was the secretary of the surgical section, for printing in the *Transactions*.

The following summer, while in the Adirondacks on my vacation, I received a cablegram from Prof. von Bergmann, the president of the congress, saying that if I did not send my full paper at once, only the abstract could be printed. I at once cabled that I myself had personally placed the full paper in the hands of the secretary (Sonnenberg), as soon as I had read the résumé. I followed this with a letter to von Bergmann, giving a full account of the facts. How the abstract was preserved while the full paper was lost I do not know. From then till now, I have never received any letter of explanation--or apology--from either Sonnenberg or von Bergmann. Also, I had no carbon copy of the original paper. I could sympathize with Carlyle, whose MS of one whole volume of the history of the French Revolution was burned up, by a careless housemaid who lighted fires with it, but I had not his undaunted industry. A year had passed. I had many other things to do. To re-read all my authorities and to re-write the paper was a task that I had not the time or the courage to attempt. A year's labor thrown away--and in the 21 years since then, no

one has written any similar paper.

At various congresses and other surgical meetings since 1890, I have

repeatedly met Sonnenberg, now a distinguished professor of surgery in

Berlin. I have scorned to allude to his carelessness, and he has never

been manly enough to confess his fault. On three occasions, I have taken

Frau Sonnenberg out to dinner, and I confess to have taken a rather mali-

cious pleasure in making myself as agreeable as possible to *her* while

being only frigidly polite to *him*.

But I learned my lesson: Never, since then, have I written *anything*

of consequence without retaining a carbon copy.

THE ABILITY TO ENDURE PHYSICAL PAIN*

In 1887, while Professor of Surgery in the Woman's Medical College

of Philadelphia, I had the following unique experience.

A member of the class consulted me about numerous tubercular glands

in her neck. As they were threatening to degenerate into abscesses and

cause very ugly scars (and possibly become a source of wider infection),

I advised their removal.

To this she readily consented, but added the condition that it must

be done without ether or chloroform! On asking her the reason for this

singular condition, she said that she had already had two operations by

the late Prof. Henry B. Sands (in his day, the foremost surgeon in New

York), one under ether, the other under chloroform, and that she had suf-

---

* A printed version of this episode, included in a W.M.C. anniversary-
dinner speech entitled "Auld Lang Syne," appears in the Appendix.

272

fered so horribly and for so long, from the distressing nausea, that she would far rather suffer the pain of an operation, no matter how severe.

I remonstrated with her, pointing out that the operation meant severe and prolonged pain; that the incision would extend from the ear to the breastbone, and probably outwards along the collarbone; that the inner and outer flaps would have to be dissected from the underlying tissues and the glands dissected away, in an operation almost certainly to last an hour and a half; that the glands would be adherent to the carotid artery, the jugular vein, and the nerves of the neck; and that any sudden movement on her part might cause my knife to cut these important blood vessels or nerves--and even endanger her life. But all to no purpose: No anesthetic, or else no operation!

I then told her that I had just recently seen a notice of a new local anesthetic called cocaine, which was said to possess a remarkable power of preventing pain, and that, although I had never yet used it, or seen it used, I would try it in her case if she were willing. To this she instantly consented. Accordingly, I got an ounce of cocaine solution (then so rare and costly that I paid $5 for what I could now buy probably for 10 cents), and we set the day for the operation (May 27, 1887).

My predictions were fulfilled, as to the long incision, the tedious and dangerous dissection, by reason of the many and dense adhesions, and the duration of the operation. The cocaine dulled but did not wholly abolish the pain, due, doubtless, to my inexperience in its use.

A few minutes after I had begun the dissection, the patient said to me that she would like to watch the operation and asked if I would object to her doing so by means of a hand mirror! By that time, I was so thoroughly convinced of her self-control that I consented. One of the assistants brought a hand mirror, and almost continuously, for perhaps an hour and a quarter, that young woman watched every stroke of my knife and never flinched by a hair's breadth, even when I was dissecting the adherent glands from the great jugular vein, the carotid and subclavian arteries, or the nerves. Never before or since have I had such a spectacular operation.

Her subsequent experiences are a still further exemplification of her courage and endurance. After a year or so of slum work in New York, Dr. Rosetta Sherwood Hall was sent to Korea. Cupid, whose wand waves over Korea as well as over America, took a hand in the game, and she was married to a young medical man with whom she had been associated in her work in New York. Then came the Sino-Japanese War of 1895. After the devastation of Pyongyang, she and her husband went to minister to the wounded of both armies. Malignant typhus fever broke out, and her husband fell a victim.

Then she returned to America with her little son. Soon after her arrival, a daughter was born, now a sweet girl of sixteen and a great help to her mother.

In Korea, Dr. Hall has not only carried on the usual medical and missionary work, but she also has twice built a fine hospital (the second time, after its destruction by fire) and established both a home for the blind and another for the deaf and dumb, the first institutions of their kind in that country. They are two fine examples of the broad Christian charity which reaches out the helping hand to the defectives even more than to those who can help themselves.

274

The ability to endure pain varies greatly. The more highly civilized races do not bear pain nearly as well as those lower in the scale of development. So too, man in general feels pain far more acutely than do the lower animals. A horse with a leg so badly mangled that he had to be destroyed has been known to hobble around and quietly crop the grass as if nothing had happened, in the interval before a weapon could be obtained.

Many missionary surgeons have commented on the fact that Asiatics and Africans, even after very extensive operations, suffer little, as a rule, from the shock, which is almost always seen after operations on Europeans and Americans.

One of my patients needed the removal of a considerable portion of a rib just over the heart, because the bone was irreparably diseased (or, in fact, dead) and threatened further mischief. On account of a serious valvular disease of his heart, I did not wish to give him ether or chloroform and instead used cocaine. But he tossed about so badly, when I began the operation (in his case, as with a small percentage of persons, cocaine had little effect), that I was compelled to run the lesser risk of using ether, so as to avoid the greater risk of the shock to his nervous system--and also the possibility of my knife's penetrating his chest, and even wounding his heart, so violently did he struggle. The operation was then successfully finished, and he recovered nicely.

One of those present was Dr. Thorn, a missionary in Mardin, in Asia Minor. After the operation, he said to me, "Do you know, Dr. Keen, what I would have done in Mardin if a Kurd had needed such an operation? "No," said I, "What would you have done?" He replied, "I should never have even thought of cocaine or ether, but would have told him to lie down on the table and would have proceeded at once to operate; and he never would have budged or uttered a cry or moan."

Another man, but an exceptional one in America, well illustrated this same stoicism or indifference to pain. He was a man of, say, 30, a total stranger who came to consult me, one evening, about a lump on his back. On examination, it proved to be a fatty tumor as large as two fists. I told him that the only way to deal with it was to cut it out. Instantly, he threw himself face foremost on the lounge and laconically said, "Go ahead!" "Don't you want any ether?" I asked. "No, go ahead."

Accordingly, as soon as I could make my antiseptic preparations, I "went ahead." The incision was perhaps 6 or 8 inches long, and the tumor, by reason of fibrous adhesions, required considerable cutting--and not a little force--to enucleate it. He never moved a muscle or uttered a groan. It was more like operating upon a cadaver than upon a living, sentient human being. I sewed up the wound with silver wire (it happened a good many years ago, as a surgeon would know by this fact), carefully dressed the wound, and, as this was in the evening, I said to him, "If you have any pain, or if any bleeding shows through the dressing, come in to see me tomorrow morning. In any case, I want you to see me the day after tomorrow, and again a few days later, when I will remove the stitches." "How much shall I pay you?" he quietly asked, at the same time producing a very encouraging roll of bills from his trouser pocket. As a young and impecunious surgeon, I remembered, fortunately, that a bird in the hand is worth two in the bush, and instead of suggesting that he wait till he was well and that he then could pay for the operation and any later care, I mentioned an amount. This he willingly paid and left the office. Who re-

276

moved the stitches I do not know. I never saw him again!

The introduction of anesthesia has, happily, abolished pain. The older surgeons have often described to me the horrors of the pre-anesthetic era, which, fortunately, I never saw. Ether was first publicly used, on Oct. 16th, 1846, by Dr. Morton and Prof. John C. Warren, at the Massachusetts General Hospital. Sir James Y. Simpson, of Edinburgh, discovered chloroform in 1847. (I did not begin the study of medicine till 1860.)

In the dreadful earlier days, as may be seen in pictures of the surgeries, the patient bent his knees and clasped his ankles, the ankles and hands being securely bound together by bandages. He was also held by strong assistants, who kept him in comparative quiet. But his uncontrollable struggles and his screams were something terrible to see and hear. Meantime, as the means for the control of hemorrhage were then very imperfect, the operating rooms were veritable bloody shambles.

The careful and painstaking, long-lasting operations of today were impossible, first, because human nerves could not endure one or two hours of horrible pain (and sometimes operations last even longer); and second, because the struggles of the patient absolutely prevented the kind of fine and delicate operations that are now so common. He was the best surgeon (and held in the greatest repute) who could slash off an arm or leg, or extract a stone from a bladder in five, ten, or fifteen seconds less than any other operator. While this developed great dexterity, it was inconsistent with the exact and careful surgery of the present day. *Tuto, cito, et jucunde* had its principal stress, before 1846, on the *cito* ("quickly"); now it is on the "safely" and the "successfully."

LIFE IN AMERICA ONE HUNDRED YEARS AGO*

The custom of serving dinner in courses was not practiced as we now practice it. Ordinarily, the whole dinner was on the table at the same time, but for a special feast there might be two courses of the same character and each a dinner in itself. The attractiveness of the table depended upon the symmetrical arrangement of the dishes and upon their garnishment. There would be nine or ten large dishes upon the table, besides a number of smaller ones. The tablecloth would hardly be visible. An opulent man giving a dinner party would serve something like the following: for the first course, a cod's head, being the head and shoulders of a fresh codfish, a dish much esteemed at the time; pea soup, venison, roasted chickens, boiled ham, beef collops, which corresponded with beefsteak; potatoes, celery, parsnips, jelly, pies, and marrow pudding. For the second course, turkey poults (young turkeys), scalloped oysters, roasted rabbits, wild ducks, lamb, smelts, haricot (usually written "harrico"), being a mutton ragoût, several vegetables, cherry tarts, and stewed pippins. Then there would be brought in some ice cream by itself. It was considered to be a great luxury, and it was eaten on rare occasions. The decanters of wine were distributed about the table. The servants placed the dishes on the table and changed the plates and knives and forks, from time to time. The largest dishes of meat were carved by the host and hostess, and the person nearest a dish was expected to help his neighbors to it. Thus they all fed one another, and everybody was busy.

SPEECH AT THE ANNUAL DINNER OF THE
BRITISH MEDICAL ASSOCIATION, LONDON,
August 1st, 1895**

Dr. W. W. Keen said that they had been told by the Lord Chancellor

that the most difficult thing for a speaker to do was to sit down. He

found most certainly that the next most difficult thing for a speaker to

do was to get up. It was bad enough to make an after-dinner speech in his

own country, but in England, and with that distinguished assembly before

---

* Hunt, Gaillard (Litt.D., LL.D.). *Life in America One Hundred Years Ago*. Harper & Bros., New York, 1914. p. 222.

** Published in the *British Medical Journal*, August 10, 1895. p. 367.

him, he could assure them that it was with great trepidation that he rose to his feet. He felt very much like the Irishman who during the American War was wounded and came before the Pension Board to apply for a pension. The surgeon asked him where he was wounded, and he placed his hand directly over his heart. "No, no," said the doctor, "It is not possible, Pat, that you were hit there; it would have gone through your heart." "Faith, sir," said he, "and when I was hit, me heart was in me mouth."

They had heard the thanks presented to this noble association by their distinguished guest, Professor Stokvis, as representing the eastern hemisphere; it was his (Dr. Keen's) pleasant duty to return thanks for his brethren of the western hemisphere. Only the other day he met an American friend at dinner, at the hospital table of the president of their surgical section, who said to him, "I think I dine with you more frequently in London than I do in New York." This brought forth a remark from an English friend, that the Americans seemed to think nothing of crossing the big pond, to which Dr. Keen replied, as he justly might, "It is no wonder that we can come over here, and do so frequently, when we have such attractions upon this side." Though a good many Americans were prodigal sons, somewhat over a hundred years ago, yet whenever they did come home, he noticed that Englishmen were always ready to kill the fatted calf, and by reason of it there was great danger--and he had found it so--to their digestion. He could assure them that nothing pleased an American so much as to come to the old home, Old England, to be welcomed by its capacious heart, big enough to hold all of them, yea, and all the world besides. The roast beef of Old England had been celebrated, but it had given way, with Americans at least, to their appreciation of the old and great Eng-

lish heart. In saying "English," he meant not only England, but Scotland,
Wales, Ireland, and the colonies as well. It was very much on the principle of the commencement of the church service which said, "Dearly beloved
brethren" on the ground that it was not necessary to mention the sisters,
because the brethren embraced the sisters.

Another reason why they would come over was that they had all been
taught in the English school. When he was a student of medicine, he was
cradled in Gray's *Anatomy*, he hardened his gums on *Watson's Practice*, that
admirable book by the Addison of modern English medicine. He was guided,
in his first obstetric case, by the light of *Ramsbotham's Obstetrics*,
whilst his surgical patron saint was Sir James Paget. He wished that the
members of the association could come to America, where they would receive
as hearty a welcome as the descendants of the old English stock could show
them. He was glad to know that there were many American physicians who
were held in just as great esteem on this side of the water as distinguished English physicians were on their side. They all knew Gross, Da
Costa, and others. Mr. Heath said of one of their Americans, at least,
that his name was in all their mouths, and his button was in their bowels.

He had lately seen, in the *Boston Medical and Surgical Journal*, a
proposal which out-Murphied Murphy by far. It was written under the name
of Paul Pry, Junior, and was dated in 1995. It related the procedure his
ancestor, a century before, had introduced into American practice, and from
that it had spread all over the world, an immense improvement, especially
in celiotomy. At that distant time, it was not uncommonly necessary, after
having made an abdominal section, when the bowels got tangled up, to make
another, in order to disentangle them. Paul Pry's grandfather had taken a

hint from Nature and had improved the common practice greatly. The hint

was a very simple one. There, thought he, as he was about to begin his

operation, was the belly button; doubtless, thought he, the remnant of a

row of buttons that ran up and down, and, thereafter, in order to induce

a return to atavism whenever he had a celiotomy, he made a row of buttons

and buttonholes and simply closed the abdomen in that way. Then if the

bowels got tangled and twisted up, he could readily reopen and disentangle

them. In fact he narrated, as a remarkable proof at that time existing

of the truth of Darwinism, that a number of children had been born of par-

ents who had been operated upon by his grandfather with a row of brass

buttons all the way down the median line of the abdomen.

He could assure them, speaking seriously, that he brought to them

most hearty thanks for the welcome that had been given to them, and that

had been as cordial, as widespread, and as universal as the members of the

British Medical Association.

(Meeting Prof. W. T. Lusk, of New York, a year or more after the

above address had been made: He told me that his son had been present at

the dinner, and that next to him sat an Englishman, drinking it all in

until I came to the "row of brass buttons," at which he turned to him and

said, "Oh pshaw, he can't expect us to believe that anyway!")

SPEECH AT THE ANNUAL DINNER OF THE
BRITISH MEDICAL ASSOCIATION, MONTREAL,
September 2nd, 1897*

Dr. Keen said that when he was asked to respond to the toast, he felt

very much like the Irishman belonging to one of their regiments in the

---

* *British Medical Journal.* September 25, 1897. p. 820.

Civil War, who was intercepted by his colonel when he was running away. "Where are you going, you cowardly scoundrel?" demanded the officer. "Begorra, Colonel," said he, "I'd rather be a coward for five minutes than be a corpse all the rest of me life." He too felt very much like running away like a coward. In the absence of Prof. Bowditch, who was also expected to respond to this toast, he now found himself called upon to make two speeches, at 2 o'clock in the morning. He would promise them, however, that the two speeches should be short.

The organization of that meeting did credit to the profession of Canada, and above all to the profession of Montreal. He only hoped that in Moscow they had a Roddick, and Adami, a Bell, an Armstrong, a Shepherd, and so on; he might go through the whole list of officers. They had also admired the learning gathered in the association, which met not for the purpose of hoarding trade secrets, but of casting them broadcast over the whole world. They had found in Montreal a most unbounded hospitality, a hospitality as royal as the mountain that had given its name to their city, a name which now graced their first citizen. They had found in Montreal a friendship as spontaneous as the clear crystal springs that flowed from their mountains, as broad as the acres of their great wheat fields, the granaries of a nation. He was sure he was the spokesman of every guest, nay, of every host also, when he said that the hardest tie to break would be that which bound them to one who was peerless as a benefactor to mankind, under every sun and in every clime, not only in the last years of a waning century, but in all centuries to come, around whose head the gathering years were weaving a chaplet of honours intertwined with reverent love, Mr.--Sir Joseph--Lord Lister.

282

Nor did they forget the land to which their departing friends would go. It was historic ground, the land of Hampden, of Pym, and Harry Vane and John Milton, hallowed by the blood of Roundheads and Puritans, hallowed by the fires of Smithfield and of Oxford, in the glorious struggle for liberty; and as in this jubilee year of a glorious reign some of them would rest by Canadian firesides and others go to dear old England, their cousins across the border, Britons only by one or two removes--for did not U.S. spell not *you* nor *me*, but *US*?--as they waved a last farewell, would join with all their hearts in singing "God save the Queen."

ADDRESS* IN REPLYING TO THE TOAST "AN IMPOSSIBLE WAR"

Mr. Toastmaster, my Lords, Ladies and Gentlemen:

The chairman and other speakers have all very naturally, and very rightly, referred to the captivating idea of celebrating the completion of 100 years of peace between Great Britain and America.

But there is an earlier instance of the splendid magnanimity of Great Britain to which no one has alluded tonight, and to which scant justice has been done by anyone in the past. In 1876, we celebrated 100 years of our national independence by an extensive and most successful universal exposition, in which all nations joined. Each nation erected a building to house its commissioners. Among the foremost, in the extent and value of its exhibits and the importance of its official building, was Great Britain. Without British aid, the exhibition would have been shorn of much of its luster. At the close of the exhibition, this British building

---

* May 13, 1913, the Bellevue-Stratford Hotel [Philadelphia], at the banquet to the Foreign Delegates to arrange for the Celebration of the 100th Anniversary of Peace Among English-Speaking People in 1914-1915.

was presented to the city of Philadelphia. It still stands, in full view from the Belmont Drive in Fairmount Park, a mute but eloquent witness to the magnanimity of a great nation.

To assist, not grudgingly but heartily, in making such a celebration by another nation a great success is an incident unique in history.

Recall the startling facts: We were celebrating a war which began at Bunker Hill and was ended by the surrender of Cornwallis at Yorktown; we were the victors, and the British were the vanquished; at the end of a century, they joined with us in celebrating our victory and their defeat. I challenge you to find a parallel event in the world's international relations. A war with a nation so magnanimous as to celebrate, in 1876, their own defeat and to treat us not as foreigners but as transatlantic brethren ought to be, and *is*, "an impossible war."

Think, gentlemen of the British delegation, of the great gifts you have bestowed upon us! Chaucer and Bacon, Shakespeare and Milton, Hampden and Burke, Jenner and Lister! How many memories cluster around each name! Recall too what we in turn have given to you: Washington and Lincoln, Longfellow and Emerson, Henry C. Lea and Horace Howard Furness; and the blessed sleep of ether!

It is not unbecoming in me, on this occasion, to vaunt my own profession. The three boons, vaccination, anesthesia, and antisepsis--an everlasting trinity of benedictions--and all three, thank God! sprung from Anglo-Saxon loins, have already done more to mitigate suffering, prolong life, and promote human hapiness than all the warriors, from Genghis Khan to Napoleon, have done to produce suffering, destroy human life, and make the earth a desert.

Your civil liberty and orderly processes of law, gentlemen, have found a congenial soil in America, and we have even bettered your religious liberty by totally severing all relations between Church and State.

I repeat, then, my assertion that a war between two such kindred nations is impossible, unthinkable. It would be a crime against humanity!

I have spoken of the action of Great Britain in 1876 as an unparalleled instance of magnanimity. But it is to remain without a fellow for only a few weeks more.

Six weeks from now, on the field at Gettysburg, hallowed by the blood of heroes and by Lincoln's immortal address, the soldiers of the Blue and the Gray--those who, after 50 years, are still living--will meet again. There, on the very spot where they had done their utmost to slay each other, a half-century ago, with clasped hands they will bow their heads over the graves of their brave comrades and breathe a prayer of thanksgiving for peace. Show me, if you can, another such meeting on any other battlefield!

But while there never has been such a one before, permit me to express the fervent hope that there *may* be yet another.

A few days ago, as president of the American Philosophical Society, I signed a remarkable address. Its signers consist of the presidents of fifty-five scientific, educational, and philanthropic institutions in the United States. The address is beautifully engrossed on vellum and is to be presented to the German emperor on June 15th, 1913. It extends to his Imperial Majesty our collective congratulations on the completion of 25 years of his reign, and especially that it has been a reign of unbroken peace!

I cast a forward glance, and in the near future--only seven years away--I see the year 1920, exactly half a century after 1870! What a glorious augury it would be for the peace of the world, for the Golden Age that is sometime sure to come, if France and Germany could then again meet on the field of Sedan, not in armed conflict but to celebrate the liberté, egalité et fraternité which should never again disappear from the earth!

Then would we be able to sign, not "Peace hath her victories no less renown'd than war," but "Peace hath her victories *far more* renown'd than war."

ADDRESS TO THE GRADUATING CLASS OF NURSES
ALLENTOWN HOSPITAL
May 27th, 1915

When I received the kind invitation to address you, I hesitated a good deal, at first, for I am no longer as young as I was 78 years ago, and I have so much to do that I have had practically no leisure.

But when I learned what you are doing here, and how extraordinarily well you are doing it, I said I will surely *make* time to go, for I want to see the place and encourage those good people--and by "those good people" I mean to include the trustees, the doctors, the nurses, and the general community.

Your last report shows 181 beds and 1869 patients, during the year; that is, over 10 patients in each bed, not simultaneously but tandem, if I may so express it. Imagine what it must have been in the Hôtel-Dieu in Paris, 150 and 200 years ago, when there were literally from two to six patients (and such patients!) in one bed, simultaneously in this case.

You reported also 1035 operations, which meant almost six operations per bed. This quick turnover means quick recovery, which in turn means a well-administered hospital, an able staff, and devoted, competent nurses.

You could hardly imagine the state of affairs when I graduated, 53 years ago. The newly-fledged doctor had never auscultated, or percussed the heart or the lungs, had never examined an abdomen, and had never even so much as touched a patient to find out if there was a fever. No thermometers were in general use until the '70s. He had never looked through a microscope, handled a test tube, himself examined any secretion, and had never seen a necropsy.

The nurse (but there *were* no nurses as we now understand the term), or any woman (practically never a man) who wished to become a nurse, simply helped this doctor or that, or nursed a friend through typhoid or a maternity case, gradually becoming very fairly skilled by mere practice, learning, that is, how to nurse *you* by her mistakes on *me*--or the reverse, as I should much prefer.

When I opened my office, in 1866, I did not need any nurses, for I had no patients, for many weary weeks. When, at last, the need arose, I knew not where or how to get one. So I obtained from one of my much older friends, who was in active practice, a list of names and addresses. Then when I needed a nurse, I gave the patient's family a copy of this list, and he spent from a few hours to a day or more, driving from place to place, in a hired hack, only to find one nurse out nursing, another out shopping, another sick in bed, and so on, but finally he would get one. Happy was he if he got a nurse within the first few hours, or even during the first day.

Ever since 1882, at the College of Physicians of Philadelphia, we have had a directory of nurses, in which certified nurses, men and women, are registered, with lists of those who are at work and those who are free, of those who specialize in accident or other surgical cases, or those in contagious diseases, etc. Rarely does one have to wait more than an hour or two, and often the nurse is secured (usually by telephone) within half an hour. In accidents, in cases of sudden delirium tremens, or insanity, or unexpected obstetrical emergencies, this is a boon indeed.

If you have no such directory of nurses in Allentown, why should not this hospital inaugurate such a service, not only for its own graduates but for all the nurses in town?

When you have patients like myself, for instance, you will need unlimited patience. Twice I have needed the kindly services of good nurses. The first time, I had a bad fall and had broken a collarbone (just to establish an equilibrium, a few years later, I broke the other one by yet another fall) and some ribs, and had gotten a general shaking-up from head to foot. The first night in the hospital, I ached intolerably and everywhere asked to be turned, again and again. This "turning" consisted in only budging me half an inch one way or the other, I am sure, but it relieved my mind, if not my body, and kept the night nurse busy and out of mischief.

In the morning, my conscience pricking me, I said to her (she was one of that class of fine nurses whose winsome ways and very attractive uniform make one, if well, half-glad to be sick and, if sick, half-loath to get well), "I'm afraid that I was a *very* troublesome patient last night." "Oh well," she replied, in a cheerful, forgiving tone, "you did have to be turned rather often." Rather often! You bet. Pardon the slang, but no other expression quite fits the case.

The second time I required similar services was after a very serious abdominal operation, and my day and night nurses were equally patient, tender, and, again, forgiving. Two events stand out, during that illness, one of which has given me great pleasure, and the other, great amusement, ever since. When I was convalescent, one of the former graduate nurses of the Jefferson, to whom I had handed the gold medal of honor, at her graduation some years before, and who had risen to the responsible position of superintendent of a training school for nurses in a large hospital, when she had heard that I was "so near," as she put it, took a whole night's journey by rail to pay me a visit of congratulation on my recovery and spent another night returning to her hospital. That was indeed the loyalty of an old friend.

The day after I was operated on, I had only hot water to sip. The next day, I was allowed albumen water. Now if you could devise more tasteless stuff than that, you would deserve a leather medal. So I asked if I might have some albumenized milk.* I had used it for years in my own surgical work and knew its virtues. This gave me great comfort. Naturally, the nurses discussed it among themselves, as it was new to them. A patient in the adjoining rooms, hearing of it, asked if she could have some, to which her surgeon assented. Her nurse, not being able to ask my nurse, who was out, went to the refrigerator and, finding the bottle with my name on it, poured out a generous dose. But when her patient had tasted a sip,

---

* Recipe (from an old, experienced nurse): Shake together, for 5 minutes, 3 oz. of lime water and the whites of 3 eggs. Add ½ pt. of hot--not boiled --milk and shake again for 5 minutes. Add sugar or sherry to taste. Use more or less lime water as needed. Give in doses (hot or cold) from a spoonful to half a tumblerful.

of it, she said to her nurse, "Throw it away. If that's what Dr. Keen calls good, I pity his taste." When my own nurse was told the story, on her return, she burst into a fit of laughter and explained that, as I had emptied the bottle during the night, she had decided to wash it out thoroughly and had filled it with soapsuds. But I'm bound to add that the soapsuds washed out the other patient so well that her recovery was speedy and complete.

Remember that for doctors and nurses, the most important canal in the world is not the Panama, the Suez, the Soo, the Kiel, or any other of the great geographical canals of the world, but, as has been well said, the alimentary. Watch, therefore, with scrupulous care everything that enters it. Learn how to cook the little appetizing *bonnes bouches* and (do not forget this) to serve them with the daintiness which stimulates or even evokes an appetite, just as slovenliness dulls or even destroys it.

I wish you all might read those delightful volumes, *Horae Subsecivae*, of Dr. John Brown, of Edinburgh. (I could also wish that the English title read *Leisure Hours*, instead of *Spare Hours*, which, to me, at least, always suggests spare ribs.) In those volumes you would find much homely wisdom that bears on medicine, including the most charming and pathetic of all medical stories, "Rab and His Friends."

In another story, I find this: "Pray, Mr. Opie," asked someone of the painter, "with what do you mix your paints?" "With brains, sir," was the crusty but illuminating reply.

If you wish to succeed in nursing, in medicine, in blacksmithing, in business, or anything, you must use your brains, something, both volatile and valuable, which will ensure success. Lacking that, you may not starve,

290

you may even get along, but more than "get along" you never will.

Among the uses to which you must put your brain is to make yourself one of the family, not drawing too rigid a line around yourself within which lie your duties and without which you ignore everything. Remember the golden rule for nurses (and for doctors as well, for I have often gladly done the not-always-agreeable work of a nurse myself): *Whatever is necessary for the comfort, well-being, and recovery of your patient, that is your duty.*

Don't always expect to be waited on. To wait on yourself, in many cases, will be a necessity, and when this is so, do it cheerfully, and wait not only on your patient and yourself, but, in many cases, you will oil the machinery by waiting on others of the patient's family.

You will find many people unreasonable. They expect you to be made of Bessemer steel and vulcanized rubber, to know no such thing as weariness or sleepiness, but to be on duty 24 hours, every day. The doctor, in that case, should be your confidant and succor. There are times, for a day or so after an operation, when prolonged hours are a necessity, but once this emergency is past, the doctor should insist on good sleep, as regular meals as is possible, and at least one hour in the open air every day. He should point out to the family that to them, sickness is, happily, a rare emergency, but to you, a constant companion; and that to *nurse* well you must *be* well, and that proper sleep, food, and fresh air are the prime requisites for health.

If, after all, you find (and rarely you may find) an unreasonable family who will not heed the doctor and self-evident common sense, then you owe it to yourself, and your health, to give up the case. But if you do, always stay for at least 24 hours, and even longer, if necessary, in order to afford time for procuring another nurse. Abruptly and at once to leave a very ill patient is a sin of the first magnitude for any nurse, unless the circumstances are wholly exceptional.

You will go forth from this hospital well trained in your honorable profession. You will be a comfort and a joy to many a patient and many a family. You will be the doctor's right hand. On you rest the honor of your profession, the responsibility of caring for your patient, in the intervals between the doctor's visits, and, in not a few cases, the recovery of your patient.

This last is especially true of typhoid fever, To notify the physician at once, if a typhoid patient complains of abdominal pain, is the golden rule in typhoid, for this is the very first symptom of perforation. If you are prompt, and if the doctor is prompt in calling in the surgeon, and if he too is prompt in operating, the mortality from typhoid perforation can be far less than at present. The same rule should prove valid in appendicitis, and similar promptness would be followed by similarly happy results.

If you do your work thus, faithfully "as ever in your great Taskmaster's eye," each day's duty will be a joy to you and a blessing to your patients. I bid you farewell and Godspeed.

AFTER-DINNER SPEECH BEFORE THE
ALUMNI ASSOCIATION OF THE JEFFERSON MEDICAL COLLEGE
June 4th, 1915

1825 . . . 1860 . . . 1915. What do these three dates mean? The first is the date of the founding of the Jefferson Medical College; the second is the year when I entered its halls as a student; the third is the present year of grace.

In 1860, the Jefferson was only 35 years old. From 1860 to 1915, I have been connected with the college, as student, alumnus, lecturer, professor, and emeritus professor--for 55 years, or almost two-thirds of its entire existence.

In 1860, the faculty included only the "sacred seven," plus one solitary demonstrator (in Anatomy). There are now 49 active professors, of various grades, and 100 demonstrators and other assistants. Then there was only one laboratory (Anatomy); now there are fifteen. Then one could walk right in from the anvil, or the plow, and after two so-called years could walk out a full-fledged doctor. I say "so-called years," for all medical schools spurned the Ptolemaic, the Julian, and the Gregorian calendars: they had their own. This might be called a Hippocratic (or, perhaps better, hypocritic) calendar, in which the year consisted of only five months, with a liberal allowance for bracing official holidays, in addition to those when our numerous beloved grandparents had to be buried.

Then, a capital operation was a rarity (and rumored for days), and the front seats were rushed for, on the momentous occasion. But the blasé student in 1915 hardly hastens his step for anything less than a suture of the heart or a hip-joint.

The undergraduates were much less studious than those of today, and the number of roisterers (who had more or less serious differences of opinions with the police) was much larger. Scarcely a week went by when some member of the faculty was not routed out of bed to go bail for some student offender.

I remember a story told me, by Dr. S. Weir Mitchell, of a young man from Texas who wished to enter as one of his office students--for every student then had a preceptor. After some conversation as to his education, Dr. Mitchell innocently asked him if he had any accomplishments. Thereupon the young man reached behind his neck, drew out a bowie knife, and, after a preliminary pass or two, let fly and deftly planted the knife blade between two panes of glass, near the top of the window. Mitchell complimented him upon his high, not to say accurate, aims but advised him to enter a more war-like office than his own, one in which students were prepared for the army and navy.

The first year was, to a large extent, wasted. But the second year had to be one of more or less serious work, for while there was no examination at the end of the first year, what passed for an examination really did take place at the end of the second.

At the end of my first year, I coached a second-year student, in Anatomy, Physiology, and Surgery, for graduation. I sprinkled over him the thimbleful of knowledge I possessed, some of it soaked in, and he passed.

This was the way in which alumni were made, half a century ago. I am not, as you perceive, a *laudator temporis acti*. I believe that the present is far better than the past and that if our honored ancestors were to return, they would gladly recognize the enormous progress we have made.

The only wonder is how the men of my time ever have amounted to anything. The explanation is simply this (an explanation which will apply to you in your turn): From the day of our graduation until now, we have had to work our fingernails off; we have had to "scorn delights and live laborious days" (aye, and laborious nights as well); we have had to read books

294

and journals (in English, French, and German), and to card-catalog what we read; we have had to take full notes of our cases, in laborious long-hand, till of late years; and we have had to remember Bacon's dictum that "reading maketh a full man, conference a ready man, and writing an exact man": From writing brief articles we grew up to the level of longer essays, finally coming to write textbooks and systematic treatises. The moment that, by study, observation, and experience, you know more than other doctors about any disease, symptom, or operation, in that moment you owe a duty to our profession, and to suffering humanity, to publish that knowledge. But never write or speak unless you have something to say that is *worth saying*, and when you have said it, *STOP.*

Thus far, I have described the way in which our medical colleges made alumni, fifty years ago, and how the alumni of those early years made up for the defects in our education. What has been the harvest? What have our alumni done?

Homer's catalog of the ships has always seemed to me an example of useful dullness. Any extended list of graduates of the Jefferson, including those identified with her as teachers, would be even more tedious. I shall, therefore, recite only a short list of the more eminent, omitting, with two exceptions, the living. Each name will call up some memories, especially for those among you who have passed the half-century mark. I shall not even attempt to place them in chronological order, but, rather, in the order in which their names occur to me:

> George McClellan (the founder)
> George McClellan (his grandson)
> Nathan R. Smith
> Daniel Drake
> Joseph Pancoast
> Thomas D. Mütter

295

Robley Dunglison
John K. and S. Weir Mitchell (father and son)
Samuel D. and Samuel W. Gross (father and son)
J. Marion Sims
Robert Battey
Levi C. Lane
David Brainard
William Goodell
Washington L. Atlee
Thomas Addie Homet
Charles D. Meigs
J. M. DaCosta
John H. Brinton
Roberts Bartholow

Only a score, and yet, how much they suggest, and how much they did!

The number of our alumni who have founded other medical colleges, including the Rush Medical College of Chicago, and who have taught (and are teaching), in more than a score of such institutions, is far too large to recount.

Two names among the living I feel that I must speak of: Thomas W. Jackson and Victor G. Heiser, both students of my own.

You all know the sad plight of Serbia, now involved in a third war in as many years, and suffering from a severe epidemic of typhus fever, that age-old foe of armies often more deadly than the enemy. To venture into that zone of death is fraught with danger. But when did the men of our guild ever flee, in craven fear, before danger? Eighty-odd years ago, Gross hurried *into* New York when everyone else was hurrying *out*, because the cholera was daily slaying its victims by the hundreds. So, now, another graduate of the Jefferson, Thomas W. Jackson--his very name is an inspiration--has hastened with other doctors and nurses to aid that little nation in its heroic fight. God grant that they may win, without themselves falling victim.

Victor G. Heiser has had a fine record as Director of Health of the Philippines but is about to leave the government service to undertake a wonderful work for the Rockefeller Foundation, no less a task than to endeavor to stamp out leprosy over the whole round globe. And I believe he will do it.

The school, which has produced a roll of honor embracing the names of such men as those I have read, has more than justified its existence. It occupies a high position among the beneficent institutions of this whole country.

But what of the thousands of graduates who are among our undistinguished alumni? Have I not a word for them? Yea, verily.

You remember Mr. Lincoln's happy saying, that the Lord must have loved the plain people because he made so many of them. To play a distinguished rôle in life is given to only a few. But the Great Father in Heaven does not judge by man's standards. Those thousands of our alumni who, in their daily rounds of arduous duties, are faithful, tried and true, cheering the faint-hearted, bringing health to the sick and the maimed, consoling the dying and the bereaved, endearing themselves to their patients by the kindly sympathy that only the doctor can give, leading pure and unselfish lives before their Maker, such men and women, whether their lives be long or short, have lived complete and worthy lives. They are sure of the welcome, "Well done, thou good and faithful servant." Of such is the kingdom of heaven.

THE AMERICAN PHILOSOPHICAL SOCIETY

During my absence in Europe (from the spring of 1907, after I had re-signed my chair at the Jefferson, until October of the following year), I was elected, in January, 1908, president of the American Philosophical Society.

As I learned after my return, I had been proposed for the presidency a few years earlier, on the resignation of General Wistar. The only other name put forth, so far as I know, was that of Dr. Edgar F. Smith, the provost of the University of Pennsylvania. Dr. C. C. Harrison put his foot down, asserting positively that Dr. Smith, as the representative of the university, must be elected and I must not be chosen (why, I don't know). When Dr. Smith resigned, there was no opposition, so far as I know.

My election was all the more a compliment as it was known that I was not to return to America until the autumn of 1908, at the earliest. I had been informed of my proposed election and had consented to serve, but, of course, I had done nothing whatever to promote it.

It was certainly the highest scientific honor I have ever received. To sit in the chair which had been occupied by Franklin, Rittenhouse, Jefferson (for eighteen years), and their distinguished successors, was far above anything I had ever dreamed of. I had been elected to membership in 1884 but had never taken a very active part in the society. I had served on the council for three years.

While abroad, I had laid my plans for a vigorous administration in various ways, and as soon as I returned, I threw myself into the work, with all the ardor I could command.

The meetings, then, were held twice a month, on the first and third

Fridays from October through May.

On my arrival, only a few days before the first of October, I found that on October 2nd, A. E. Kennelly and Walter E. Upson were to read a paper on "The Humming Telephone," and that E. B. Titchner and W. H. Pyle were to read a paper on "The After-Images of Subliminal Colored Stimuli," but that no other speakers had as yet been provided. I was fortunate in immediately securing Dr. E. O. Hovey, of the American Museum of Natural History, for October 16th, the first meeting at which I personally pre-sided. He read a very interesting paper entitled, "A Contribution to the History of Mt. Pelée, Martinique." In New York, I also secured Dr. Alexis Carrel, of the Rockefeller Institute, who presented a paper, on November 6th, entitled, "Recent Studies in Transplantation of Organs in Animals." On November 20th, Mr. Rosengarten read a paper on "The Early History of the American Philosophical Society," and Prof. T. H. Montgomery read one on "The Recapitulation Theory of Embryologists."

Meantime, I had gone to Washington and spent several days there, in-terviewing our own Washington members, as well as the heads of several of the scientific bureaus of the government. I obtained several promises of additional papers. All of the gentlemen I saw, both members and non-members, were most kind and cordial. This gave us a little breathing spell.

Two years later, April 1st, 1910, we wisely decided to hold only one meeting a month (on the first Friday). In the beginning, when life in Philadelphia was very simple and engagements very few, the meetings were held every Friday evening (as is still the case with the Royal Society), but with the increasing complexity of modern life in a large city, when everyone has many interests and many engagements, both private and public, the society has been led to schedule less and less frequent meetings.

I have found excellent support from a number of our members, and we have never missed a meeting and have never been without a speaker except twice, as I remember, on those occasions when the meeting came in the first two or three days of October and we could hardly expect to gather an audience. On the two occasions when our speakers failed us, on account of illness, I filled the breach myself.

We have had several special meetings when we were addressed by especially distinguished speakers, such as the Hon. Charlemagne Tower; Signor Guglielmo Ferrero, of Rome; Sir William Ramsay (on November 1st, 1912, he presented to the society the first photograph ever taken showing the paths of individual electrons); Prof. J. C. Bose, of the Presidency College in Calcutta, who demonstrated electrically the similarity of rhythmical impulses in plants to the nervous impulses in animals; and on April 23rd, 1909, we had also a special memorial meeting to celebrate the 50th anniversary of the publication of Darwin's *On the Origin of the Species*, with addresses by Mr. Bryce, the British ambassador, Prof. Goodale, of Harvard, and Prof. Fullerton, of Columbia.

Besides the monthly meetings, some 14 years ago (1902), at the instance of Dr. I. Minis Hays, the society (which had fallen into an almost somnolent condition, for a number of years) inaugurated a general meeting of all our members. This has been a great success and has re-established the society in the dignity and importance to which it is rightly entitled. Nearly 100 members usually attend, and the papers read are of the most important character. By an amicable arrangement with the National Academy of Science, the two societies meet in the same week, dividing the time between them equally, so that, as many persons are members of both, they can attend both with the outlay of time and money for one journey.

Beginning in 1912, the Saturday afternoon of the general meeting has been given over to a symposium on some topic of general interest, such as: 1912, "Stellar Spectroscopy;" 1913, "Wireless Telegraphy;" 1914, "The Physics and Chemistry of Protoplasm;" 1915, "The Constitution of Matter;" and 1916, "International Law."

This last one was of exceptional interest. It was organized by Prof. John Bassett Moore, who introduced the subject. He was followed by the Hon. Charlemagne Tower, Prof. G. G. Wilson, of Brown (now of Harvard), Prof. Philip M. Brown, of Princeton, and the Hon. David Jayne Hill.

At various general meetings, there have been presentations of medallions: for example, one of Hooker and another (with a fine steel engraving) of Darwin. In 1913, my portrait, by Vonnoh, was presented by Mr. Rosengarten and received by Prof. Pickering.

In 1906, a special and splendid Franklin bicentenary celebration was held in memory of his birth. The meeting was a remarkable success in every way. By order of Congress, a special medal was struck, and while I have a copy in bronze, the original, in solid gold, was presented to the government of France.

The society has held three memorial meetings, following the death of each of three distinguished members: in 1909, in honor of Henry C. Lea; in 1912, in honor of Horace Howard Furness; and in 1914, in honor of S. Weir Mitchell. In each, a number of other organizations took part, and notable addresses were delivered.

Our dinners are unique. We always have on the menu appropriate quotations, prepared by various members, such as Shakespearean scholars Howard Howard Furness, père et fils; Dr. Holland, Prof. Gummere, and Prof. Schelling, with prominence given to other Elizabethan writers. The last (in 1916), with a number of legal quotations, was prepared by Hampton L. Carson.

The toasts are always four in number, as follows: "To the memory of Franklin;" "To our sister societies;" "To our universities" (or "To our institutions of learning," depending on the speaker); and "To the American Philosophical Society."

One dinner will always stand out in my memory for the most distinguished and brilliant speeches I have ever heard. On my right sat Ambassador Bryce, an Englishman who had written the best book on the American commonwealth; and on my left sat President A. Lawrence Lowell, an American who had written the best book on the government of England. Both they and President Pritchett, of the Carnegie Foundation for the Advancement of Science, spoke, and spoke admirably. But the gem of the occasion (and, I think, the best after-dinner speech I ever heard) was by President Francis L. Patton, of Princeton, on Franklin. He used not a note and hesitated not for a word; and the word chosen was always the right word. He was logical, witty, learned, and, in fact, he was everything that was brilliant and fascinating.

At the April dinner of 1912, I presented to Mr. Charles H. Burr the Phillips Law Prize of $2000. His essay was chosen out of nine, by a committee of judges consisting of Messrs. Joseph H. Choate, of New York; J. M. Dickinson (late Secretary of War), of Tennessee; John C. Gray, dean of the Harvard Law School; Henry W. Rogers, dean of the Yale Law School; and

James Brown Scott, of Washington, D.C., a notable set of judges.

The subject was "The Treaty-Making Power of the United States and the Methods of its Enforcement as Affecting the Police Powers of the States." Mr. Burr wrote, so say all good judges, the best essay on the subject ever written. From it has arisen a very large and remunerative practice in international law for him, I am told, and he deserves it.

The committee who selected the subject consisted of Chief Justice Mitchell and four other lawyers. Several subjects were proposed by them. It may interest my children to know that the topic chosen was the one which I had proposed. I proposed it because I had felt deeply the weakness of the United States in dealing with injuries to the persons and property of aliens, in New Orleans, California, and some states in the Northwest. This essay showed clearly the supreme power of the United States as to treaty rights.

I sent copies of the essay to ex-presidents Roosevelt and Taft, to President Wilson, Senator Elihu Root, Secretary of State Bryan, and many others. Every one except Mr. Bryan acknowledged it. Judging by his policy in foreign affairs, I conclude that he has never even opened it.

We have had as members ten presidents of the United States. Two (Roosevelt and Taft) were elected to membership while in the White House. All the other eight had been members of the society for a number of years prior to their election. When Mr. Wilson became president, in 1913, a committee, consisting of Messrs. Root, Woodward (president of the Carnegie Institute), Walcott (secretary of the Smithsonian Institution), Tittman (superintendent of the Coast and Geodetic Survey), General Greeley, and myself, were directed to present to President Wilson (who had been a mem-

ber since 1897) a congratulatory address. In subsequent conversation, al-
luding to the fact that he was the 8th member of the society to enter the
White House, I said to him that I sometimes even shook in my shoes myself.

On my 75th birthday, in 1912, Florence invited all the local members
of the American Philosophical Society--and members of the Franklin Inn
Club--to greet me, between 3 and 6 o'clock. The occasion (more fully described in a former note, pp. 220-2) was a most delightful one.

The Commonwealth of Pennsylvania owned all of Independence Square*
and the buildings on it (which the city later acquired from the state),
and in 1785, the state donated the 5th-Street site to the society, which
erected its building in 1787. But by 1911, we were convinced, after much
debate in several meetings, that we ought to move. After all, our original site is, at present, so far out of the way; our building was not fire-
proof--and could not be made to be--so that all our treasures were in danger of being entirely destroyed (with imminent danger to Independence Hall
itself, as well); our walls were already weighted to the limit of safety,
so that we had to store 10,000 volumes in a nearby fireproof building; and
we had long outgrown our building, in that we needed a reading room and a
relic room, both to be open to the public. The first vote on removal came
at a special meeting in May, when the votes were 57 to 7 in favor. At the
June 2nd meeting, the vote was unanimous. Finally, on November 29th, 1911,
the society unanimously voted to accept a contract with the city to give
us a lot, bounded by the Parkway and 16th and Cherry Streets, in exchange
for our old lot and building. We obtained the contract a year later.

The main trouble has been a lack of funds. About 1913-14, the stock exchange moved from 5th and Chestnut to Broad and Walnut, and the brokers (and others) soon followed, of course. This left us with only one tenant instead of four, who had occupied the lower rooms, which we could not use for our own purposes. Our income from these rooms had been $5500, but we now get only $1500--and very likely shall get less than that, when the present lease expires.

The burden of raising the money has practically fallen on my shoulders. I have had a hard time. The business depression of 1913-14 made it impracticable to obtain any subscriptions, and now that prosperity has returned and the war profits are being made, the endless appeals for the sufferers from the Great War interfere seriously with my success.

Still, to date (May 1st, 1916), I have raised $50,000 for the building fund, with a contingent subscription of $10,000, by Messrs. Alba B. Johnson and Samuel M. Vauclain, to be added to every $90,000 I raise and to be repeated up to $650,000. For publication funds, I have obtained $13,500 in endowment funds, and from Dr. C. F. Brush, of Cleveland, a $10,000 donation for our general support.

I have also some prospects which I hope will materialize. I have been twice to New York, with no result so far, and once to Boston, with $600 as a result. If my life is spared, I hope to attain our object, viz.: $300,000 for the building, $250,000 for the endowment, and, if possible, $200,000 for the promotion of research. The total, $750,000, is a tidy little sum, and if I don't get it, it will not be for want of persistent work.

Among the names of those who have died, since I became president, are the following. They indicate the resplendent names on our roll of membership:

Wolcott Gibbs	Charles Francis Adams
Simon Newcomb	Samuel Dickson
Henry C. Lea	James T. Mitchell
Anton Dohrn	Sir James A. H. Murray
H. P. Bowditch	Frederick W. Putnam
F. A. March	Lewis Boss
Jacob H. Van't Hoff	Horace Howard Furness
Rear Admiral George W. Melville	W. W. Goodwin
Sir Joseph D. Hooker	Rt. Hon. Joseph Lord Lister
Jules Henri Poincaré	John S. Billings
Lester F. Ward	Rt. Hon. Lord Avebury
Sir William Henry Preece	Alfred Russell Wallace
S. Weir Mitchell	B. O. Peirce
Sir David Gill	W. S. Holden
W. A. Wright	August Weismann
Charles S. Minot	Rear Admiral Alfred Thayer Mahan

MY OWN IMPRESSIONS AND REFLECTIONS ON THE GREAT WAR

That Germany had been preparing, ever since 1870, for this war is clear from many evidences. These are perhaps best shown in Paul Vergnet's *France in Danger.*

The German "White Book" admitted that there had been communications between Berlin and Vienna, in reference to the relations between Austria and Serbia, and that Germany supported Austria. Neither power has ever dared to publish the *text* of these conferences.

The moment was opportune, as Germany judged:

I. Great Britain was on the verge of civil war over home rule for

Ireland, and the spreading disaffection in India would cause an uprising probably as serious as the Sepoy Rebellion of 1857.

II. France was about to lengthen the term of service to the colors from two to three years, and it was important to strike before the full effect of this change was realized.

III. Russia was emerging from her defeat by Japan and would soon be too formidable.

IV. The Kiel Canal had finally been widened and deepened, so that all German ships of war could pass through it, between the Baltic and the North Sea.

V. The German navy had been increased until it was approaching equality with that of Great Britain.

VI. The German army had been notably increased several times, by large additions to the peace force--and still more in case of war. The excuse was that a new power had arisen in the Balkans and that all eventualities must be provided for.

The favorite toast, in German army circles, was *Der Tag!*

The assassination of Archduke Ferdinand at Sarajevo was merely the pretext for, not the cause of, the war. The Austrian ultimatum was brutal and allowed no time for the other powers to mediate or to stop the war. Germany and Austria were determined on war and would brook no interference-- or even delay. Finally, on August 1st, 1914, Germany declared war on Russia, and the conflagration was started.

The brutal treatment of M. Cambon, the French ambassador to Germany (as related in the French "Yellow Book"), was in marked contrast to that of Herr von Schön, the German ambassador to France. The latter was sent in a special train to the German frontier. (On its arrival, the Germans seize the train.) M. Cambon, on the other hand, suffered indignities which a spy or a servant would have rightly resented.

On August 4th, a few hours after Belgium had been assured, by the German minister, of her safety, German troops entered the country and also occupied all of Luxembourg. Germany had solemnly guaranteed the neutrality of both. Luxembourg could not resist, for by treaty she was forbidden to have an army or fortifications. Thus were two solemn treaties reduced to "scraps of paper." Since then, a third treaty also has been torn into scraps of paper: In 1888, Germany, Austria, and Turkey (with the other great powers) were cosignatories of a treaty guaranteeing that the Suez Canal should always be free and open, "in time of war as in time of peace, to every vessel of commerce or of war, without distinction of flag."

Germany has never even attempted to defend her invasion of Luxembourg. She has asserted that documents found in Brussels justified her invasion of Belgium. These documents were only unofficial conversations with British officers which indicated that IF Germany invaded Belgium, Great Britain would come to her rescue. But granting the German claim, the motives and acts of Germany on August 4th are to be judged by what she knew on August 4th, and not what she pretends she found on, say, August 14th in Brussels.

But the frank avowal of von Bethmann-Hollweg, in the Reichstag, is conclusive that Germany had perpetrated a wrong on Belgium. The only excuse was "military necessity."

By terms of a treaty, neutral Belgium was obliged to enforce her own neutrality by arms, and this was not to be considered a warlike act. Yet

Germany, again, has disregarded this proviso and has committed cruelties

and barbarities unspeakable on Belgium and the Belgians. Lord Bryce's re-

port, and the testimony of reliable witnesses I have known personally (or

known of), have set these forth with great force. The atrocities in Ser-

bia and Poland, and the wholesale slaughter of Armenians by the fiendish

Turks--the allies of Germany--are horrible beyond belief. Joseph Shimoon,

one of my own students at the Jefferson (the class of 1903), and a Persian

whose splendid character none of us then fully appreciated, has been

burned to death because he would not renounce Christianity for Mohammedanism.

Besides all this, Germany has ruthlessly destroyed cities and splen-

did monuments of the past, such as the library at Louvain and the cathe-

dral at Rheims; has exacted enormous tribute from captured cities; has

seized civilian hostages--and shot them on flimsy pretexts; and has made

war more frightful than ever with her flaming shells and by poisonous gases.

The submarine warfare has been carried on by Germany with brutal dis-

regard of international law, of the laws of humanity, and of the lives of

Americans and other neutrals. The fine stand taken yesterday (April 19th,

a significant date) by President Wilson expresses exactly the sentiment

of the great bulk of Americans. His chief fault is that this note should

have been written a year ago, when the *Lusitania* was sunk without warning.

Our dead cry to us, from the waters of the Atlantic, for the expiation of

their murder.

The Germans whine over the inhumanity of the attempt of Great Britain

to starve a nation into defeat. Does any one outside an insane asylum be-

lieve that if Germany (instead of Great Britain) had had command of the sea, at the beginning of the war, she would have hesitated for an instant to blockade all the ports of Great Britain and thus starve *her* into submission? The food supply of Great Britain, as estimated by many writers, is usually only sufficient for about six weeks. Had not the British fleet commanded the seas, England would have been beaten almost before she began. Never were Admiral Mahan's views of the value of sea power in history more splendidly vindicated.

In August of 1914, Belgium saved the day. But for her heroic resistance, the Germans would surely have invested and possibly have captured Paris.

After 20 months of war, the Kaiser's troops, halted on the Marne, have achieved little further progress. In the East, the Russians are gradually driving back the once-victorious Germans and Austrians. In Armenia, they have captured Erzerum and Trebizond and may easily threaten Constantinople. On the Tigris, the British bid fair to be victors. In Arabia and Egypt, the attacks on the Suez Canal have been halted; and in the Balkans, the Anglo-French troops are almost ready for a drive against the Germans and the Bulgarians.

The Italians have not yet captured Trieste.

The miserable fiasco at the Dardanelles ought never to have occurred.

Meantime, the possible entrance of Holland and Rumania (as I hope) will hasten the inevitable victory of the Allies.

The titanic struggle is between two great principles:

I. Germany and Austria represent autocracy, military ascendency, the state as the sole arbiter, and the subservience of the individual, whose worth is negligible, save as a small unit to be exploited by the state.

II. The Allies represent democracy, civil ascendency over the military, and the primacy of the individual, for whom and for whose welfare the state exists, having no right to infringe on the individual's life, liberty, or pursuit of happiness.

And where does my country stand? The bulk of the people are, I believe, loyal to our republican principles. They hope fervently for the success of the Allies, who are fighting *our* battle for *our* future freedom--and even possibly for our future existence.

We have made great fortunes out of the war and are now the great creditor nation of the world. But I still believe that our ideals are our beacons and that we shall choose national honor and national duty to ourselves and to humanity and, if need be, fight and even die for them. We will not be recreant sons of the partiotic sires of 1776 and 1861.

Wholly apart from the money gained from making munitions for the Allies, we remember that to place an embargo on such exports would be a gross violation of international law, as well as a gross violation of the official neutrality which the government of the United States must adhere to. Germany went into the war knowing that Great Britain had command of the sea. She voluntarily took the risk. As a neutral, we may by law sell to both belligerents, as Germany did in the Russo-Japanese War and the Boer War. To prohibit such sales to one belligerent because the other has lost command of the sea (or for any other reason) would be the greatest possible direct aid to Germany--which God forbid.

My only regret is that we did not long ago enter the war, as an ally of Great Britain, France, and Russia. We may yet bitterly repent that we did not. The positive demands of President Wilson's note, and his address to Congress yesterday, may result, as I hope, in our entering the war.

But no words can express my humiliation at our unpreparedness, or the failure of Congress--especially of the House--to appreciate the gravity of the situation and the need for prompt and adequate relief.

Our army has been on the Mexican frontier for four years. Any moment, we might expect a raid, or possibly war itself. Yet Villa's raid on Columbus, N.M., on March 9th, apparently caught our troops without even pickets to warn them; our machine guns did not work; so little were we prepared that we had no motor trucks ready to carry supplies to our troops; of six aeroplanes, four were worthless; and our troops did not start in their pursuit of Villa till he had had a start of six days, and only on the 11th day after his raid did the first fifteen auto trucks (of the one hundred "ordered!") start with supplies. Practically our whole army at home is in Mexico or on the border, for this one little episode, leaving only about 4,000 men available in case of any serious riot or other emergency requiring action.

May we yet heed the warning and be ready when the call of duty comes.

THE COLLEGE OF PHYSICIANS OF PHILADELPHIA

I was elected a Fellow of the College of Physicians upon the nomination of Dr. S. Weir Mitchell, in 1867. Before that, I had attended some of the meetings of the college, down in the old "picture house" of the Pennsylvania Hospital, on Spruce Street between 8th and 9th. (This was so called because it was built for the purpose of holding, and enabling the public to see, Benjamin West's *Death on a Pale Horse*, which is now in the possession of the Academy of the Fine Arts.) In 1863, the college had

312

moved to the building at the corner of 13th and Locust Streets.

When I was first elected, Robert Bridges, the assistant to Dr. Bache (the Professor of Chemistry at the Jefferson), was the librarian, and the library was open for, I think, only one or two hours a day, and only one or two days in the week, instead of, as now, from 10 until 6 every week-day, with extended evening hours for two evenings in the week.

The entire library, when we moved to 13th and Locust, was carried in three or four wagon-loads. The early meetings of the college were pretty dull, for we had a series of reports on meteorology, and the effects of weather on health, which could better have been read by title and printed for those who wished to consult them. After we had moved, however, the library and the college took on a new life. Samuel Lewis, in particular, was a source of great encouragement. Owing to the fact that he stuttered quite badly, and that his means, while not extremely large, enabled him to live in comfort and have considerable to spare, he never entered into practice. He started the Lewis Library, for which he was constantly buy-ing books; for years, it has been a large and important part of the college library.

I was elected president in 1900. I had been elected vice president in 1897, assuring my election as president three years later. We always have a contest over the vice-presidency, but whoever wins there is auto-matically elevated to the presidency. I resigned in 1901, on account of my starting on a trip around the world, which prevented me from serving the third year of the usual allowable term in office.

On my election, I found that we had only $10,000, or possibly $15,000, endowment funds for our library. This made it almost impossible for us

to purchase any books, as the money was used up in binding and in the subscriptions to journals. Accordingly, I got busy, while I was president,
and raised about $60,000 in various funds (giving one of $5,000 myself),
whose purpose was the purchase of books and bindings for the library, with
$2,500 for a building fund.

In 1882, at the insistence of Dr. S. Weir Mitchell, the college established the directory for nurses. The committee which organized this
consisted of Drs. Mitchell and Sinkler and myself as chairman. We worked
very hard over the the organization of it, and it became a great success
from the very start. From the date of its establishment until now, it has
paid about $2,000 every year into the treasury of the college, exclusively
for the use of the library, so that we now have received over $68,000
since it was started. After a long service as chairman, I retired from
that position and was succeeded by Dr. James C. Wilson. This directory
has been the greatest boon, to physicians, to the sick, and to those who
have met with serious accidents or emergencies.

Our quarters at 13th and Locust finally became so crowded with books
that they were sometimes two, and occasionally three, rows deep on our
shelves, and it was simply impossible not to make some radical change. A
number of the conservatives, led especially by Arthur V. Meigs, bitterly
opposed moving, and there was a great division of opinion over the matter.
They wished to buy the adjoining lot and put an addition on to the inadequate building. Dr. Mitchell and I particularly, with the help of some
of the younger man, held out for entire removal. After several years of
debate, we carried the day by a large majority. Even then, the feelings
ran so high that it almost severed some early friendships, a very absurd

thing. We bought the lot, about 130 by 180 feet, on 22nd Street above Chestnut, for $80,000. Later, the adjoining lot was bought by Mr. Eckley B. Coxe, Jr., for $40,000, and given to the college. This was brought about by Dr. Sinkler, then vice president and prospective president of the college, who was ill at the time (though we little dreamed that it was his last illness). No better service was ever done the college than this. The lot had been occupied by a stable but was then bought by a syndicate of gentlemen whose purpose was to transform it into a garage, which, filled with barrels of gasoline and oil, would be a serious menace of fire, not only to us on the north but still more to the church on the south, to which it was so much closer. This building was pulled down and the lot made into a very attractive garden, as a memorial to Dr. Sinkler.

During my lifetime, two members of the college have served as president for two terms, Dr. S. Weir Mitchell and Dr. J. M. Da Costa, graduates of the Jefferson both.

Mitchell was the dominating force in the college for many years and was its greatest friend, giving not only money but also gifts of all sorts of curios, rare books, pamphlets, and manuscripts; and, most important of all, his personal devotion and the spirit which he infused into nearly all the members. Our later presidents also have done very much for the college, in raising and giving money, and in obtaining additions to our bibliographical and medical treasures.

It was a proud day, November 10th, 1909, when we opened the new building, and, following the president of the college, in walked Mitchell with Andrew Carnegie, who had donated $100,000 toward it.

The building cost somewhere about $300,000, and the rooms were furnished

315

by the descendants of deceased fellows--especially officers--of the college. in addition to that, we have had some notable gifts, especially the bequest, just received, of Dr. Lewis A. Duhring. By will, he has given us $5,000 for a special fund, the income to be used for the purchase of books on dermatology, plus one-fifth of his residuary estate, which amounted to about $200,000. As we already had something over $100,000 in library funds, this gives us now an endowment of $300,000 for the library alone. I suppose that our real estate would be worth between five and six hundred thousand dollars, and our invested funds, I think, amount to over a hundred thousand. Our library, of over 110,000 volumes would be worth probably $150,000, for our collection of incunabula alone amounts now to nearly 200 volumes and is worth a large sum. I suppose that our entire worth (real estate, furnishings, investments, and library) would amount to not far from $1,250,000--possibly even $1,500,000. What a contrast to the conditions when I was first elected a Fellow!

In 1876, while preparing the Toner lecture on "Surgical Complications of Typhoid Fever" (which afterward was expanded into my book on the same subject), I had to get from Washington two large dry-goods boxes full of books, not in the college library, that I wished to consult. If I had to do the same work today, I doubt if there would be more than half a dozen volumes--possibly not even so many--that would not be available in the library of the College of Physicians.

[ADDENDUM]

SOME AMUSING STORIES

Prof. Martin, of the University of Wisconsin, told us the following:

He was the only student in a course in geography, at Harvard, under Prof. William Morris Davis. One day, he handed in a carefully prepared paper embodying certain quotations. Prof. Davis read it and then pounced upon the modest student with "What in the world did the author mean in this quotation?" He violently opposed the views stated in the quotation and ended with a repetition, "What did the author mean?" Mr. Martin very quietly replied, "I really don't know just what you did 'mean' when you wrote it." Instead of seeing the funny side of the situation, Prof. Davis at last said only, "Let's go on."

 *   *   *   *   *

On my 79th birthday, when I was in St. Augustine, a friend telegraphed me his warm congratulations on my natal day. On delivery, in typewriting it read congratulations on my *fatal* day.

 *   *   *   *   *

When Polly Butcher was nine years old, we dined at Ardmore. I sat next to Polly and said to her, "Polly, yesterday you were eight, weren't you?" "Yes, grandfather." "And today you are nine?" "Yes, grandfather." "Then I suppose tomorrow you'll be ten?" "No, grandfather, Nature doesn't do it that way."

 *   *   *   *   *

When Corinne was a child of nine (or it may be twelve, on anywhere in between) she wrote a composition on Napoleon. It ended somewhat after this fashion: "Napoleon said that he abdicated for the good of his country, but I think it was because he had to."

*   *   *   *   *

When Margaret was a small child, I had a colored man named Thomas in
my employ. He was very swift-footed in answering the bell. One morning,
I heard Margaret call him "Tom." Sitting in my office (at 1729) with her
on my lap, I told her that "Tom" was unduly familiar, for a little girl
speaking to a man, and that she must call him "Thomas." Just then, the
front-door bell rang, and Thomas passed the open office door at full speed.
Margaret turned around and said "Hello, Tom." I said to her, "Why Margaret, I just told you that you must say "Thomas" and not "Tom." "But
Papa," she replied, as quick as a wink, "He went so fast that I didn't
have time to say more 'n "Tom."

*   *   *   *   *

Miss J. L., of Buffalo, went on a visit to New York, one of her first
journeys alone. Her mother directed her to telegraph her safe arrival
promptly. This she forgot to do. Remembering it later, she agreed to
let the husband of her hostess attend to it. After her mother had gone to
bed, she was awakened by a telephone call, and the telegraph girl could
hardly repeat the message on account of her giggling:

> Arrived here safe, o Mother dear / A-ridin' on my bustle,
> And now that I am here, by gosh / New York has got to hustle.

--M[argaret] K[een] B[utcher]

*   *   *   *   *

Corinne, while at Cape May, had a bag from which a hook was broken
off. Walter brought the bag up to Philadelphia to have it mended, along
with a note from Corinne to the person who was to do the job which read:

318

"Please call at 1832 Spruce Street for a bag. The hook
is inside My sister Mrs. Butcher recommended you to me."

Walter wrote to Corinne, in a disguised hand, a postal card saying, "Called at house. Mrs. Butcher not there. Please advise." Corinne thought
she recognized the handwriting as Howard Butcher's and that it was to per-
petrate a neat little joke. So she wrote Howard, who knew nothing at all
of the whole matter, "Please call again and bring an emetic."

--M. K. B.

*   *   *   *   *

Prof. Shorey, of Bryn Mawr College (and later of the University of
Chicago), was planning a lecture. He discussed with his wife Emma whether
he should select his lecture on "The Pace that Killed Athens" or a recital
of his experiences as Roosevelt exchange professor in Berlin. Finally, he
sent a telegram, by telephone from his home to the telegraph operator, who
tried, at least, to make it read, as she thought, as though it made somewhat good sense:

"Emma prefers Pace that kills. Thinks Roosevelt professor
too thin and trifling for college lecturer."

The Athenian theme was chosen.

--D[ora] K[een] [Handy]

319

A list of the positions I have occupied and of the honors
so generously given me and of the books and papers I have written
and edited numbering over 300 (see list) will be found in the drawer
of the table in the front office, and to some extent are given in
"Who's Who in America".   Of two of the highest professional distinctions, one European and one American, I only learned while traveling in India in 1901-2.   In 1901 I was elected one of the eight
Honorary Fellows at the German Surgical Society, the largest and
most distinguished Surgical Society in the world.   I am the only
                    when Halsted was elected
American surgeon who, up to 1914, has ever received that honor.   In
1902 I was elected President of the Sixth Triennial Congress of
American Physicians and Surgeons to be held in 1903--the blue ribbon
of the American Profession.   The list of Presidents is a very distinguished one; viz,- (1) 1888, John S. Billings; (2) 1891, S.
Weir Mitchell; (3) 1894, A. L. Loomis; (4) 1897, Wm. H. Welch; (5)
1900, Henry P. Bowditch; (6) 1903, W. W. Keen.   Following me have
been (7),1907, R. H. Fitz; (8) 1910, E. L. Trudeau. *1913 Sir Wm. C. Gorgas* *1916 W. S. Thayer*

In the late '90's I think it was I made a serious effort
to initiate a movement for an International Surgical Congress.
                      Billings
I corresponded with Czerny, Kocher, Gussenbauer,vonBergmann, *Nera*
                       the U.S.
and other leading surgeons in Germany, France, Great Britain and
Italy.   They all approved on the idea and it would have materialized but for the attitude of the British surgeons.   They
had no Surgical Society with scientific meetings, transactions,

etc.   The Royal College of Surgeons of England is a Society
charged with (1) The examination (with the Royal College of
Physicians of England and the Society of Apothecaries) and
granting of degrees in medicine; (2) The care of the Hunterian
Museum and (3) Certain funds for stated courses of lectures

KEEN'S OWN RÉSUMÉ

WILLIAM W. KEEN, Surgeon, 1729 Chestnut Sy., Phila.
Born Jan.19,1837.

$\phi B K - \Sigma \Xi - \Lambda \Delta \phi$

DEGREES
A.B. and A.M.,Brown,1859
M.D. Jeff.Med.Coll,Phila.1862
LL.D. Brown, 1901
LL.D. Northwestern Univ. 1903
LL.D. Toronto Univ. 1903
LL.D. Univ.of Edinburgh 1905
LL.D. Yale 1906
Hon.M.D. Univ.Greifswald 1906
Hon.Ph.D. Univ. of Upsala 1907
LL.D. Univ.St.Andrews 1911
Hon.Sc.D. Jeff.Med.Coll.1912

SOME FOREIGN HONORS

CORRESPONDING MEMBER
Soc.de Chir. de Paris
Soc. Belge de Chir.
Clinical Soc. of London

HONORARY FELLOW
Roy.Coll. of Surg. of Eng.
 "   "   "   " " Edimb.
Deutsche Gesellsch.f.Chir.
Italian Surg.Soc.
Palermo Surg.Soc.
Berlin Med.Gesellsch.

PROFESSIONAL CAREER
Assist.Surg. 5th Mass.Regt.1861
 "   "   U.S.A. 1862-64
Studied in Europe 1864-66
In practice in Philadelphia since 1866

AS AN EDUCATOR
Conducted Phila. School of Anatomy 1866-'75
Lecturer on Path.Anatomy,Jefferson Med.Coll.1866-'75
Prof.Artistic Anat.,Penna.Academy of Fine Arts 1876-1890
Prof. Surgery, Woman's Med.Coll. 1884-1889
 "   "   Jefferson Med.Coll.,1889-1907
Prof. Emeritus   "   "   "   1907-

AS AN ADMINISTRATOR
Trustee Brown Univ.1873-1895. Fellow 1895-
 "   Shaw University
 "   Crozer Theological Seminary
 "   Pennsylvania Dental School

PRESIDENT
American Surgical Association 1898
American Medical Association 1899
College of Physicians of Philadelphia 1900
Congress American Physicians and Surgeons 1903
American Baptist Missionary Union 1906
American Philosophical Society 1908-

AS AUTHOR (Partial List)
Reflex Paralysis the Result of Gunshot Wounds 1864
Clinical Charts 1870
Early History of Practical Anatomy 1874
History of Philadelphia School of Anatomy 1875
Anat. Pathol. & Surgical Uses of Chloral 1875
Medical Missionary Work in Japan 1874
History of First Baptist Church,Philadelphia,1898
Surgical Complications and Sequels of Typhoid Fever 1898
Cholecystotomy 1884
Our Recent Debts to Vivisection 1885
Surgery of the Brain 1889
Surgery of the Spine 1889
Removal of the Gasserian ganglion 1894
Operation Wounds of the Thoracic Duct 1894

AS EDITOR (Partial List)
Heath's Practical Anatomy 1870
Fowler's Diagrams of the Nerves 1872
American Health Primers 1879-80
Holden's Medical & Surgical Landmarks 1881
Gray's Anatomy 1883
American Text Book of Surgery 1692
Keen's System of Surgery, 6 vol. 1905-1913
Bulkeley's Skin in Health & Disease
Dercum's Diseases of the Nervous System

KEEN'S DEGREES AND HONORS CITED IN THESE MEMOIRS

American Academy of Arts and Science: Fellow (1901)

American Baptist Missionary Union: President (1906)

American College of Surgeons: Honorary Fellow (1913)

American Medical Association: President (1899)

American Philosophical Society: President (1908-13)

American Surgical Association: President (1898)

Belgian Surgical Society: Honorary Fellow; Corresponding Member

Berlin Medical Scoiety: Honorary Fellow

Brown University: A.B., Valedictorian (1859); A.M. (1860); LL.D. (1901);
   Trustee (1873-95); Fellow (1895-   )

Clinical Society of London: Corresponding Member

College of Physicians of Philadelphia: Fellow (1867); President (1900)

Crozer Theological Seminary: Constituent Trustee (1867)

German Surgical Society: Honorary Fellow (1901)

International Congress of Surgery: President (1917)

Jefferson Medical College: M.D. (1862); Honorary Sc.D. (1912)

Northwestern University: LL.D. (1903)

Palermo Surgical Society: Honorary Fellow (1908)

Paris Surgical Society: Honorary Corresponding Member

Pennsylvania Anatomical Board: President

Pennsylvania Dental School: Trustee

Philadelphia Academy of Surgery: President

Philadelphia School of Anatomy: Owner/President

Royal College of Surgeons of Edinburgh: Honorary Fellow (1905)

Royal College of Surgeons of England: Honorary Fellow (1900)

Shaw University: Trustee

Toronto University: LL.D. (1903)

University of Edinburgh: L.L.D. (1905)

University of Greifswald: Honorary M.D. (1906)

University of Saint Andrews: LL.D. (1911)

University of Uppsala: Honorary Ph.D. (1907)

Yale University: LL.D. (1906)

AULD LANG SYNE

A ~~REPRINT OF~~ *Reply to* THE TOAST, BY W. W. KEEN, M.D., AT
THE ANNIVERSARY DINNER OF THE WOMAN'S
MEDICAL COLLEGE OF PENNSYLVANIA,
MAY 4, 1915

I heard recently the story of a man who owned a circus with which
of course went a menagerie. Sometimes he indulged a little too freely in
the flowing bowl and had suffered for it. On this occasion he was rather
more frazzled than usual, but was sober enough to know what to expect if
he showed himself to his not over-indulgent spouse. Instead, therefore,
of seeking his own bed he finally unlocked the lion's cage and lay down there.
In the morning his wife, after much searching, at last found him in the
cage. Her only greeting was two words and a double gesture. Shaking
both fists at him, she exclaimed, "You coward!"

Now, on the contrary I have boldly ventured in here facing even a whole
battalion of women without any fear, for I know by nearly thirty-five
years of experience in the Woman's Medical College of Pennsylvania how
good and friendly you have been and, I am sure, still are towards
myself. About 1880 I accepted the post of lecturer in the College and in
1884 I became full Professor of Surgery. After five years I was obliged
to resign, as other duties became too urgent and absorbing, but I have
never lost my interest in the College and am glad to attest it by my presence on this festal occasion.

Your genial Dean gave me my marching orders in advance. I was to
tell you, first, how I liked you when I was with you; second, how I like
you now, and third, what I hope for you in the future.

When I was with you I found you—or rather the predecessors of those
before me—a body of enthusiastic, hard working, intelligent students who
were daunted by no task, were equal to any emergency and were ever faithful to your duties.

Two, or rather three, of my students stand out in an individualized way
from among the large number I had the pleasure of teaching at the Woman's
Medical College of Pennsylvania.

First, Mrs. Joshee and her friend Ramabai who was occasionally a hearer
though not an enrolled student. They were the first two in a long line of
Oriental students,—a line still persisting, for one from Ramabai's school
and her husband are our fellow guests to-night. No women in the whole
Far East have done finer and more valuable work than that inaugurated
and still carried on by Ramabai for her fellow countrywomen, and the
work of our many graduates in the Orient.

A third student who lives vividly in my recollection furnished me in
May, 1887, a wholly unique surgical experience—unique, I fancy, even in
the annals of Surgery. The student referred to sought my advice for a
number of tuberculous glands in the neck. As they were on the point of
becoming abscesses I advised their removal. To this she immediately
consented but added "upon one condition." "And what is that?" "That
I shall not take either ether or chloroform." "But, my dear child," I
said, "surely you do not understand. This operation will last probably
an hour and a half. I must make an incision from your ear to the breast
bone and then along the clavicle nearly to the shoulder, raise both flaps
over a large area and dissect the glands most carefully from the jugular
vein, carotid artery, probably the great subclavian vessels and certainly
from all the numerous nerves in the neck. If you jump from sudden pain
I do not know where the point of my knife may go."

"Yes," she replied, "I quite understand. I will stand any amount of pain without budging, but I will not take either ether or chloroform." "Why not?" "Because I have already had two operations for similar glands elsewhere, both done by Prof. Henry B. Sands of New York, one with ether and the other with chloroform, and I suffered so intensely from the after effects that I prefer to endure the pain of the operation. If I can not have the glands removed without the anesthetic, I will not have the operation performed." "Well," said I, seeing her absolutely fixed determination, "only within a few days I have seen an account of a new local anesthetic called *cocain*, and if you are willing I will try that, but I can't promise how much it will dull the pain as I have never used it." "Anything except ether or chloroform," was the quiet but decided answer.

A few days later I operated. As I had never used cocain before I am well aware that it was but partially effective but she never so much as winced. Now, however, comes the additional and unique surprise. I had made my incisions and had begun to dissect the flaps when she said to me, "Would you mind if one of the residents (the operation was done in the Woman's Hospital and the residents, of course, were women) were to get me her hand glass and let me watch the operation?" For a moment I confess I was—if I may venture to use the word—"flabbergasted." But I instantly made up my mind that any one who could face fearlessly an hour and a half of pain without any anesthetic would be able to watch the operation without flinching. And so it proved. For over an hour she held the glass and watched every stroke of my knife even when shaving the great jugular and without a single movement of head, hand or foot.

Her later history is interesting, instructive, and worthy of her. She was sent to Seoul, Korea, as a medical missionary. There (for Cupid flings his darts in Korea as elsewhere) she married a doctor. After the battle of Pyang Yong in the Chinese-Japanese War of 1895, they went up to attend the wounded. There her husband fell a victim to typhus. She at once came home on furlough and her second child, a daughter, was born in the United States; her first had died in Korea. Later she returned to Korea, and for some time she has worked in a fine large hospital built for the Mission by the late Mr. L. H. Severance of Cleveland. Some years ago she established the first school for the blind and later the first school for the deaf and dumb ever founded in Korea. When her daughter was old enough she efficiently aided her mother. About three years ago both of them called to see me and I was proud of their work, as well I might be. The Woman's Medical College of Pennsylvania, also, may well count such a woman as one of many who have conferred honor upon the College and benefits untold upon humanity.

The second command of Dr. Marshall was to tell you how I like you now. The answer shall be short, sharp and decisive. If I didn't like you now, I wouldn't be here!

And, third, what do I hope for your future? I believe in you "up to the hub." There *is* a place for an exclusively woman's medical college in this country. Your splendid record for sixty-five years is one to be proud of. That you will not only be sure to equal it in the future but will surpass it I have not the slightest doubt. May your most ardent hopes be more than fulfilled!

NOTES

1   *then a residential part of the city*: This area of Philadelphia is being restored to its residential character.

2   *Uppsala*: Not to be confused with Upsala College, East Orange, N.J.

2   *Linneaus*: Carolus Linneaus (1707-78) was the originator of modern scientific classification of plants and animals. He taught botany and medicine at the University of Uppsala.

2   *Chester*: Originally named Uppland.

2   *oldest adult grave*: The oldest tombstone in the location described is that of *John* Keen, the great-grandson of Kyn.

5   *Jeffreys*: A notoriously cruel judge, George Jeffreys was sent to punish those involved in the rebellion of the Duke of Monmouth. He caused nearly 200 persons to be hanged, some 800 transported, and many more imprisoned or whipped. James II made him lord chancellor, in 1685. When James fled the country, three years later, Jeffreys was imprisoned and died in the Tower of London.

8   *man named Miller*: In 1831, convinced from his study of the Bible that prophecies pointed to the second coming of Christ in 1843, William Miller went about spreading his belief among large audiences. Many prepared for the Day of Judgment, and when the year passed without a fulfillment of his prophecy, a date in 1844 was set. In 1845, Miller and his followers founded the Adventist Church.

10 *Woodlands*: This "large yellow mansion" is now the centerpiece of Woodlands Cemetery, where the Keen family plots are located.

12 *nine buildings in all*: An 1849 map of the area (see plates) reveals not only the Keen property but also the school, the church, and the residences of several neighbors mentioned.

12 *"looking through nature . . . "*: "Slave to no sect, who takes no private road / But looks through Nature up to Nature's God." From Pope's "Essay on Man" (Epistle iv, line 331).

13 *Thomas W. Evans*: See Gerald Carson's *The Dentist and the Empress: The Adventures of Dr. Tom Evans in Gas-Lit Paris* (Houghton Mifflin, Boston, 1983).

15 Great Western: Her first crossing, in 1838, took fifteen days.

15 *Cape Race*: Avalon Peninsula, Newfoundland.

15 *the first cable*: See James Dugan's *The Great Iron Ship* (Harper and Brothers, New York, 1953).

21 *University of Lewisburg*: Since 1866, Bucknell University.

23 *simple football*: Probably a combination of soccer and rugby.

30 *to my consternation*: Keen doth protest too much, methinks.

34 *friendship that has endured*: Mitchell and Keen appear in a rare photograph (see plates) of a dinner at the Franklin Inn Club.

35 *I entered the service*: After the first battle of Bull Run, in 1861, Keen's regiment was demobilized and he returned to finish medical school. After the second battle of Bull Run, a year later, he was captured (see p. 156) and released.

35 *Loyal Legion*: The Military Order of the Loyal Legion was awarded to all Union officers who served in the war.

36 War of the Rebellion: The official Union designation. The South considered it the War of the Northen Aggression, though in some circles this was softened to "The Late Unpleasantness."

40 *Pennsylvania Academy of the Fine Arts*: Frank Furness's Victorian wonder of 1876 was beautifully restored in time for the country's bi-centennial.

40 *thirty lectures*: Keen's fee was $10 per lecture. Thomas Eakins, who taught painting at the school, was one of his students of anatomy.

40 *cadaver, skeleton, and living model*: This trio, conducted by Keen, is immortalized in Charles Stephens's painting (see plates), which is sometimes on display at the Academy.

42 *wiser to remain in Philadelphia*: Keen's "successful practice" and congenial associations are typical of the city's magnetic forces, according to Digby Baltzell's *Puritan Boston and Quaker Philadelphia* (Macmillan, New York, 1979).

46 *new edition*: This was the first American edition and followed the 11th English edition.

59 *for my children only*: Bryant died in 1914. Keen published his own account of these operations in 1917.

72 *"Fuller" of that day*: The latter-day Fuller appears on page 184.

86 *stirred to its depths*: In retrospect, shallow waters indeed.

86 *they could take a hint as well as Queen Elizabeth*: This obscure catch phrase might have its origin in the fabled Parliamentary act requiring Elizabeth to take a bath once a month, "whether she need it or no."

89 *demonstrating the steps*: At the Jefferson, there is a new conference room (recently dedicated to Keen) featuring closed-circuit television from the operating table. How he would have admired the technology-- and appreciated the honor.

98 *111-pound tumor*: Awesome, but the 1988 *Guinness Book of World Records* cites a 328-pound tumor successfully removed in 1905.

100 *massage of the heart following a chloroform collapse*: A pioneering effort at cardio-pulmonary resuscitation?

105 *imperturbable coolness*: J. Chalmers Da Costa wrote that the worse
the surgical situation, the "calmer, quieter, kinder, pleasanter"
Keen became. When he had the hemorrhage under control, he would
say, "Now we have the whip-hand of it"--an expression which became
proverbial at Jefferson. (From "The Art of Philadelphia Medicine,"
a 1965 exhibition at the Philadelphia Museum of Art.)

130 *Fortunately . . . his father-in-law died*: Every cloud has a silver
lining.

134 *"wrath of the Lamb"*: Rev. 6:16.

136 *such a paper*: A pioneering effort at malpractice insurance?

175 *"Ben Butler!"*: Gen. Benjamin Franklin Butler was a scalawag, with
a reputation for beastly habits as a dinner guest, including steal-
ing the flatware. (Described also in Kennedy's *Profiles in Courage*
as "the butcher of New Orleans," he ordered that when any Confederate
female "shall by word, gesture, or movement, insult or show contempt
for any officer or soldier of the United States, she shall be regarded and held liable to be treated as a woman of the town plying her
avocation." He was removed as military governor of New Orleans.)

176 *not a Polish prince*: Or one of the ladies!

179 *alienist*: That is, a psychiatrist.

181 "Jacob Wrestling with the Angel": Hos. 12:4.

181 *descendant of Jehu*: "[T]he driving is like the driving of Jehu the
son of Nimshi; for he driveth furiously." 2 Kings 9:20.

192 *free from any further pain*: Will Mayo asked the convalescing Keen
for suggestions and was told to "write more" and "make more reports
to the profession." (See Helen Clapesattle's *The Doctors Mayo*, U.
of Minnesota Press, Minneapolis, 1941).

193 *Robert Vonnoh*: Vonnoh's portrait is one of four Keen icons on display at the College of Physicians. Others include a 1901 oil, by
James L. Wood; a 1920 plaster bust, by Samuel A. Murray; and the 1932
plaster of Paris death mask, by R. Tait McKenzie.

197 *"prophet is not without honor . . . "*: Matt. 13:57.

197 *"How great a fire a little matter kindleth."*: James 3:5.

198 both *arms in slings*: Adding to the volume of this genre of anecdota,
I pass along the "clearly remembered" report, from a retired attorney
of unquestioned veracity, of a Philadelphia newspaper's front-page
picture of Keen sitting on an operating table, having just removed
his own appendix. The newspaper and edition in question have, to
date, eluded my detection.

207 *"man of blood and iron"*: "Not with dreams, but with blood and with
iron / Shall a nation be moulded at last." (From Swinburne's "A
Word for the Country.")

218 *Charles, as a broker*: A pioneering effort at insider trading?

219 *all reaching the* Oneida: This account omits White House physician Robert O'Reilly, who had examined the president's "bothersome" mouth two weeks earlier. For the latter half of the first operation, he administered the anesthesia.

221 *cheek retractor*: This instrument is exhibited (along with the excised tumor and section of Cleveland's jaw) in the Mütter Museum of the College of Physicians.

224 *skillful dentist*: New York prosthodontist Kasson Gibson made the artificial jaw from vulcanized rubber. (A note from Cleveland to Gibson, dated June 9, 1896, commented that his recent loss of a gold filling indicated how completely he had been on the gold standard.)

224 *Hasbrouck*: Persuaded by Holland that the story was already publicly known, at least in outline, Hasbrouck confirmed it in full detail. When the doctors vigorously denied everything, the reporter was repudiated as a scandal-monger and died discredited. When the truth came out (Keen's account appeared in 1917, in *The Saturday Evening Post*), there was an attempt to make amends. Although Holland had died, no president was ever again able to just drop out of sight.

227 *necropsy*: Cleveland's cited heart failure, with edema and pulmonary thrombosis.

248 *proper woman's voice*: "Her voice was ever soft, gentle, and low-- an excellent thing in a woman." *King Lear*, V, iii.

263 *"Anti-Kamnia"*: At the turn of the century, the Antikamnia Chemical Co., of St. Louis, marketed a full line of medicinal tablets (along the generic lines of snake oil) designed to treat a wide range of maladies. The line included Antikamnia & Codeine; Antikamnia & Heroin; Antikamnia & Quinine; and Antikamnia & Salol.

266 *actively hostile*: When the Female Medical College of Pennsylvania held its first graduation, in 1851, awarding M.D. degrees to women, "the action was so controversial that 500 medical students . . . protested the ceremonies and threatened to interrupt them," accord- to the account in John Francis Marion's *Philadelphia Medica*.)

280 *his button was in their bowels . . . out-Murphied Murphy*: In 1892, Chicago surgeon John Murphy introduced the Murphy button as a device for performing enteroanatomoses--surgery on the intestines.

286 *"Peace hath her victories . . ."*: Milton to Lord General Cromwell.

294 *"scorn delights and live laborious days"*: From Milton's "Lycidas."

298 *representatives of the university*: When McClellan first sought the charter for Jefferson Medical College, the university tried to block it. Nothing daunted, he persuaded Jefferson College, of Canonsburg (near Pittsburgh), to open a medical branch in Philadelphia, and the race was on! The smaller school has resolutely maintained its independence from the larger.

303 *Chief Justice Mitchell*: Of the Pennsylvania Supreme Court.

308 *Belgium . . . Luxembourg*: The perpetual neutrality of Belgium was guaranteed at the London Conference of 1838-39; that of Luxembourg, in the London Conference of 1867.

310 *Admiral Mahan's Views*: Mahan's two major works were *The Influence of Sea Power upon History, 1660-1783* (1890); and *The Influence of Sea Power upon the French Revoultion and Empire, 1793-1812* (1892).

SOME ACHIEVEMENTS OF THE FRIENDS OF MEDICAL RESEARCH IN 50 YEARS*

1. Discovered and developed antiseptic surgery.

2. Made possible abdominal surgery and brain surgery.

3.   "   "   modern surgery of the chest.

4. Almost entirely abolished lockjaw following operations and accidents.

5. Abolished yellow fever.

6. Reduced the mortality from compound fractures: 66% to less than 1%.

7.   "   "   "   "   ovariotomy: 66% to 2.3%.

8.   "   "   "   "   hydrophobia: 12-14% to 0.77%.

9.   "   "   "   "   cerebro-spinal meningitis: 75-90% to 20%.

10.   "   "   "   "   hernia, mastectomy, tumors: now negligible.

11.   "   "   "   "   diphtheria: less than ¼ of previous rates.

12.   "   "   "   "   tuberculosis: by 30 to 50%.

13. Enormously diminished the ravages of malaria.

14. Devised a method for the direct transfusion of blood, saving many lives.

15. Made operating for goitre almost perfectly safe.

16. Reduced Malta fever in the British army and navy: 1300 cases to one case, in four years.

17. Reduced puerperal fever following childbirth: 10-57% to less than 1%.

18. Discovered a remedy for syphilis.

19. Discovered a vaccine that totally abolishes typhoid.

20. Discovered the cause of infantile paralysis.

21. Discovered the cause, method of transmission, and the means of treating sleeping sickness.

22. Enormously benefited animals be discovering the cause of (and in many cases the means of combating) tuberculosis, rinderpest, anthrax, glanders, lumpy jaw, and hog and chicken cholera.

Note: These achievements have been made, in every case, through animal experimentation.

----

* Written in 1912.

SELECTED BIBLIOGRAPHY, KEEN AS AUTHOR

Addresses and Other Papers. Saunders, Philadelphia, 1905.

Animal Experimentation and Medical Progress. Houghton Mifflin, Boston, 1914.

Bi-Centennial Celebration of the Founding of the First Baptist Church of the City of Philadelphia, 1698-1898. American Baptist Publication Society, Philadelphia, 1899.

Brief History of the Sunday School of the First Baptist Church in Philadelphia on the Completion of Its First Centenary, 1815-1915. American Baptist Publication Society, Philadelphia, 1915.

Concerning Human Vivisection. American Humane Association, Philadelphia, 1901.

Gunshot Wounds and Other Injuries of Nerves [with Mitchell and Morehouse]. Lippincott, Philadelphia, 1864.

Henry Charles Lea. American Philosophical Society, Philadelphia, 1911.

History of the Philadelphia School of Anatomy and Its Relation to Medical Teaching. Lippincott, Philadelphia, 1875.

I Believe in God and in Evolution. Lippincott, Philadelphia, 1922.

Influence of Antivivisection on Character. American Medical Association, Chicago, 1912.

Medical Research and Human Welfare. Houghton Mifflin, Boston, 1917.

Modern Antiseptic Surgery and the Role of Experiment in Its Discovery and Development. American Medical Association, Chicago, 1910.

Progress of Surgery as Influenced by Vivisection. Reprinted from the *Philadelphia Record* of Sep. 14 and 21, 1901.

Selected Papers and Addresses. Jacobs, Philadelphia, 1923.

Sketch of the Early History of Practical Anatomy. Lippincott, Philadelphia, 1874.

Surgical Complications and Sequels of the Continued Fevers. Smithsonian Institution, Washington, 1877.

Surgical Complications and Sequels of Typhoid Fever. Saunders, Philadelphia, 1898.

Surgical Operations on President Cleveland in 1893. Jacobs, Philadelphia, 1917.

Treatment of War Wounds. Saunders, Philadelphia, 1917.

Use of Roentgen X Rays in Surgery. N.p., New York, 1896.

What Vivisection Has Done for Humanity. American Medical Association, Chicago, 1910.

Bulkley, Henry Daggett. *Skin in Health and Disease: A Concise Manual*. N.p., 1849.

Burnett, Charles H., et al. *American Text-book of Surgery, for Practitioners and Students* [with J. William White]. Saunders, Philadelphia, 1892.

Dercum, Francis Xavier. *Journal of Nervous and Mental Diseases*. Dec. 1903.

Flower, William Henry. *Diagrams of the Nerves of the Human Body, Exhibiting Their Origins, Divisions, and Connections*. Hamilton, Philadelphia, 1874.

Gray, Henry. *Anatomy, Descriptive and Surgical*. Lea, Philadelphia, 1887.

Heath, Christopher. *Practical Anatomy: A Manual of Dissections*. Lea, Philadelphia, 1870.

Holden, Luther. "Landmarks, Medical and Surgical." Lea, Philadelphia, 1881.

Lindsay & Blakiston. *American Health Primers*. Blakiston, Philadelphia, 1879-80.*

[Various authors]. *Surgery, Its Principles and Practice*. 6 vols. Saunders, Philadelphia, 1906-21.

---

* Titles in this series, for 1879 and 1880, are as follows: "Long Life and How to Reach It;" "Our Homes;" "Sea-air & Sea-bathing;" "The Summer and Its Diseases;" "The Throat and the Voice;" and "Winter and Its Dangers." Forty years later, yet another title appeared: "Brain-work & Overwork."

DOCTORS MENTIONED IN THESE *MEMOIRS*

Adami, John George (1862-1926), 282
Agnew, David Hayes (1818-92), 44, 90, 93
Anschütz, Wilhelm (1870-1954), 248
Armstrong, Robert (1844-1920s?) 282
Atlee, Washington Lemuel (1808-78), 296
Bartholow, Roberts (1831-1904), 296
Bassini, Edoardo (1844-1924), 176-7
Battey, Robert (1828-95), 296
Bell, James Munsie (1880-1934), 282
Beni-Barde, Joseph Marie Alfred (1834-1919), 38
Bergman, Ernst von (1836-1907), 61, 68, 243, 258, 271
Bernard, Claude (1813-78), 149
Bier, Karl Gustav August (1861-1949), 258
Bigelow, Henry Jacob (1818-90), 209
Billings, John Shaw (1838-1913), 49, 61, 306
Billroth, Christian Albert Theodore (1829-94), 38
Bowditch, Henry Ingersoll (1808-92), 61, 282, 306
Brainard, Daniel (1812-66), 296
Braun, Heinrich Friedrich Wilhelm (1862-1934), 243, 246
Brinton, John Hill (1832-1907), 33, 39, 51, 296
Brown, John (1735-88?), 290
Bryant, Joseph Decatur (1845-1914), 59, 217-28
Buck, Gurdon (1807-77), 158-9
Bulkley, Henry Daggett (1803-72), bibliography
Carrel, Alexis (1873-1944), 299
Cattell, James McKeen (1860-1944), 100
Championnière (See Lucas-Championnière)
Collins, Howard Dennis (1868-1947), 188
Conner, Phnieus Sanborn (1839-1909), 128-9, 231
Cunningham, Daniel John (1850-1909), 41
Czerny, Vincenz (1842-1917), 61, 62, 68, 244
Da Costa, John Chalmers (1863-1933), 57, 69, 105n, 167, 209
Da Costa, Jacob Mendez (1833-1900), 33, 39, 56, 69, 208, 280, 296, 315
Depage, Antoine (1862-1925), 62, 63
Dercum, Francis Xavier (1856-1931), bibliography
De Schweinitz, George Edmund (1858-1938), 17-8, 209, 228
Drake, Daniel (1785-1852), 295
Duchenne de Boulogne, Guillaume Benjamin Armand (1806-75), 36
Duhring, Louis Adolphus (1845-1913), 316
Dunglison, Robley (1798-1869), 33, 296
Durante, Francesco (1844-1934), 61, 68, 195
Dyer, Ezra (1836-87), 17
Eiselsberg, Anton von (1860-1939), 191, 245, 246
Erdmann, John Frederic (1864-1954), 221
Esmarch, Johannes Friedrich August von (1823-1908), 68, 246, 258
Evans, Thomas Wiltberger (1823-97), 13
Ewald, Carl Anton (1845-1915), 243-4
Ferrier, David (1843-1928), 49-50
Flint, Austin (1812-86), 96

Flower, William Henry (1831-99), bibliography
Forbes, William Smith (1831-1905), 39, 131
Freeman, Walter Jackson (1860-1920), 98, 242
Friedrich, Paul Leopold (1864-1914?), 234
Fritz, Reginal Heber (1843-1913), 61, 188
Gibson, George Alexander (1854-1913), 188-9
Gibson, Kasson Church (1849-1925), 224n
Godlee, Rickman John (1859-1925), 48, 69
Gorgas, William Crawford (1854-1920), 61
Gray, Henry (1825-61), bibliography
Gross, Samuel David (1805-84), 33, 39, 51, 90, 125, 168, 280, 296
Gross, Samuel Weissel (1837-89), 39, 51, 296
Guéneau de Mussy, Noël François Odon (1813-85), 131-2
Gurlt, Ernst Julius (1825-99), 38
Gussenbauer, Carl (1842-1903), 61
Guyon, Jean Casimir Félix (1831-1920), 68
Hall, Rosetta Sherwood (1865-1951), 272-4
Halsted, William Stewart (1852-1922), 61, 67, 68, 69, 229
Harlan, George Cuvier (1835-1909), 48
Harte, Richard Hickman (1855-1925), 63
Hasbrouck, Ferdinand (1844-1904), 220-4, 224n
Hays, Isaac Minis (1847-1925), 51, 300
Hearn, William Joseph (1842-1917), 167
Heath, Christopher (1835-1905), bibliography
Heiser, Victor George (1873-1972), 296
Hildebrand, Otto (1858-1927), 243
Hodge, Hugh Lenox (1836-81), 43
Hoffa, Albert (1859-1908), 243-4
Holden, Luther (1815-1905), bibliography
Holland, James William (1849-1922), 302
Holmes, Oliver Wendell (1809-94), 42, 164
Honan, James Henry (1839-1917), 248
Horsley, Victor Alexander Haden (1857-1916), 49-50
Huntington, Thomas Waterman (1849-1929), 201
Hyde, James Nevins (1840-1910), 42
Igelsrud,* Kristian (1867-1940), 198
Jackson, Thomas Wright (1870-1925), 164, 296
Jacobs, Henry Barton (1858-1939), 179-81
Janeway, Edward Gamaliel (1841-1911), 188, 219, 221, 224
Jenner, Edward (1749-1823), 122, 284
Kausch, Walther (1867-1928), 243, 245
Keen, William Williams (1837-1932), passim
Koch, Robert (1843-1910), 57
Kocher, Emil Theodor (1841-1917), 61, 62, 67
König, Franz (1832-1910), 68, 243, 244
Körte, Werner (1853-1937), 243, 245, 246
Krause, Friedrich (1858-1936), 243-4, 248
Kümmel, Werner (1866-1930), 246
Küster, Ernst Georg Ferdinand (1839-1930), 244, 24

---

* Name changed to Egilsrud in 1907.

Lane, Levi Cooper (1830-1902), 296
Langenbeck, Bernhard von (1810-87), 38, 162, 208, 246, 258
Lannelongue, Odilon Marc (1840-1920), 181
Le Conte, Robert Grier (1865-1924), 63
Leidy, Joseph (1823-91), 44
Lewis, Morris James (1852-1928), 48
Lewis, Samuel (1813-90), 313
Lister, Joseph Lister [sic] (1827-1912), 68, 122, 282, 284
Long, Crawford Williamson (1815-78), 161
Lovett, Robert Williamson (1859-1924), 91
Lucas-Championnière, Just Marie Marcellin (1843-1913), 62
Lusk, William Thompson (1838-97), 281
MacCormac, William (1836-1901), 67
Maclaren, Peter Hume (1837?-1911), 188
Madelung, Otto Wilhelm (1846-1926), 246
Maisonneuve, Jacques Gilles Thomas (1809-97), 36
Mayo, William James (1861-1939), 190-2, 192n
McClellan, George (1796-1847), 295, 298n
McClellan, George (1849-1913), 295
McLean, Angus (1862-1939), 43
Mears, James Ewing (1838-1919), 130
Meigs, Arthur Vincent (1850-1919), 314
Meigs, Charles de Lucena (1792-1869), 296
Mills, Charles Karsner (1845-1931), 50
Mitchell, John Kearsley (1793-1858), 296
Mitchell, Silas Weir (1829-1914), Keen's mentor, 33-5, 42, 43, 48, 51, 92, 93, 104, 148; A.P.S. Memorial, 301; memorial volume, 35; research and writings, 35; anecdote, 294; president, Congress of Physicians and Surgeons, 61; president, College of Physicians, 314-6
Mitchell, Thomas Duché (1791-1865), 33
Morehouse, George Read (1829-1905), 34, 51, 95, 194
Morton, William Thomas Green (1819-68), 161-4, 277
Murphy, John Benjamin (1857-1916), 280n
Mütter, Thomas Dent (1811-59), 295
Nélaton, Auguste (1807-73), 36, 208
Oliver, Charles Augustus (1853-1911), 48
Olshausen, Robert Michaelis von (1835-1915), 244
O'Reilly, Robert Maitland (1845-1912), 219n
Osler, William (1849-1919), 100, 229
Paget, James (1814-99), 208, 280
Pancoast, Joseph (1805-82), 33, 39, 295
Pancoast, William Henry (1835-97), 39
Park, Roswell (1852-1914), 50
Parkes, Charles Herbert (1842-91), 42
Parkman, George (1790-1849), 110
Pepper, William (1843-98), 44
Picqué, Robert (1877-1927), 246
Playfair, Lyon (1818-98), 161-2

Porter, George Loring (1838-1913), 154, 211
Pry, Paul, Jr. (-   ), 280-1
Putnam, James Jackson (1846-1918), 35n
Ramsbotham, Francis Henry (1800-68), 280
Rehn, Ludwig (1849-1930), 246
Ricketts, Howard Taylor (1871-1910), 169
Riedel, Bernhard Moritz Carl Ludwig (1846-1916), 243, 246
Roddick, Thomas George (1846-1923) 282
Rovsing, Niels Thorkild (1862-1927), 244, 246
Rugh, James Torrance (1867-1942), 215
Sands, Henry Berton (1830-88), 162, 272
Schaeffer, Charles (1838-1903), 194
Schede, Eduard Hermann Wilhelm (1844-1902), 98
Schleich, Karl Ludwig (1859-1922), 248
Seguinn, Edward Constant (1843-98), 50
Shepherd, Francis John (1851-1929), 282
Shimoon, Joseph (c. 1879-1915), 309
Simpson, James Young (1811-70), 161-2, 277
Sims, James Marion (1813-83), 296
Sinkler, Wharton (1845-1910), 80, 314, 315
Smith, Albert Holmes (1835-85), 266
Smith, Nathan Ryno (1797-1877), 295
Sonnenberg, Eduard (1848-1926), 97, 271-2
Spencer, George Wicks (1870-1926), 198, 212, 216
Starr, Moses Allen (1854-1932), 50
Stillman, Charles Frederick (1853-92), 216
Stokvis, Barend Joseph (1834-1902), 279
Strawbridge, George (1844-1914), 170
Sutton, Rhoads Stansbury (1841-1906), 93
Taylor, William Johnson (1861-1936), 166-7, 218, 225
Thayer, William Sydney (1864-1932), 61
Thomson, William (1833-1907), 17, 95, 132
Thorn,   (-   ), 275-6
Toland, Hugh Hughes (1806-80), 43
Trendelenburg, Friedrich (1844-1924), 68, 243
Trudeau, Edward Livingston (1848-1915), 57-8, 61
Velpeau, Alfred Louis Armand Marie (1795-1867), 36
Virchow, Hans (1859-1940), 243-4
Virchow, Rudolf Ludwig Karl (1821-1902), 38, 206-7, 244, 246
Warren, John Collins (1778-1856), 67, 69, 229, 277
Webb, Gerald Bertram (1871-1948), 197
Webster, John White (1793-1850), 110
Weir, Robert Fulton (1838-1927), 48, 50, 67, 69, 158, 180-1, 229
Welch, William Henry (1850-1934), 61
White, James William (1850-1916), 53
White, William Hale (1831-1913), 189-90
Wilson, Ellwood (1822-89), 266
Wilson, James Cornelius (1847-1932), 314
Wood, Hoartio Charles (1841-1920), 48

INDEX

Alpha Delta Phi, 26, 89, 204
American Academy of Arts and Science, 69, 113
American Baptist Missionary Union, 89, 100
American Baptist Publication Society, 196
American College of Surgeons, 69
American Human Association, 215
American Medical Association, 89, 92
American Philosophical Society: Keen as delegate,
    60, 68, 189, 272, as president, 60, 65, 89,
    284, 298-306, as honoree, 192; annual dinner,
    215; atmosphere, 113; attendance, 300; Frank-
    lin bicentenary, 230-2; Linneaus bicentenary,
    60, 68, 232-3; friendships, 104, 300, 304;
    meetings and papers, 299-303; members notable,
    304, 306; real estate, 85, 304; work of, 69;
    sesquicentennial, 230-1; records, 230
American Surgical Association, 50, 89, 104
Angell, Prof. J. B., 24-5, 27, 32, 102
Anglo-American Medical Association, 248
Animal experimentation, 64, 89, 95, 123, 149,
    157-9, 168, 169, 172, 216
Antisepsis, 63, 64, 89, 93, 123, 284
Antivivisection, 64, 123, 157, 216
Army Medical Museum, 36
Athos, 259-66

Banes, Mary (Keen's cousin), 73
Baptist Church, 3, 9, 21, 27; First Philadelphia,
    7, 9, 10, 12, 60, 89, 94, 213, 230-1; Chestnut
    St., 9, 11, 71, 72
Belgian Surgical Society, 62, 69
Bloody Assizes, 5
Borden, Spencer (Keen's brother-in-law), 223, 226
British Medical Association, 235, 278-83
Brooks, Rev. Phillips, 209
Brown University, 21-32, 63, 66, 88, 118, 188,
    236
Buchanan, James, 152, 154
Budd, Susannah Britton (Keen's grandmother), 5,
    7, 188
Budd, Rev. Thomas ("jail bird"), 4-5
Burtis, Helen Keen (Keen's aunt), 73
Burtis, Jane (Keen's cousin), 76
Butcher, Howard, Jr. (Keen's son-in-law), 7, 21,
    243
Butcher, Margaret Keen (Keen's 4th daughter), 46,
    179-81, 189, 192, 224, 229, 245, 249, 318-9
Butcher, Polly (Keen's grandaughter), 317

Centennial Exhibition, 111, 112, 182, 185-6, 283-4
Christian Street Hospital, 35, 148, 194
Cleveland, Grover, 59, 211, 217-28
College of Physicians of Philadelphia, 17, 70,
    104, 228, 287-8, 312-6
"Colonel," 184
Commission to Investigate Abuses in the Spanish-
    American War, 212-3, 231
Congress of American Physicians and Surgeons, 49,
    55, 68

Disraeli, Benjamin, 207-8
Dowling, Rev. Dr., 22

Eckington Military Hospital, 125
Edinburgh, University of, 66, 67
Edison, Thomas Alva, 88
Edwards, E. J. ("Holland'), 224
Evans, Rudolph, 12, 13
Everett, Edward, 204-5

Fauntleroy, A. M., 156
Franklin, Benjamin, 193, 232, 301
Franklin Inn Club, 104, 193, 304
Freeman, Corinne Keen (Keen's 1st daughter), 3,
    6, 70, 192, 242, 317, 318-9
Freeman, Walter Jackson (Keen's son-in-law), 98,
    242, 248

"George," 181-4
German Surgical Society, 61, 67-8, 70, 228, 246
Gladstone, William E., 207-8
Grant, Ulysses S., 185, 211
Gray's Anatomy, 33, 45-6, 55, 58, 280
Greifswald, University of, 66, 234

[Handy], Dora Keen (Keen's 3rd daughter), 62, 175,
    179-81, 187-92, 195, 197, 198, 200-1, 214, 224,
    229, 233, 236-42, 242-9, 249-58, 260-5, 319
Harrison, Benjamin, 128-9
Hay, John, 26, 211
Hearst, William Randolph, 100, 198-201
Hospital for Diseases and Injuries of the
    Nervous System, 34, 148

Independence Hall, 84, 95, 202, 211
International Congress of Surgeons, 61-3
International Exposition (Chicago, 1893), 224;
    (Paris, 1900), 179
International Humane Conference, 215-6
Irwin, Agnes, 232
Italian Surgical Society, 69, 195-6

Jefferson Medical College: Keen as student, 33-6,
    as lecturer, 38, 47, as tutor, 294, as profes-
    sor, 47, 294, as chairman of surgery, 51-5, as
    alumnus, 292-7, as retiree, 57, 60, as honoree,
    68, as benefactor, 57, as clinician, 164; the
    early days, 292-3; logrolling, 39-40; labora-
    tory, 91, 240; friendships, 104; alumni, 295-7;
    Civil War student sympathies, 153-4
Jeffreys, George, 5

Kaiserin (Augusta Victoria), 242-8
Keen, Baron Stow (Keen's brother, "Benjamin"),
    6-7, 77, 82
Keen, Charles (Keen's uncle), 73
Keen, Charles Burtis (Keen's brother), 4, 6, 7,
    9, 38, 76, 82, 154-5, 212, 218
Keen, Charley (Keen's cousin, "The Count"), 73
Keen, Emma Corinna Borden (Keen's wife), 45, 81,
    185, 194
Keen, Fanny Louisa Colladay (George Keen's wife),
    12, 77
Keen, Florence (Keen's 2nd daughter), 5, 62, 175,
    179-81, 187-92, 195-8, 214, 224, 234, 236-42,
    245, 249-58, 304

Keen, Frank (Charles B. Keen's son), 6
Keen, George Budd (Keen's brother), 4, 6-7, 9, 10, 12, 72, 75, 82
Keen, Gregory B. (great-grandson of Mathias Keen [II]), 2, 3, 4
Keen, Harriet Emily Ide (Charles B. Keen's wife), 9, 73
Keen, Helen (Keen's cousin), 73
Keen, Isaac, Joseph Keen's brother), 3
Keen, John (Keen's great-great-grandfather), 3
Keen, Joseph (Keen's uncle), 4, 12
Keen, Joseph Swift (grandson of Mathias Keen [II]), 4, 12
Keen, Margaret Thomas (2nd wife of Mathias Keen [II]), 3
Keen, Margaret Williams (Keen's grandmother), 3-4
Keen, Mary Swift (1st wife of Mathias Keen [II]), 3, 4
Keen, Mathias [I] (Keen's great-great-great-grandfather), 2
Keen, Mathias [II] (Keen's great-grandfather) 3-4
Keen, Matilda Frick (Charles Keen's wife, "Mattie"), 73
Keen, Moses (Keen's "collateral ancestor, 'Moons'"), 236
Keen, Sarah Knowles (Isaac Keen's wife) 3
Keen, Susan [I & II] (Keen's sisters, died young), 6, 11
Keen, Susan Budd (Keen's mother), 5, 6, 15, 70-1, 76-80
Keen, Matilda (Keen's cousin, "Tillie"), 73
Keen, William [I] (Keen's brother, died young), 6
Keen, William Williams (Keen's father): descent, 2; birth, 3; education, 21; character, 4, 21, 28, 74-6, 79-80; health, 8; merchant, 4; grief, 6, 8, 82; property-owner, husbandman, 1, 9, 12, 71-81; churchman, 9, 11, 71; slave-owner, 170-1, style, 16, 75; retirement, 4; blindness, 81; death, 4, 9, 80-1; estate, 4

Keen, William Williams, Jr.
    Career
Approach, 27-8; choices, 13, 42-4; start at Jefferson, 33-4; Civil War, 35-6; M.D. degree, 36; artistic anatomy, 41; Paris offer, 13; first office and practice, 38, 287; foundation in pathology, 38-9; first surgery, 104-5; turning point, 47-9, 55, 97; pioneer, 51; success, 61; leader, 97; ideals, 117-8; retirement, 60, 298
    Childhood Recollections
Ice cream and A.P.s, 7-8, 76; skimmings, 77; comet of '43, 8; reading, 14; games and parties, 13-4, 72; academy lectures, 12; "Millerites," 8; "Santa Anna," 11; Chestnut St. house and garden, 9, 71-81; trundle bed, 79; Mexican War, 16; Harvard murder trial, 110; travel to New York, 6, 81-2; solar spectrum, 78; hunting, 71; Sunday school, 7
    Education, Pre-Medical
Newton Grammar School, 17; Central High School, 17, 24; Greek & Latin tutoring, 22-3; Brown University, 21-32, 102

    Emotional Concerns
Childhood terror, 8; disappointment, 39, 40; delusion, 8; grief, 45; gratification over family and friends, 167, 193
    Esthetic Concerns
Artistic anatomy, 41; melodeon player, 28; singer, 21, Centennial chorus, 185; orators, 203-11; movies and vulgarity, 88
    Financial Concerns
Inheritance, 4; loan at Brown, 23-4; vis-à-vis professional choices, 42-3, 45; first earned income, 28; pecuniary necessity, 167; insurance 85-7; half the pay, twice the work, 56; success of textbook, 90; purchase of school, 93; insider trading, 218, 224, 226; Keen as fundraiser, A.P.S., 305, College of Physicians, 313-6
    Family
Genealogy, 2, 4; documents, 2, 4; ancestors, 5, 69, 233, 236; genes, 4; feud, 3-4; parents, 6, 8, 11, 15, 28, 79-80; children, etc., 1, 25-6, 35, 39, 45, 46-7, 61, 64, 66, 81, 192, 218-9
    Health
Not robust as a child, 14; near-sighted, 14-7; short, studious, 14; accidents: cheek, 13, knee 59, forefinger, 70-1, icy fall, 24, tumble in the dark, 29, collarbone, 198, collarbone & ribs, 288, knee, 200; insomnia, 34, 38; grippe 70; depression, 45; infection, 165-7; tough, not strong; abdominal tumor, etc., 106, 187-92
    Humanitarian Concerns
Allies, 311; altruism, 171-2; animal research, 123; Christianity, 105
    Industry
Quotes: nose to the grindstone, 23, 46; not the idle life, 101; diligent performance, 58; work our nails off, 294; painstaking preparation, 102; I loved work, 56; unstinting work, 61; I never tired in my efforts, 102; I worked as hard as I could, 39; I had done my level best, 40; all my spare time, 46; each day's duty, 26-7, 46-7; I never worked so hard in my life, 52; enormous amount of labor, 66; doing my work as thoroughly as I could, 58; I gave far more time, 56
    Intellectual Concerns
Brown's new system, 22; History, Latin, sciences, 25; Mathematics, 26-7, 102; stimulation of friends, 104; analytical method, 102
    Medical Chairs
Anatomy: Harvard, 42, Jefferson, 39, 44, 47, 54, Penn, 43; Therapeutics: Jefferson, 39; Surgery California, 43, Jefferson, 39-40, 51-5, 60, 90 Rush, 42-3, Woman's Medical College, 44, 47
    Moral Concerns
Marriage vows, 179; plagiarism, 92; slavery, 149-55; yellow journalism, 100, 198-201, 222, 227; antivivisectionists, 123; nepotism, 39
    Patriotism
Loyal Legion, 35; inventions, U.S. and others, 114; manifest destiny, 118-20; defectors and traitors, 152-4; Taft as exemplar, 216

Political Concerns
Kossuth and liberty, 18; national ideals, 311; Lincoln-Douglas debates, 150; colonialism and changing maps, 118; peace in Europe, 286; Democrats & Republicans, 118, 150, 216, 217, 220; seapower in history, 310; allies vs. barbarians, 311; election of 1912, 216; German responsibility for war, 107, 306-11

Philosophical Concerns
After-life, 106; divine love, 187; God's approval, 40, 297; God's guidance, 53-4, 64; God's reward, 47; Keen's gratitude to God, 1, 192; God-fearing Keen, 8; service to God, 63; valley of the shadow of death, 191; Christian life, 9, 106; Keen not called to ministry, 27; baptism into the life of the Church, 9

Professional Concerns
Standards, 63-4; malpractice insurance, 135-7; ideas, ideals, 44; personal errors: ligation of femoral vein, 93-4; post-op mismanagement, 49; rule transgressed, 159

Residences
232 South 3rd, 1, 4, 7; 37th & Chestnut, 9, 70; 3621 Chestnut, 9, 11-2, 70-2, 78; college, 27; 1619 Chestnut, 74; 1729 Chestnut, 86, 156

Social Concerns
Women in medicine, 44-5, 265-6; Keen modesty, 1, temerity, 18; health of college students, 23; silver panic, 222; proper woman's voice, 248; unwashed prince, 176; borrowed toothbrush, etc., 252; boots and spurs in bed, 256

Socialization
Games, 13-4; pre-college outing, 21-2; lecture outing, 29; "harem," 30; football, rowing, 23 fraternity, 26

Teacher
Sunday school, 24; lectures, 25-6, 29; explaining science, 25-6, 102; tutoring, 28, 37, 47; best among candidates, 39; analytical approach, 102; revelations 102; artistic anatomy, 94; surgery, 93; the Jefferson, 38, 47, 102, as professor, 54, 60, 91; P.A.F.A., 40-1; Pennsylvania Museum, etc., 41; School of Anatomy, 34, 35, 38, 47, 92; Woman's Medical College, 44, 55, 60, 265, 272

Kossuth, Lajos, 18-20
Kyn, Jöran, 2, 3

Lewisburg, University of, 21
Lincoln, Prof., 24, 25, 27, 102
Lincoln, Abraham, 151-2, 153, 205, 211, 297
Linneaus, Carolus, 2, 60, 68, 232-3

Massachusetts General Hospital, 161, 165, 209, 277
McKinley, William, 58, 212-5, 231
Miles, Rebecca Keen (daughter of Isaac and Sarah Knowles Keen, "Cousin Becky"), 3

Newton Grammar School, 12, 17
Northwestern University, 66, 98

Oneida, 217-28
"Opportunity," 57-8
Orthopedic Hospital, 35
Oxenstierna, 69, 233

Palermo Surgical Society, 69
Paris Surgical Society, 69
Pennsylvania Academy of the Fine Arts, 40-1
Pennsylvania Anatomical Board, 130
Pennsylvania Museum and School of Industrial Art 41
Pennsylvania Railroad, 14-5, 21, 81, 154, 211
Pennsylvania, University of, 33, 43-4, 53, 88, 104, 130
Philadelphia: R.R. depot, 14; stock exchange, 6, 305; city limits, 10, 84; 1837 population, 110 banks, 83; post office, 16; firefighting, 85-6 polls, 84-5; West Philadelphia, 4, 7, 9, 10, 11-2, 17, 71-2, 78, "Hamiltonville," 10, 70
Philadelphia School of Anatomy, 34, 35, 38, 47, 56, 93-4, 129
"Prince," 73, 76

Quarantine, 236-42
Quakers, 5, 110

Reeves, Anna Keen (Keen's aunt), 73
Roosevelt, Theodore, 217, 303
Royal College of Surgeons, Edinburgh, 66-7, 233
Royal College of Surgeons, England, 62, 67, 69, 177, 228-9

Saint Andrews, University of, 66, 193-4, 232-5
St. Mary's Hospital, 48
Saunders, W. B., 90

Taft, William H., 215-6, 303
Thiersch, of Leipzig, 56
Toronto, University of, 66
Twain, Mark, 206

United States, growth, 118
Uppsala, University of, 2, 60, 68, 232-3

Valley Forge, 5
Vivisection, 64, 95, 123, 147-8, 157, 161-2, 169 215-6
Vonnoh, Robert, 193-4, 301

Washington, George, 5
Wayland, Francis, 22, 151-2, 209-11
Weir, Helen Keen (Keen's cousin), 78
Wilhelm II, 107-9, 117-8, 230, 258-9, 285, 306-1
Wilson, Woodrow, 216-7, 303-4, 309, 311-2
Woman's Hospital, 50, 170
Woman's Medical College, 44, 47, 52, 60, 266-70

Yale University, 66
Yellow journalism, 100, 198-201, 222, 227